STEREOCHEMISTRY

PROGRESS IN
STEREOCHEMISTRY
2

Editors

W. KLYNE, M.A., D.Sc., Ph.D.

Reader in Biochemistry
University of London
(Postgraduate Medical School)

P. B. D. de la MARE, Ph.D., D.Sc.

Reader in Chemistry
(University College)
University of London

LONDON
BUTTERWORTHS SCIENTIFIC PUBLICATIONS
1958

BUTTERWORTHS PUBLICATIONS LTD.
88 KINGSWAY, LONDON, W.C.2

AFRICA: BUTTERWORTH & CO. (AFRICA) LTD.
DURBAN: 33/35 Beach Grove

AUSTRALIA: BUTTERWORTH & CO. (AUSTRALIA) LTD.
SYDNEY: 8 O'Connell Street
MELBOURNE: 430 Bourke Street
BRISBANE: 240 Queen Street

CANADA: BUTTERWORTH & CO. (CANADA) LTD.
TORONTO: 1367 Danforth Avenue

NEW ZEALAND: BUTTERWORTH & CO. (AUSTRALIA) LTD.
WELLINGTON: 49/51 Ballance Street
AUCKLAND: 35 High Street

U.S.A. Edition published by
ACADEMIC PRESS INC., PUBLISHERS
111 FIFTH AVENUE
NEW YORK 3, NEW YORK

Set in Monotype Baskerville type
Printed in Great Britain by Bell & Bain, Ltd., Glasgow

CONTENTS

CONTENTS

PREFACE

THE favourable reception given to Volume 1 of this series in 1954 has led us to produce a second volume, which contains chapters dealing with topics in physical, inorganic, organic and biological chemistry. As for the previous volume, drafts of many chapters were circulated to other contributors for comment, and much valuable criticism resulted. The literature has been covered, as far as possible, up to late 1956.

The recent book entitled *Steric Effects in Organic Chemistry* (Wiley, New York, edited by Professor M. S. Newman) has appeared since most of the chapters of the present work were completed. It covers a number of subjects related to those considered in the organic chapters of this and the previous volume. Specific references have been made to *Steric Effects* in a few places in this book, but it seems desirable to draw attention in a general way to the valuable complementary collection of articles contained in Professor Newman's book.

We are again indebted to many colleagues, including fellow authors, who have made useful suggestions or who have supplied unpublished information. We are grateful also to the authors and publishers of figures which have been reproduced from other books and journals (*Journal of the Chemical Society*: Chapter 5, Figures 1, 2, 4, 5 and 6; *Advances in Science, London* and Sir John Lennard-Jones, F.R.S. : Chapter 8, Figure 6). The editors are again indebted to the staff of Messrs Butterworths for their constant and willing help at all stages of the production.

W. KLYNE

P. B. D. DE LA MARE

CRYSTALLOGRAPHY AND STEREOCHEMISTRY

J. C. Speakman

By diffraction analysis it is theoretically feasible to determine the positions of all the atoms in a crystal. In favourable cases this objective can actually be attained ; and then all the questions asked qualitatively by classical stereochemistry are answered quantitatively—at any rate for the molecule as it exists in the crystal. Of course it is true that modern stereochemistry may also be concerned with subtler details of structure and reactivity, details which are only partially supplied by crystal structure analysis, or not at all. It is also true that the molecule in the solid may differ from that in the gaseous or dissolved states, though, on the whole, the changes in molecular dimensions between solid and gas are surprisingly small. The extreme instance of phosphorus pentachloride is described on page 220, and slight differences are sometimes found (see p. 29). With molecular crystals, however, significant differences are exceptional ; for the crystal-lattice forces are small compared with those needed to bring about serious distortion of a covalent molecule. Therefore, as a method of winning information of stereochemical value, crystal-structure analysis occupies a special position. It is perhaps rather less accurate than is electron diffraction when applied with current refinements to very simple molecules in the gaseous state, and is considerably less accurate than are spectroscopic and micro-wave methods ; but it can be applied to a far wider range of substances.

For these reasons most of this chapter is devoted to the method of x-ray analysis, which is what crystallography chiefly signifies in the context. The author's intention is to outline and to illustrate the principles rather than to catalogue again the many published results —to bring out the potentialities and limitations of the method—and thus to help the reader to assess the significance of the recorded data and the practicability of solving any particular problem by this means. As to the published results, they soon find their way into the successive volumes of *Structure Reports*. Together with their predecessors, the seven volumes of the *Strukturbericht*, these reports include a critical review of all results obtained by x-ray analysis, and by some other physical methods, down to 1951 (at the time of writing).

CRYSTALLINITY AND DIFFRACTION ANALYSIS

The essence of crystallinity is the manifold repetition of some *motif* in three-dimensional space. This repeat-unit may be a single atom (as in diamond or a metallic element), or an ion-pair (as in rock-salt), or half a molecule (as in benzene), or a whole molecule (as in hexa-methylbenzene), or some more complex combination. The distance at which the unit is exactly repeated, as regards identity, environment and orientation, is known as a *primitive translation*. When the magnitudes and relative directions of at least three independent primitive trans-lations have been ascertained, it is possible to characterize a *unit cell*, which is the 'brick' with which the whole crystal can be regarded as having been built. The unit cell (if it is a true one) must contain a discrete number of molecules.

This regular arrangement of a vast number of molecules (or other entities) makes it possible to apply special methods of investigation. For example, anisotropy in the optical, electrical, magnetic or mechanical properties of the crystal can be related to an anisotropy in molecular properties—such as the enhanced polarizability of an aromatic molecule in the plane of its ring system. By far the most important consequence is the possibility of diffraction analysis. As was first suggested by von Laue in 1912, a crystal constitutes a three-dimensional grating of mesh suitable to produce diffraction effects with x-rays; and this was quickly confirmed in practice for x-rays, whilst analogous effects have subsequently been obtained with beams of electrons, neutrons and other radiations. Most structural investiga-tions hitherto have used x-rays, and it is with these that this chapter is primarily concerned.

When a beam of 'monochromatic' x-rays falls on to a crystal, it is diffracted ('reflected from the different crystallographic planes') in certain directions, with various intensities. A characteristic diffraction pattern can be recorded by photographic, or other, means. The task is to deduce the crystal structure—the positions and natures of the atoms in the unit cell—from the diffraction pattern. This task can be broken down into a series of steps of increasing difficulty and increasing informativeness.

Dimensions of the Unit Cell

The geometry of the pattern (in three dimensions) at once leads to the primitive translations, and so to the unit-cell parameters. Provided they are used with discrimination, these can occasionally be made to yield information of stereochemical value. The most celebrated example arose from Bernal's (1932) determination of the unit cells of certain compounds of the steroid group. As he pointed out, the cell dimensions were not consistent with the formulae then attributed to these molecules, and his results had great influence in leading to the recognition of the correct skeletal plan for these compounds. A much simpler example is Hargreaves' (1943) measurement of the unit-cell dimensions of calycanine. At that time, two molecular formulae were under consideration: $C_{16}H_{10}N_2$ and $C_{21}H_{15}N_3$. Had the latter been correct, it would have implied the presence of $1\frac{1}{2}$ molecules in the cell, which is an unacceptable result. The former requires there to be two molecules, and is now regarded as much the more likely on chemical grounds also (Robinson and Teuber, 1954).

The Space-group and its Possible Significance

When to the unit-cell parameters is added information about systematically missing reflexions (' absences '), it becomes possible to draw conclusions as to the internal symmetry of the cell, as defined by its *space-group*. There are 230 possible space-groups, and most of them are not determined unambiguously by the absences alone. This is because x-rays always supply a centre of symmetry, whether one be in fact present or not. For instance, in their characteristic absences, the space-groups *P*2 and *Pm* are indistinguishable from each other, and from $P2/m$* into which they are each converted by addition of a centre. However 70 space-groups (including 10 enantiomorphous pairs) can be diagnosed unambiguously; and fortunately they include $P2_1/a$, which is the group of most frequent occurrence amongst the several thousands of crystals so far examined. (Nearly 25 per cent of all organic crystals belong to it.) Even when the absences admit of an ambiguity (as they usually do), it is normally possible to make a reliable assignment by applying physical tests for pyro- or piezo-electricity, by considering the morphology of the crystal as indicated by classical methods of goniometry, or by examining the statistics of intensity distribution amongst the various reflexions (a method of greater power recently developed by Wilson, 1949, and Rogers, 1950).

From a knowledge of the unit-cell dimensions and space-group, along with the density of the crystal, significant deductions can often be made. Hargreaves' study of calycanine showed it to belong to $P2_1/a$: this group has four-fold multiplicity; any atom, or group of atoms, in a general position must be repeated in three other positions in the cell by the implied symmetry operations; and, since there are only two molecules in the unit cell, the asymmetric unit must be the half-molecule, and the molecule itself must possess a centre of symmetry. The nickel and palladous compounds of salicylaldoxime (I) crystallize isomorphously, and again in the space-group $P2_1/n$, with

* Space-groups (and point-groups) will normally be represented in this chapter by the Hermann–Mauguin symbols. In some cases the symbol is changed by a change of axes. Thus $P2_1/a$, $P2_1/c$ and $P2_1/n$ represent the same space-group ($= C_{2h}^5$).

two molecules in the unit cell. The molecules must therefore possess a centre of symmetry, at which the metal atom M must be situated. This evidence alone (found by Cox, Pinkard, Wardlaw and Webster, 1935, and without the complete analysis recently reported by Merritt, Guare and Lessor, 1955) proves that the four atoms coordinated to M are in a co-planar *trans*-arrangement; and it provided one of the

I   II

earlier experimental demonstrations of coordination in accordance with dsp^2-hybridization. At an early stage in Wheatley's analysis (1954) of *N*-methyl-2 : 2-di(methylsulphonyl)vinylideneamine (II), the space-group was proved unambiguously to be *Pbcn*. Each of the four molecules in the cell must therefore have either a centre, or a two-fold axis, of symmetry. The latter must in fact obtain, since the chemical formula of this molecule rules out the possibility of a centre. The implication then is that the $> C = C = N - CH_3$ chain must be strictly linear—a stereochemical feature borne out by the subsequent structure analysis, but by no means wholly to have been expected *a priori*.

A number of recent investigations give warning that deductions based on space-group symmetry may be invalidated by disorder in the molecular arrangement. *p*-Dichlorobenzene and *p*-dibromobenzene crystallize isomorphously with two molecules in a cell belonging to the space-group $P2_1/c$; and the molecules of each are required to be centro-symmetric, as was to be expected. But *p*-bromochlorobenzene also proves to be isomorphous, as was found by Hendricks (1933). Molecular centro-symmetry is therefore indicated here, as with the other two substances—a conclusion that is formally unacceptable. The explanation is that the symmetry is statistical; that the lattice contains a random distribution of molecular orientations between the two alternatives represented as $Cl.C_6H_4.Br$ and $Br.C_6H_4.Cl$. A more detailed study by Klug (1947) has confirmed this explanation, and shown the halogen positions to be identically occupied by 'mean atoms'—$\frac{1}{2}(Cl+Br)$.

In Rollett's (1955) analysis of phenylpropiolic acid, the space-group was deduced to be *Pnnm*; and the structure then proved to consist of planar dimeric molecules (as suggested in III) which were perpendicularly bisected by a crystallographic plane of symmetry parallel to the length of the dimer. Amongst other things, this implied that the $C = O$ and $C - OH$ bonds are of precisely equal length. A very

4

careful refinement showed, however, a decidedly better agreement with the experimentally observed intensities when it was supposed that these bonds did in fact differ slightly in length (as would be expected), but that the difference was concealed because there was, throughout the crystal, a random arrangement of molecules in the senses represented by III and IV.

III

IV

In certain acid salts of the general formula MHX_2, where M is a univalent metal and HX the parent monobasic acid, crystal-structure analysis (Speakman, 1948, 1949; see also Brown *et al.*, 1949) shows that oxygen atoms of two different carboxyl groups are separated by 2·5–2·6 Å, and are related by an intervening centre of symmetry. They must be united by a ' short ' hydrogen bond, in which the acidic hydrogen atom participates; and this bond must be crystallographically symmetrical. In a bond of such inter-oxygen distance, it is unlikely that the proton actually occupies an equilibrium position at the mid-point. More probably it oscillates between two positions of minimum energy about 1·1 Å from each oxygen atom (Davies and Thomas, 1951; Skinner, Stewart and Speakman, 1954; Bacon and Curry, 1956; see also p. 16). (*Cf*, however, Speakman, 1956.)

In all these examples the disorder enhances the effective molecular symmetry. Such cases are probably exceptional, though they are likely to be found more often as methods of analysis become more accurate. But at present they certainly do not constitute any general ground for rejecting all space-group evidence of molecular symmetry.

Provided disorder can be excluded, the molecular symmetry required crystallographically is always a lower limit, as was pointed out by Bernal many years ago. The crystal rarely makes full use of the total point-symmetry of the idealized molecule, as it may exist when in its ground state in the gas. The benzene molecule belongs to the point-group $6/mmm$ $(=D_{6h})$; but, of the 23 symmetry elements comprised in this group, only one—the centre—is actually used in the space-group to which the benzene crystal belongs. The deviations of the molecule from the atomic positions proper to the full point-group symmetry are, however, very slight (Cox *et al.*, 1955). Again, though polycyclic aromatic hydrocarbons usually have planar molecules, no case is yet known where such a molecule lies in a plane of crystallographic symmetry.

Complete Structure Analysis by means of Intensity Data

For the fullest exploitation of the diffraction method, the intensities of the reflected rays must be measured. It may then become possible to deduce coordinates for all the atoms in the unit cell, and hence to determine the structure completely. A number of procedures are available. Of these, the Fourier-series method is perhaps the most powerful, and it is certainly the most directly pictorial. It will be outlined here because it serves well to illustrate the inherent difficulties of deducing the crystal structure from the diffraction pattern, by any method. [This whole problem, and those of refinement, have been reviewed by Jeffrey and Cruickshank (1953).]

Any linear pattern, which can be represented by a quantitative function, $p(x)$, and repeats itself along the x-axis at regular intervals, a, can be reproduced by summing a sufficient number of cosinusoidal terms; *i.e.* by a single Fourier series:

$$p(x) = \frac{1}{a} \sum_{h=0}^{h=\infty} |A_h| \cos 2\pi\left(\frac{hx}{a}+\alpha_h\right),$$

where $|A_h|$ is the amplitude and α_h the phase-angle of the hth term. A crystal can be regarded as an electron-density pattern, $\rho(x, y, z)$, repetitive in three dimensions, as it is by the electrons that the x-rays are scattered. Hence the electron-density can be represented by an analogous triple Fourier series:

$$\rho(x, y, z) = \frac{1}{V} \sum_h \sum_k \sum_l |F_{hkl}| \cos 2\pi\left(\frac{hx}{a}+\frac{ky}{b}+\frac{lz}{c}+\alpha_{hkl}\right) \quad . \quad . \quad (1)$$

where V is the volume of the cell, with a, b and c as edges, and where $|F_{hkl}|$ is the amplitude and α_{hkl} the phase-angle of the wave scattered from the hkl crystal plane. [The *structure factor* (F_{hkl}, as distinct from $|F_{hkl}|$) is properly the complex quantity involving both amplitude and phase-angle.] The amplitude can be readily found from the intensity observed for the appropriate reflexion; and, although it is not possible to measure the infinite number of terms needed to yield a perfect image of the electron-density, a number adequate for a good approximation is usually accessible. Atoms appear as roughly spherical regions of high electron-density.

But an essential part of the information needed for the use of equation (1) is lacking. The phase-angle, α_{hkl}, cannot be recorded. This is the fundamental difficulty in structure analysis by any diffraction method.

The Phase Problem

The phase-angle depends on the point in the unit cell chosen as origin. Even when this choice has been made, the angle for any particular reflexion might *a priori* have any value from 0° to 360°;

therefore, when a large number of terms is to be summed in (1), an infinite number of solutions for $\rho(x, y, z)$ is mathematically possible. For the special case of a centrosymmetric structure (and provided the origin is taken at a centre of symmetry), α_{hkl} is restricted to $0°$ and $180°$, which is equivalent to saying that the structure amplitude can be converted to the structure factor by ascribing to it a positive or a negative sign. Though the number of solutions of (1) is now no longer infinite, it is still very large (2^N for N observed reflexions), and it is wholly impracticable to test all combinations of signs, even for a few dozen of the strongest terms only.

Most of these sign-combinations will lead to results that are physically unacceptable; the electron-density must never be negative and it must be distributed so as to correspond to discrete atoms, in the right numbers and of the right kinds, arranged in a way that is chemically valid. The problem is to find the set of signs (or phases) which leads to the correct, and probably unique*, structure. At present there is no recognized general method for solving the phase problem, though it is suspected that one may exist, at least for centrosymmetric crystals. Should such a method be found, and proved to be practicable, the way would become open for almost unlimited progress in structure analysis.

Hitherto the many hundreds of structures that have been established have depended on circumventing the phase problem by a number of methods of limited applicability. The first is that of *trial and error*. When the structure is known, it is always possible to calculate the structure factor (*i.e.* including the phase-angle). Hence in a sufficiently simple case it is practicable to try various atomic arrangements until one is found which yields a reasonable agreement between observed and calculated amplitudes. This structure is then taken to be nearly correct, and the *calculated* phase-angles are used with the *observed* amplitudes in a series of successive approximations, usually by the Fourier method. This approach is practicable when only a few atoms have to be located, or when the structure is already known chemically and has favourable features (*e.g.* planarity). It becomes impracticable with substances having large, non-planar molecules, or molecules of unknown chemical structure.

When the structure includes an atom of relatively high atomic

---

* In one instance—that of the mineral bixbyite (Pauling and Shappell, 1930)—two distinct structures were found to give *exactly* the same set of calculated structure amplitudes, and hence to correspond to the same diffraction pattern. This phenomenon of *homometric* structures is believed to be rare; and in any case only one structure for bixbyite was acceptable on chemical grounds.

The phenomenon of *pseudo-homometric* structures is commoner. Besides the correct structure, there may exist other more-or-less plausible sets of atomic positions which give some measure of agreement with the observed structure-amplitudes. Should one of these structures be postulated, the analysis may appear to confirm it up to a point, but a *close* agreement is not attainable. Recent experience should have put crystallographers on their guard against being misled in this way.

number, the x-ray scattering is largely dominated by this atom. In the centrosymmetric case, this means that the sign of any structure factor is probably (though not certainly) that which would be required by the heavy atom alone. If, then, the position of the heavy atom can be found (and this is often possible), an approximation to the electron-density can be computed with equation (1), using the observed amplitudes with the signs calculated for the heavy atom. Once this approximation has yielded recognizable positions for the other, lighter atoms, the process of refinement can be carried through as explained above. This *heavy-atom method* becomes particularly elegant when the atom occupies a special position in the cell, such as a centre of symmetry in platinum phthalocyanine (Robertson and Woodward, 1940). Then all (or almost all) the signs may be taken as positive, and the Fourier series leads directly to an absolute structure determination, in which no chemical assumptions have had to be made.

A striking application of the heavy-atom method in a more complex situation has enabled the hitherto unknown structure of the alkaloid, cryptopleurine, to be discovered. The problem was solved via 'generalized' or 'modulus' projections, using the methiodide of a closely related compound (Fridichsons and Mathieson, 1955). Mathieson (1955), in reviewing recent structure determinations in the organic field, has considered how heavy the heavy atom must be to give a good prospect of a successful analysis. Following Lipson and Cochran (1953), he took $N^2/\Sigma n_i^2$ as an index of the prospect, where N is the atomic number of the heavy atom and n_i that of each of the lighter atoms. Success may be reasonably anticipated when the ratio exceeds unity, though it has sometimes been achieved when the ratio was much smaller. Since it neglects a number of other factors, favourable and unfavourable, this rule must be a rough one.

A more powerful method, though narrower in its applicability, is based on *isomorphous replacement*. It depends upon the possibility of replacing one atom by another of appreciably different scattering power, without significantly changing the rest of the structure; *i.e.* upon the availability of isomorphous crystals (*e.g.* K and Rb compounds). By comparing corresponding intensities for the two crystals, it is usually possible to infer the position of the replaceable atom. In the centrosymmetric case, it then becomes possible to calculate, not only the magnitude, but also the sign of the difference between corresponding structure factors. (Thus if, for compounds of rubidium and potassium, $F_{Rb} - F_K = +35$, and if $|F_{Rb}|$ and $|F_K|$ are respectively 25 and 60, then each of these terms must have a negative sign.) This method was used in the early work on the structures of the alums (*e.g.* Beevers and Lipson, 1935), and with especial elegance with phthalocyanine and its nickel derivative (Robertson, 1936).

Use of isomorphism becomes more difficult and ambiguous in a non-centric system. But it played an all-important part in elucidating the structure of vitamin B_{12} (Hodgkin *et al.*, 1955). The molecule, with formula $C_{63}H_{88}N_{14}O_{14}PCo$, contains a cobalt atom; but this would be quite inadequate by itself to give a solution to the phase problem in an unknown structure of such complexity. There is also a CN-group attached to the cobalt atom, and this can be replaced by CNS- and by CNSe-groups without greatly altering the rest of the structure (though there is not strict isomorphism). This circumstance (along with the fortunate discovery of a crystalline degradation product, in which the heterocyclic ring-system round the Co-atom was preserved) ultimately led to the determination of the total structure of the vitamin. This analysis is undoubtedly the greatest achievement in structural crystallography thus far.

In recent years greater use has been made of the *Patterson synthesis*. This uses the Fourier series of equation 1, with the difference that F^2 replaces F, so that the question of the phase-angle does not arise. The resulting synthesis, $P(x, y, z)$, contains the interatomic vectors for all pairs of atoms. Thus the number of 'Patterson peaks' increases as the square of the number of atoms; with growing complexity the peaks tend to overlap, and the synthesis becomes more and more difficult to interpret. Nevertheless, in suitable cases, especially where three-dimensional data are used, this method has often indicated an approximate structure when the others were not applicable, or had failed (*e.g.* P_4S_7, Vos and Wiebenga, 1955).

A number of other methods for solving the phase problem have been suggested, and have been used successfully in individual analyses. Some of them are of great theoretical interest and potential importance. But it is still true to say that the great majority of structures have been, and are, solved by one of the four methods described above, or by some combination of them. It is also true that they all become much more difficult as more complex structures are undertaken; and that they must ultimately become impracticable.

Refinement of Atomic Positions and Molecular Parameters

When the phase problem has been solved to the extent of finding a correct, approximate structure, there comes the straight-forward, though usually laborious, task of refining the atomic coordinates to the limit permitted by the intensity data. In a repeat-unit comprising N atoms, $3N$ coordinates are needed to define the structure, and there is rarely any difficulty in obtaining more than $3N$ observational data; an excess of 10-fold or more is commonly accessible. The intensities of x-ray reflexions are not very accurately measurable by the usual photographic-visual techniques. (Considerably greater accuracy, if less convenience, attends the use of counter methods*.) The refinement process, whether it be by Fourier series or other routes, takes advantage of the excess of not very exact data to achieve relatively more exact coordinates.

In the past refinement was done ' two-dimensionally ', and to a considerable extent it still is, by applying the double Fourier series

$$\rho(x,y) = \frac{1}{A} \underset{h\ k}{\Sigma\Sigma} \mid F_{hk0} \mid \cos 2\pi \left(\frac{hx}{a} + \frac{ky}{b} + \alpha_{hk0}\right) \quad . \quad . \quad (2)$$

to data derived from the reflexions of a single zone [$hk0$ in (2)], so as to yield a projection of the electron-density on to a plane perpendicular to the (c-)axis, A being the projected area of the unit cell in this direction. With a desk calculating machine, the computational labour is not excessive. When the structure has been studied in two, or more, projections, all three coordinates of each atom can be found in principle. However, two-dimensional analysis does not make full use of the diffraction pattern; first because only in very favourable cases are all the atoms resolved in a given projection (and, even if they are so along one axis, they are almost certain to overlap along the others); and secondly because only a fraction of the accessible data is included in the principal zones of reflexions.

The diffraction method is fully realized when it is applied ' three-dimensionally ', using all accessible (hkl) reflexions in a triple Fourier series (equation 1), or in some equivalent procedure. Since atoms are always separated in space by at least the sum of their covalent radii, overlapping cannot now occur. On the other hand, the amount of computational labour is very great—almost prohibitively so unless some form of electronic calculating machine is available. The number of published three-dimensional analyses during recent years has run parallel with the availability of such machines, which are especially plentiful in the United States.

When the Fourier-series method has been pursued to the point where all the observed terms can be included, the atomic positions found may not be the best attainable. Errors arise from the use of a non-infinite series. The importance of these errors, and the methods for their elimination, have come to be recognized during the past ten years.

There remain the observational errors. Their effect is less serious than might be supposed, provided that they are random, and that there is a large excess of data over parameters. Making these assumptions, Hughes (1941), Cruickshank (1949) and others have applied statistical methods to assess the standard deviations (σ) of the final coordinates and of the derived bond-lengths and valency angles.

* Attempts to raise the precision of intensity measurements are important; but they are only partly rewarding, since there is great difficulty in making the necessary corrections for absorption and extinction with parallel precision.

It has recently become the practice to report these estimated standard deviations (e.s.d.) in all analyses in which any claim to accuracy is made. It by no means always follows that the real accuracy is as high as the e.s.d. makes it appear; for the assumption that experimental errors are random may be at fault. Furthermore, the refinement process is based on the principle of selecting a model structure, and then adjusting its parameters to give the best possible agreement between observed and calculated structure-amplitudes. But errors in the model may not always be apparent. At one stage in the precise analysis of solid benzene (Cox *et al.*, 1954) it was found that the C—C distance was 1.378 ± 0.003 Å. This low result was later proved to be a consequence of neglecting the considerable torsional oscillation of the molecule about its 6-fold axis. When this feature was included in the model (Cox *et al.*, 1955), the C—C length rose to 1.392 Å, in agreement with that found from an accurate study of the Raman spectrum of the vapour (1.397 Å, Stoicheff, 1955).

The stereochemist is often anxious to know what reliance can be placed on x-ray results. An assessment must depend on the complexity of the structure (*i.e.* on the number of independent coordinates to be determined), on the thoroughness of the analysis in the sense discussed above, and on the date of publication. In very simple structures, where all the atoms are in special positions, the errors in bond-lengths will be relatively no greater than those in the unit cell dimensions. These can be measured within $\frac{1}{2}$ per cent very easily, and much greater precision is readily attained if desired (up to ± 0.001 per cent). The C—C distance in diamond depends only on the single unit-cell parameter, and it is known to within 0.0001 Å. Usually, however, most, if not all, atoms will be in general positions. In recent publications, where the derived molecular data are accompanied by values for e.s.d., they are unlikely to be in error by more than three times the e.s.d., unless they are affected by special anomalies which have escaped detection. Earlier work, based on two-dimensional methods and without correction for finite-series errors, is almost always less accurate than its authors have supposed. As a rough rule it may be suggested that bond-lengths will probably not be in error by more than 0.05 Å, and angles by more than $3°$. The position of a heavier atom will be more exactly known than that of a lighter one; the positions of light atoms in the neighbourhood of a heavy atom are liable to be more seriously in error. When the original author has tabulated his observed structure-amplitudes, it is always possible to refine his coordinates by more recent techniques. This has sometimes been done with a striking increase in accuracy (*e.g.* Ahmed and Cruickshank, 1953).

Crystallographers often signify the precision of their analyses by reporting values of R, the 'reliability index' (or agreement factor).

11

This is the arithmetical sum of the differences between observed and calculated structure amplitudes expressed as a fraction, or percentage, of the sum of all observed amplitudes. The better the agreement, the lower is R, which might therefore more logically be termed the ' *un*reliability index '. Falling values of R usefully denote the stages of a successful refinement of coordinates. The final value of R is, however, an imperfect substitute for a set of e.s.d. values; and some care and judgment is needed in assessing its significance. In an analysis requiring the location of 15 atoms of similar weight (*e.g.* 45 coordinates), an R of 20 per cent might well indicate a more accurate determination than one of 10 per cent in another analysis where the structure factors are largely dictated by a heavy atom in a special position, the coordinates of which are exactly known by symmetry. Furthermore R tends to look more impressive when only a few reflexions have been recorded (but this is also true of e.s.d.); whereas real accuracy always increases as more reflexions are included in the calculations.

It may be appropriate to give an estimate of the amount of time and labour required in the various stages of an x-ray structure-analysis. The first stage is to determine the unit cell dimensions and the space-group. With adequate single crystals, this will need a period between a day and a fortnight, according to the symmetry of the crystal. It is then possible to forecast the prospects of a successful analysis. If they appear bright enough (in relation to the importance of the problem) to tempt the crystallographer to proceed, the second stage is to collect intensity data. When two-dimensional methods are in view, one or two weeks should suffice for the experimental work, and the visual estimation of intensities and the correlation of the data may take perhaps as long again. When three-dimensional work is intended, these times must be increased by a factor of four or five. The third stage, the solving of the phase problem, is the least predictable. The time needed depends on the crystal, on the skill and persistence of the worker, and perhaps on his good luck. Success may come in a couple of days; it may still be lacking after a year. The last stage is that of refinement, and it will occupy a period of from some weeks to some months, depending on the number of coordinates to be fixed, on the degree of refinement required, and on the computational aids available. Future developments in technical methods may diminish these times.

Other Information derivable from X-Ray Analyses

When an analysis has been carried through to the limits of refinement, a great deal of information may become available, besides that on bond-lengths and angles. Details of inter- and intra-molecular ' contacts ' cannot easily be obtained in any other way, and they have important steric implications (see p. 22). Thermal vibrations spread out the sphere of electron-density representing an atom; and they are quantitatively measured by introducing ' temperature factors ' (B) into the model. (This factor is related to the mean square displacement, $\overline{u^2}$, of the atom from its mean position by the relationship $B = 8\pi^2\overline{u^2}$; a typical value of B for an organic compound would be 3·0 Å², which would correspond to a r.m.s. displacement of about 0·2 Å.) In a refined analysis, different atoms may require different temperature factors. For instance, atoms further away from the centre of gravity of a molecule are generally subjected to a greater amplitude of vibration, as is to be expected. Anisotropy of temperature factor is often found, indicating anisotropy of vibration. The careful exploration of these effects* has a further importance; for it is only after they have been recognized and corrected for that it may become possible to investigate the finer details of the electron distribution; *e.g.* to detect inherent deviations of the atom from spherical shape, and ultimately perhaps to make the bonding-electrons manifest in the electron-contour diagram (*i.e.* in an electron-density ' difference ' map).

Low Temperatures

During recent years, techniques for taking x-ray diffraction photographs at low temperatures have been developed (*e.g.* by Lipscomb, 1950). A considerable number of analyses have now been carried out at temperatures down to 90°K, using liquid air or nitrogen, and methods for going much lower with liquid hydrogen are being developed. It then becomes possible to study substances that are liquid or gaseous at ordinary temperatures; and to locate more precisely the positions of the atoms, because the amplitudes of their thermal vibrations are diminished†.

Limitations of X-Ray Structure Analysis

First, it is necessary that the substance be obtainable in an adequately crystalline form. With materials belonging to the cubic system, or some other of high symmetry, it may be possible to analyse the structure using data from powder photographs only; remarkable results have been obtained in this way for compounds of the actinide elements (*e.g.* by Zachariasen, 1954). But structure analysis from powder photographs becomes difficult, and soon impracticable, with crystals of lower symmetry, which means with most organic and inorganic substances of stereochemical interest. Then it is necessary to work

---

* For the most thorough study yet made of these effects, see Cruickshank (1956).

† Zero-point energy, however, persists; so that with an atom as light as hydrogen the amplitude of vibration does not appreciably decrease below room temperature (Bacon and Pease, 1955).

13

with single crystals. It is not essential for the crystal to be well formed, but it must exceed a minimum size—*e.g.* not less than 0·1 mm in any dimension. Techniques for handling smaller crystals have indeed been outlined, but they are not yet widely adopted. It is highly inconvenient if the material is in the habit of giving twinned crystals.

Secondly, it must be possible to surmount the phase problem. Pending the discovery of a general method, this imposes a serious restriction. In the absence of any of the favourable features mentioned above, the prognosis would not be good for the analysis of a structure requiring the location of more than 10 atoms. However it is often possible for the chemist to contrive a suitably crystalline derivative containing a heavy atom, or one that can be isomorphously replaced. Thus an iodoacetate led to the successful determination of the stereochemical configuration of the pentacyclic triterpene oleanolic acid (Abd El Rahim and Carlisle, 1954), which was shown to be V.

V

Thirdly, it is difficult to locate light atoms in the presence of several heavier ones. This was the basis for the generalization that ' x-rays cannot detect hydrogen atoms '. The generalization is no longer valid, though it is true that their detection is more difficult and less accurate than that of other atoms. The intensity data need to be reliable, and the positions of the other atoms must first be precisely ascertained; for the hydrogen atoms show up well only after the effects of these other atoms have been accurately eliminated. The use of low temperatures is also advantageous (*cf* Hirshfeld and Schmidt, 1956; Richards, 1956).

Electron and Neutron Diffraction

A particle moving with momentum, mv, is associated with a de Broglie wave-length, $\lambda = h/mv$, and a beam of such particles can give rise to diffraction effects in appropriate circumstances. In principle, any kind of particles could be used; at present, results of value in crystal-structure analysis have been obtained with electrons, and especially with neutrons.

Beams of ' monochromatic ' electrons have been used for many years in studying the surfaces of solids and the structures of molecules in the gaseous state. During the past few years they have been applied to investigating the internal structures of crystals in a manner wholly analogous to x-ray diffraction. Work in this field (' electronography ') has been most actively pursued in Russia (*e.g.* Pinsker, 1953), but Cowley (1953) has published papers on the subject from Australia. The scattering of electrons depends on the varying electrostatic potential field in the crystal. By treating quantitative electron-diffraction measurements by the Fourier-series method, a map can be computed showing the distribution of potential in the unit cell, and having peaks at the positions occupied by atoms. There are some serious difficulties, notably because very thin crystals (thickness $< 10^{-5}$cm) must be used, and because they must be exposed to a high vacuum. The main advantage from the stereochemical viewpoint is that hydrogen atoms show themselves as peaks decidedly more prominent than those in the maps derived from x-ray data. Several impressive potential maps, in which the positions of the hydrogen atoms are strikingly evident, have been published (*e.g.* one is reproduced by Speakman, 1954) but, so far, full details of the work are not available. Cowley's analysis (1953) of orthoboric acid led him to postulate an unorthodox type of hydrogen bonding. However it is possible that the corrections needed to allow for random stacking of successive layers of atoms vitiated his map sufficiently to give spurious ' hydrogen peaks '; for Zachariasen (1954) has described a very careful refinement of his own early x-ray analysis, and the hydrogen atoms, now well manifested, occupy positions corresponding to normal bonding, as suggested at VI. The O⋯⋯O distance is 2·72 Å, and the hydrogen appears to be slightly off the direct line between the oxygens, and 0·88 Å from one of them.

VI

As concentrated sources of slow neutrons become more available, neutron diffraction (*e.g.* Bacon, 1955) is becoming a valuable adjunct to x-ray crystal-analysis. The technique at present is difficult, and the method is best applied when the structure has already been studied with x-rays. Neutrons are scattered by the atomic nuclei. This has two important consequences. First, the atom appears as a point, except in so far as it may be ' spread out ' by its thermal motions; and this makes for greater precision in its location, though it becomes even more necessary to correct for finite-series errors. Secondly, the

15

scattering power is a function of the particular nuclear species, and does not increase steadily with atomic number. Light and heavy atoms in general scatter equally well. The scattering power of ordinary hydrogen, H, is negative (*i.e.* it scatters neutrons with an anomalous change of phase), so that hydrogen atoms appear, on the map showing the distribution of neutron-scattering power, as negative peaks; but their magnitude is of the same order as those indicating oxygen or carbon atoms, and they can be located with equal accuracy. Deuterium, on the other hand, produces positive peaks.

The immediate chemical importance of neutron-diffraction is thus that it provides an effective means of locating hydrogen atoms. One of the first applications was in the study of ice. Wollan, Davidson and Shull (1949), using ice made from heavy water, obtained results which supported Pauling's (1935) proposed structure : that it consists of discrete water molecules, with the hydrogens situated along the O········O directions, but nearer to one oxygen (~ 1.05 Å) than the other (~ 1.70 Å), and, throughout the macroscopic crystal, distributed randomly between the two possible positions. Peterson and Levy (1952) have confirmed this, using ordinary ice. Bacon and Pease (1953, 1955) have carried out a detailed study of KH_2PO_4, a substance which includes a short hydrogen bond (O········O = 2.49 Å). At room temperature the negative peak was elongated in a manner consistent with either of the following interpretations : either the proton oscillates between two positions of minimum potential energy on each side of the mid-point, or it executes vibrations, of notable anisotropy along the bond direction, about a single minimum. In a parallel study at 77°K (where the substance has undergone transition to a ferroelectric phase), with the crystal maintained as a single domain by application of an electrostatic field, the hydrogen appeared as a single peak, of nearly circular section, 1.05 Å from one oxygen atom and 1.43 Å from the other. Bacon and Curry (1956) have reported a study of trona, $Na_3(HCO_3)CO_3.2H_2O$, a crystal previously known to contain a short, and crystallographically centrosymmetrical, hydrogen bond (see p. 5). The acidic hydrogen appears as a peak at the centre of symmetry, only very slightly elongated in the direction of the bond.

Hydrogen atoms are difficult to find by x-ray diffraction because of their insignificant scattering power. An opposite kind of difficulty arises when chemically different atoms, such as Mg and Al, have almost identical scattering powers, and so cannot be distinguished. Neutron diffraction can be valuable here, since it happens that Mg has nearly double the neutron-scattering power of Al. Thus it has been possible to prove that the metal atoms in spinel, $MgAl_2O_4$, are (at least very nearly) arranged in the ' normal ' way, with Mg in tetrahedral, and Al in octahedral, sites.

16

Nuclear Magnetic Resonance

In favourable instances, very precise information about the arrangement of protons, and one or two other isotopic species, in a crystal can be deduced from a study of its nuclear magnetic resonance absorption (*cf* Smith, 1953). The effect measured depends on the magnitudes and directions of the lines joining all possible pairs of neighbouring protons, rather than on the actual positions themselves; but from this *vectorial* information, it is often practicable to infer the positions of the protons with high accuracy. Amongst many other applications, nuclear magnetic resonance can be used to decide whether the hydrate of an acid, HX, is a true hydrate, $HX.H_2O$, or an oxonium salt, $H_3O^+ X^-$. The former situation obtains in oxalic acid dihydrate (as has since been confirmed via an exact electron-density projection, by Pringle, 1954); the latter obtains in the monohydrates of nitric and perchloric acids, and in the dihydrate of sulphuric acid.

The position found for a hydrogen atom tends to be somewhat closer to that of its heavier, neighbouring atom when determined by x-ray analysis than by other physical methods. Should this effect prove to be general, its explanation might be that the position of the proton needs not coincide exactly with the associated point of maximum electron-density.

DISSYMMETRIC MOLECULES IN CRYSTALS

The accommodation of dissymmetric molecules in crystals has been considered by Hägg (1944; see also Nowacki, 1942 *etc.*). A molecule is not superposable upon its mirror-image when it does not possess any symmetry element of the second sort—*i.e.* when it has no inversion axis* (*cf* Wheland, 1949; Woodward, 1955; note that an *n*-fold inversion axis is conventionally represented as $\bar{n}$). In almost all cases so far studied, this corresponds to the familiar rule that the molecule must not possess either a centre ($\bar{1}$) or a plane ($m = \bar{2}$) of symmetry. But a molecule lacking both may yet possess an inversion axis of a higher order divisible by 4, and so not be resolvable. The first case of this kind has been described recently by McCasland and Proskow (1955); the cation of the ' *meso-trans/trans* ' diastereomer of 3 : 3′ : 4 : 4′-tetramethyl*spiro*-(1 : 1′)-bipyrrolidinium toluene-*p*-sulphonate (VII) has a $\bar{4}$-axis, and is not resolvable despite the absence of $\bar{1}$ and *m*.

It follows that dissymmetric molecules of one hand only cannot occur in crystals belonging to a space-group that includes a centre of symmetry, or a mirror-, or glide-plane, or a $\bar{4}$-axis. (Axes of orders higher than 6 are excluded from space-groups; they cannot be

---

* An alternative description, now little used by crystallographers, is that it must possess no alternating axis.

embodied in the symmetry of a crystal lattice.) For, if the molecule were in a special position, where such a crystallographic symmetry element formed part of its own point-group symmetry, it would

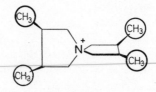

VII

necessarily be a *meso*-form, and not dissymmetric; whilst, if it were in a general position, any one of these elements would imply the presence of an enantiomorphic molecule, so that a racemate would result. This means that only 65 of the 230 possible space-groups are eligible for optically active substances. The author can find no authenticated exception to this rule. If any should be found (and this seems not impossible), it would be natural to explain it as due to some kind of disorder, such as molecular rotation, which had made the molecule simulate a higher symmetry than was inherent (see p. 5). The great majority of optically active substances crystallize in the space-groups $P2_1$ and $P2_12_12_1$. A succession of one-handed molecules arrange themselves along a two-fold screw axis (2_1).

The overcrowded compound 3 : 4-benzophenanthrene (XIV, p. 25) crystallizes in $P2_12_12_1$. It follows that in any single crystal the molecules must all be of one hand. Crystallization has led to spontaneous resolution, though the crystals were not large enough for the effect to be confirmed by direct optical means. A similar, though more complex, case is the benzene adduct with tri-*o*-thymotide discovered by Powell (1954). Here the effect has been verified optically.

Racemates, on the other hand, involve the remaining 165 space-groups. In them, *dextro*- and *laevo*-molecules are usually paired about a centre of symmetry, or occasionally about a plane. They may, however, merely be related by a glide-plane, in which case there is a regular alternation of antimeric molecules, without discrete pairs. DL-Alanine crystallizes in the space-group *Pb2n* (Albrecht *et al.*, 1943) and illustrates this possibility.

Compounds that are not resolvable frequently crystallize as racemates. Thus four molecules occupying general positions in a unit cell of space-group $P2_1/a$ are each in a dissymmetric environment, and are themselves strictly dissymmetric, with equal numbers of right- and left-handed forms present. The distinction between them may well depend on some slight—perhaps even immeasurable—detail of conformation or bond-angle, and it will then disappear when the molecules leave the lattice. (It has already been pointed out that the full point-symmetry of the idealized molecule is rarely exploited in the crystal.) In some cases, on the other hand, the distinction is obvious, even though it still disappears in solution. The *cis*-azobenzene molecule is forced to deviate considerably from coplanarity by the repulsion between the *ortho*-hydrogen atoms, so that it possesses only a two-fold axis of symmetry, and it exists in the crystal in *dextro*- and *laevo*-forms (Hampson and Robertson, 1941). Similarly the creatinine molecule (VIII) has the methyl group 0·25 Å out of the plane of the other seven skeletal atoms; it is thus dissymmetric, and the crystal is a racemate (du Pré and Mendel, 1955).

$$O{=}C\underset{\displaystyle NH-C{=}NH}{\overset{\displaystyle CH_2-N-CH_3}{\big\langle}}$$

VIII

Crystallographic evidence of molecular symmetry is therefore of much greater significance than is evidence of dissymmetry. This principle was utilized by Carlisle and Crowfoot (1941) in discriminating between isomeric $\alpha:\beta$-disubstituted dibenzyls of the *meso*- and racemic series. The solid isomer of $\alpha:\beta$-diethyldibenzyl belongs to the space-group $P2_1/c$, with two molecules in the unit cell. The molecules must therefore possess a centre of symmetry and be internally compensated *meso*-forms. The liquid isomer may then be presumed to be a racemate. Again the $p:p'$-diaminocompound of m.p. 140°C, derived from the solid dibenzyl, also had two molecules in a cell of symmetry $P2_1/c$, so that it too was a *meso*-compound. The other diamino-derivative of m.p. 97–8° had four molecules in a cell belonging to the space-group Cc, which is consistent with its being a racemate, though not decisive. Generally the *meso*-compounds were found to have the higher melting points. As was pointed out by the authors, the finding of centro-symmetry in a single compound is not conclusive, because there is a chance (though remote in a dibenzyl) that the molecule might acquire spurious symmetry through disorder; but this chance can be excluded when the results with several pairs of isomers are mutually consistent, as they are here.

Determination of Absolute Configuration

When the x-ray analysis of an optically active compound has been completed, so that x-, y- and z-coordinates can be assigned to all the atoms, the absolute configuration of the molecule is still ambiguous. The x-ray data are equally well satisfied by a structure in which the directions of the reference axes have been reversed, thus leading to the enantiomorphic structure. The reason for this is explained in principle by FIGURE 1, in which (i) represents the reflexion from an *hkl* face of the crystal, consisting of two kinds of layers of atoms, A and B. When the Bragg equation is satisfied for successive layers of either kind ($A, A, A\ldots$ or $B, B, B\ldots$), the waves diffracted from the B-layers (broken lines) lag behind those from the A-layers (continuous lines), as is suggested in (ii); and the two sets of waves combine to yield the composite wave represented by the heavy line. Reflexion from the opposite crystal face, $\bar{h}\bar{k}\bar{l}$, is shown at (iii). The waves from the B-layers are now ahead of those from A, as in (iv). The composite wave in (iv) differs from that in (ii) only in the undetermined phase-angle; the *observable* property, the amplitude (or the intensity), is the same. This is the normal behaviour covered by Friedel's law: $|F_{hkl}| = |F_{\bar{h}\bar{k}\bar{l}}|$, and the corresponding intensities are equal. In the ordinary way x-rays cannot distinguish between hkl and $\bar{h}\bar{k}\bar{l}$.

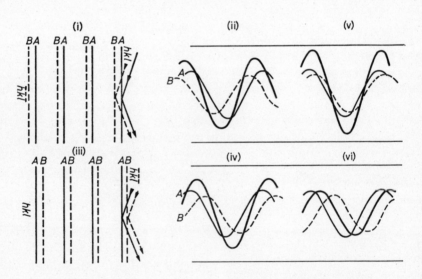

FIGURE 1. Reflexion of x-rays, at Bragg angle, from hkl and $\bar{h}\bar{k}\bar{l}$ faces of a crystal: (ii) and (iv), the normal case when Friedel's law is obeyed; (v) and (vi), the anomalous case when Friedel's law fails because of a phase-change at the B-layers.

Friedel's law breaks down, however, when the x-rays are so chosen as to have a frequency which excites the inner electrons of one kind of atom (let it be those of type B). The scattering at the B-layers is then accompanied by a change of phase, which can be evaluated. (It is shown as an advance in FIGURE 1.) The situation then becomes that represented in (v) and (vi). The phase-differences between the waves from the A- and B-layers, which were equal in amount, though different in sign in (ii) and (iv), now differ in amount too, being diminished in (v) and increased in (vi). The composite waves now differ in amplitude, as well as in phase: $|F_{hkl}| > |F_{\bar{h}\bar{k}\bar{l}}|$ —an *observable* difference.

The applicability of this principle to the present problem was first recognized by Bijvoet (1949; see also 1955), and it was realized in practice by Peerdeman, van Bommel and Bijvoet (1951) with sodium rubidium (+)-tartrate, the structure of which was already known apart from its absolute configuration. Using x-rays from a zirconium target, which excite the rubidium atom, it was possible to calculate the respective intensities for 15 pairs of reflexions, *hkl* and $\bar{h}k\bar{l}$, assuming the tartrate ion to have the configuration, shown in IX equivalent to the Fischer convention. In four cases the differences observed were uncertain; in the eleven others they were consistently in the sense calculated. By a fortunate even chance therefore, the convention corresponds to reality. As described in Chapter 5 of Volume 1 (Mills and Klyne, 1954), it thus became possible to assign absolute configurations to all other molecules that can be related to tartaric acid*.

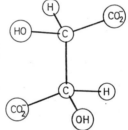

IX. The absolute configuration, and conformation, of the tartrate ion in NaRb (+)-tartrate.

This conclusion has been confirmed with rubidium hydrogen (+)-tartrate (van Bommel, 1953). In a similar way, absolute configurations have been directly determined with x-rays for D(—)-*iso*-leucine (Trommel and Bijvoet, 1954), for the inorganic complex ion in $2\{(+)[Co(en)_3]^{3+} 3[Cl]^-\}\cdot NaCl\cdot 6H_2O$ (Saito *et al.*, 1955)— and for strychnine (Peerdeman, 1956).

Mathieson (1956) has pointed out that, if an asymmetric residue of known absolute configuration is substituted in a molecule of unknown configuration, then a normal x-ray analysis of the substituted compound, without the use of special radiations, would suffice to reveal the absolute configuration of the whole molecule, including that of the unsubstituted material. This method has been applied independently by Hine and Rogers (1956) to (+)-*S*-methyl-D-cysteine-*S*-oxide (X). A straightforward x-ray analysis reveals the structure and conformation

* Grenville-Wells and Lonsdale (1954) have shown that it is possible to distinguish between the intensities of *hkl* and $\bar{k}\bar{k}\bar{l}$ reflexions in Laue photographs, using non-mono-chromatic x-rays; and hence that absolute configurations could be determined in this way. The underlying principle is the same as that described above.

of the molecule, apart from its absolute configuration; but, since the configuration at the L_s-α-carbon atom is already known, that of the whole molecule can be deduced unambiguously to be as represented in X. The configuration at the sulphur atom (which is thus determined

X

for the first time) is S in the notation proposed by Cahn, Ingold and Prelog (1956).

As was also pointed out by Mathieson, this device would be applicable if the unit of known configuration were introduced as a component in a molecular compound.

MOLECULAR OVERCROWDING AND OTHER STERIC EFFECTS

The accumulated results of structural crystallography are the chief source of information about intermolecular 'contact' distances. Non-bonded and neutral atoms, with filled shells of valency electrons, exert on each other a weakly attractive force, arising mainly from the dispersion effect. Opposed to this attraction is a repulsion, which may be attributed to the reluctance of separate electron-clouds to interpenetrate. A characteristic of these repulsive forces is that they increase very sharply with decreasing interatomic distance. For this reason a fairly definite contact can be envisaged, so long as only weak attractions are involved (cf Volume 1, pp. 145–6). Tables of standard minimum separations between non-bonded atoms were therefore drawn up by several early authorities, and their findings were systematized in Pauling's set of van der Waals radii* (see Volume 1, p. 365). Within the limitations implied by its author, this set is still generally acceptable. The value of 1·2 Å tentatively suggested for hydrogen has received a somewhat firmer basis in Russian work on the electron-diffraction from a crystalline paraffin (Vainshtein and Pinsker, 1954). An anomalously short intermolecular contact had been reported in crystalline triphenylene; but this irregularity has disappeared as the result of two independent emendations of this

* Both attractive and repulsive forces have been associated with the name of van der Waals, the references being to the a and b terms, respectively, of his equation of state.

structure analysis (Vand and Pepinsky, 1954; Pinnock, Taylor and Lipson, 1956). The anomalously close contact between an oxygen atom of *p*-nitraniline and the carbon atom *ortho* to the amino-group of another molecule (Abrahams and Robertson, 1948) appeared to gain significance from the discovery (McKeown, Ubbelohde and Woodward, 1951) that the crystal has a remarkably high coefficient of thermal expansion in a direction nearly parallel to this contact. But it now appears (Abrahams and Robertson, 1956) that an unsuspected ambiguity involving the intermolecular packing in this crystal may have affected the values derived for the contact distances, and that an alternative arrangement, with no abnormal van der Waals separations, may yield a better agreement between observed and calculated intensities.

As Pauling pointed out, a strict adherence to the contact distances deducible from a table of fixed radii is not to be expected. In particular the distance must depend on the direction of the contact with respect to the covalent bonding of the atoms concerned. The effective radius of an atom X, linked to the rest of its molecule, Y, is relatively large in a direction away from Y. It is considerably smaller in directions making angles, at X, of about 90° with X-Y, as is shown, for instance, by the absence of obvious steric stress in simple groupings such as : CCl_2, where the distance between the chlorine atoms ($\sim 2 \cdot 9$ Å) is much less than the sum of their van der Waals radii ($3 \cdot 6$ Å); or, to take a more complex case, in propane, where the distance between terminal carbon atoms ($\sim 2 \cdot 5$ Å) is very much less than twice the radius ($2 \cdot 0$ Å) attributed to a methyl group.

These oblique contacts are often critical in causing *intramolecular overcrowding*. The term was introduced by Bell and Waring (1949) in discussing aromatic compounds, the molecules of which would be expected to be planar, were it not for the steric interference between some of their atoms. Many compounds of this type have been studied, and the effects of overcrowding demonstrated by the methods of organic chemistry, as is reviewed by Campbell (1953). A remarkable example is the recent resolution of phenanthrophenanthrene (XI) by

XI

Newman and his co-workers (1955). This is the first known optically active hydrocarbon owing its molecular dissymmetry to overcrowding.

In a number of compounds the methods of x-ray crystallography have yielded quantitative measurements of the distortions caused by overcrowding, despite the fact that overcrowded molecules lack the special feature of planarity which often allows aromatic structures to be studied with an accuracy not otherwise obtainable by two-dimensional methods. In a recent review, Harnik, Herbstein, Schmidt and Hirshfeld (1954) have made the following generalizations. (i) Overcrowding sets in when the unperturbed structure would bring two carbon atoms—whether aromatic carbons or methyl groups—to within 3·0 Å of each other. (ii) When there is over-crowding, it finds relief principally by an out-of-plane distortion, which tends to be spread over the whole molecule, rather than by the stretching of particular bonds*. That the critical distance between methyl groups is much smaller than twice the conventional radius no doubt depends partly on the directional effect already mentioned; it may also depend on the fact that the exact positions of the hydrogen atoms are usually uncertain, and that hydrogens of contiguous methyl groups may 'intermesh' (see p. 28). Where chlorine–chlorine contacts are involved, overcrowding sets in at about 3·15 Å.

The first unsubstituted aromatic hydrocarbon, showing molecular distortion, to be studied with x-rays was 3 : 4-5 : 6-dibenzophenanthrene (XII) (McIntosh, Robertson and Vand, 1954). This compound is now known to exist in two polymorphic forms. The α-form (m.p. 177–8°) used was unfortunately the less convenient for analysis. The unit cell comprises 12 molecules, 8 of them in general positions, and 4 in special where the molecule makes use of a two-fold axis of symmetry. Despite this unhelpful complexity, a structure determination of moderate accuracy was achieved by two-dimensional methods. The two crystallographically distinct kinds of molecules did not differ significantly in their structures, and the common distortion is sketched in XIII, which shows the aspect of the molecule when viewed along its two-fold axis. The interfering carbon atoms, marked with asterisks in XII, are thus able to increase their separation from 1·4 Å to 3·0 Å.

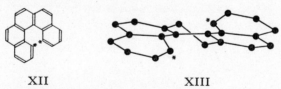

XII   XIII

Coulson and Senent (1955) have explored this distortion by a theoretical treatment involving an approximate potential function for the out-of-plane vibrations of π-electron systems. Starting from the idealized planar molecule, they suppose the atoms, including hydrogen, to have been displaced by various distances normal to the plane. The

---

* Spectroscopic evidence makes it clear that molecular distortions occur with increasing facility in the order : bond-stretching < bond-bending (deformation) < bond-twisting (torsion). The effects of overcrowding can be largely, though not wholly, described in terms of the last of these.

displacement of the interfering carbon atoms—one up, the other down
—was adjusted so as to separate them by the observed distance (3·0 Å),
and that of the attached hydrogen atoms so as to separate each of
them by 2·7 Å (= 1·5+1·2 Å) from the opposite (non-attached)
carbon. The displacement of the other 32 atoms were treated as
unknowns. The rise in potential energy due to the distortion was then
calculated by use of two force-constants derived from the vibrational
spectrum of benzene, and minimized in the usual way in terms of the
unknowns. The displacements thus calculated agreed extremely well
with those observed in the x-ray study. It was also roughly estimated
that the warping of the molecule led to a loss of resonance energy of
some 28 kcal.mole^{-1} out of the 162 kcal.mole^{-1} calculated for the
coplanar structure; but no experimental datum is yet available.
Coulson and Senent end their paper with the remark: ' the fact that
(this loss of energy) is so small in relation to the deformations shows
how relatively easy it is to build up quite large displacements in
aromatic molecules of this sort by a series of small distortions around
each of the carbon atoms of the molecular framework '. That it is
possible to make small changes in bond-directions without any
appreciable consequent change of bond-lengths is illustrated by a very
careful analysis of acridine III, recently reported by Phillips (1956).
In this polymorph, pairs of acridine molecules face one another, in
anti-parallel arrangement, across centres of symmetry. Between them
there are some short (though not very short) intermolecular contacts;
and to these with the accompanying polarization effects may be
attributed the small but significant deviations of the molecule from
strict planarity. But the C—C bond-lengths agree extraordinarily
closely with the corresponding lengths in anthracene as refined by
Ahmed and Cruickshank (1952), though the anthracene molecule is
substantially planar (see also Cruickshank, 1956).

XIV   XV

Herbstein and Schmidt (1954a) have described the structure of
3 : 4-benzophenanthrene (XIV). The analysis was done by two-
dimensional methods, and high accuracy is not claimed, so that
differences in individual bond-lengths are perhaps not generally
significant. Nevertheless their work gives an adequate picture of the
molecular distortion, which is sketched in XV, and by which the atoms
marked with asterisks become separated by 3·0 Å. The details of the
distortion and their implications are fully discussed by the authors.
For instance, the bonding at the carbon atoms must deviate from the

directions required by the sp^2-hybridized orbitals normally used in aromatic systems; at some points the bond-directions approximate more nearly to the requirements of sp^3-hybridization; and this can be correlated with chemical reactivity at these sites. Again the structure is in accord with the observation by Bergmann *et al.* (1951) of a non-zero dipole moment of 0.70 ± 0.07 D in benzene solution. On the other hand, the same workers found a smaller, but significant, moment for perylene (XVI), the molecule of which should not be

XVI

significantly overcrowded, and is certainly very nearly planar in the solid state (Donaldson, Robertson and White, 1953). Hirshfeld and Schmidt (1956) have briefly reported the refinement of the structure of benzophenanthrene, and of some other overcrowded hydrocarbons, at liquid-nitrogen temperature. The improved resolution has enabled them to locate the positions of the hydrogen atoms, even in two-dimensional projections. This should be of considerable value in studying possible changes of hybridization at the carbon atoms.

The series of derivatives of pentacene represented by the formulae XVII–XX is being studied at Glasgow (personal communication by

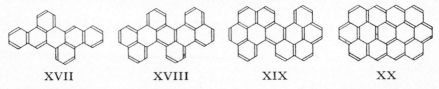

XVII   XVIII   XIX   XX

Professor Robertson). Pentacene itself has not been studied in detail, but its molecule is probably planar. The compound XVII, so far studied only in a single projection, has a molecule that is almost planar, but probably is slightly distorted. The compound XVIII has been thoroughly investigated by Rossmann. The molecule is greatly distorted, so as to maintain the usual distance of about 3·0 Å between the interfering carbon atoms. The directions in which the various parts of the molecule are displaced are such as to give a structure of approximate symmetry 2, but this is not a crystallographic two-fold axis. A warped molecule will pack less easily than a flat one; and accordingly the distance between the mean molecular planes of XVIII is about 3·9 Å, compared with the 3·4 Å characteristic of normal aromatic hydrocarbons. Compound XIX has so far received only a preliminary study. Its cell unit has an axis of 3·9 Å, which suggests that the molecules may be similarly non-planar with their mean planes nearly perpendicular to this axis. Circumanthracene, XX, has been studied (Clar *et al.*, 1956) only in one projection, but its molecules are almost certainly planar, like those of coronene and ovalene, and they are packed with about 3·4 Å between their planes.

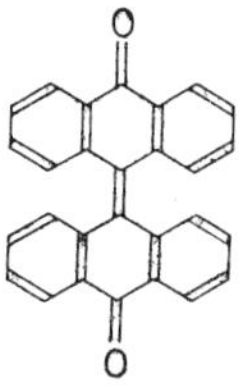

XXI

A somewhat different form of overcrowding is exemplified by dianthronylidene (or dianthrone, XXI), also studied via projections by Harnik and Schmidt (1954). Here again two pairs of carbon atoms would be only 1·4 Å apart in a coplanar molecule. Distortion of the kind sketched in XXII raises this distance to 2·9 Å. In more

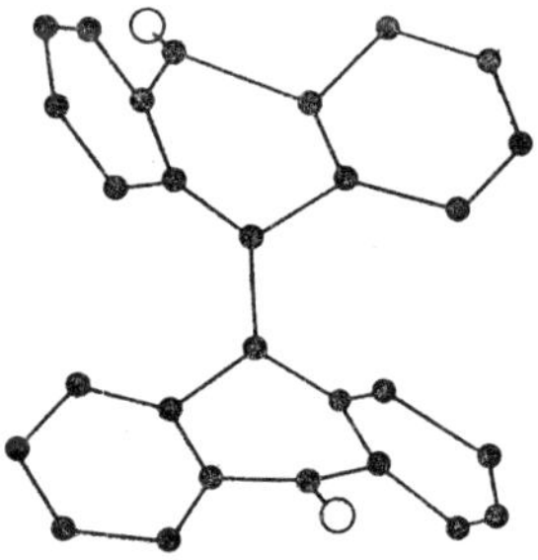

XXII

detail, the warping can be described as follows: the molecule is strictly centrosymmetric, and it approximates closely to the point-symmetry $2/m$; the plane of symmetry includes the carbonyl groups and the two central carbon atoms, and the axis is perpendicular to this plane and through the molecular centre; the central bond is effectively double (C—C = 1·31 Å), and the six atoms of the ethylenic group are coplanar; with this plane those of the benzene rings make angles of about 40°, so that resonance between each of them and the double bond is greatly reduced, the intervening C—C bonds having lengths of about 1·53 Å. The anthraquinone molecule is coplanar in the solid state; but the two anthraquinone residues in XXI are each folded along their centre-lines.

A re-examination (Nyburg, 1954) of earlier x-ray work on di-fluorenylidene (XXIII) shows that its molecules are in fact non-planar, as would be expected. An incomplete analysis, in a single projection

27

(Herbstein and Schmidt, 1954b), of tetrabenzonaphthalene (XXIV) excludes the possibility that its molecule is coplanar. The distortion is probably in accordance with the symmetry 222.

XXIII   XXIV

If all the carbon atoms in the octamethylnaphthalene molecule were coplanar, the pairs of methyl groups in the *peri*-positions would be only 2·4 Å apart. Overcrowding is therefore to be expected, and the crystal structure analysis (Donaldson and Robertson, 1953), using two-dimensional methods giving fairly high accuracy, substantiates this. By space-group requirement, the molecule has 222 symmetry. The *peri*-(α-) methyl groups are displaced from the plane by about 0·73 Å in opposite directions, so as to clear one another by 2·98 Å. The β-methyl groups are also displaced by about 0·3 Å, each in a sense opposite to that of its neighbouring α-group, so that again a separation of about 3·0 Å is maintained. A slighter deviation of the aromatic carbon atoms from the mean plane is suspected, but not proved.

However, in hexamethylbenzene, which was carefully analysed by Brockway and Robertson (1939) using two-dimensional methods, the twelve carbon atoms are certainly very close to a coplanar arrangement, though the methyl groups can then be only 2·9 Å apart. It appears that, in ' border-line ' cases such as this, a coplanar molecule is favoured in the solid state, whilst a non-planar molecule may exist in the vapour. This may well be attributed to the simple fact that flat objects can be packed together particularly conveniently. A familiar example is diphenyl. A very early x-ray study shows the crystals to have two molecules in a unit-cell belonging to the space-group $P2_1/a$. The molecule must therefore be centrosymmetric, and the two phenyl groups must be coplanar. By contrast, a reliable electron-diffraction study of the vapour (by Bastiansen, 1949) shows them to be rotated through $45 \pm 10°$ to one another. The ultra-violet spectra of solid and dissolved diphenyl are interpreted (Merkel and Wiegand, 1948) qualitatively in the same sense. More recent x-ray studies of several *m*- and *p*- (but not *o*-) substituted diphenyls have also indicated a planar arrangement in the solid state (*e.g.* Toussaint, 1948).

Proton magnetic resonance measurements have been made on solid hexamethylbenzene by Andrews (1950) at temperatures down to 95°K. They are interpreted by supposing that the methyl groups are rotating, presumably with the hydrogen atoms of contiguous methyls ' in gear '. The unit cell of this substance contains only one molecule. All the molecules in a single crystal are therefore parallel and in a known orientation. This circumstance facilitates the study of its absorption spectrum with polarized light; and such an investigation at 20°K, in the 2800 Å region, has been reported by McClure and Schnepp (1955). The interpretation of the results was difficult at some points because of uncertainty about the influence of the crystal environment on the selection rules; but it was concluded that the molecular symmetry was either $6/m$ $(= C_{6h})$ or $\bar{3}$ $(= S_6)$, the latter being the more probable. Rotation of the methyl groups apparently does not occur at this low temperature. The $\bar{3}$ symmetry would permit some puckering of the molecule, though this might be restricted to the excited state only. (Hexamethylbenzene undergoes a transition at about 108°K. The nature of the change is unknown. Since the crystal already belongs to the system—triclinic—of lowest symmetry, the change can hardly be associated with a lowering of symmetry as is often the case under such conditions.)

A similar unconformity obtains between electron-diffraction and x-ray crystallographic findings for hexachlorobenzene. Lonsdale's x-ray analysis (1931) included the earliest electron-density projection for any organic crystal, and it implied that the chlorine atoms were coplanar with the benzene ring, or nearly so. If the molecule is in fact planar, normal values for the bond-lengths then imply that neighbouring chlorine atoms are 3·12 Å apart. Bastiansen and Hassel (1947), in an accurate study of the vapour, found this distance to be larger—3·15 Å. By itself this difference might not seem impressive, though it is beyond the probable experimental error. But the distance between *meta*-chlorine atoms (5·35 Å) is *less* than would be required by a coplanar structure; and the model in which the C—Cl bonds were directed ±12° out of the plane of the ring gave a consistently better agreement with the whole range of interatomic distances found experimentally. A rather more marked deviation from the planar structure was found in *o*-dichlorobenzene and some other related compounds.

Possible explanations of these apparent discrepancies are: (i) that the molecules are non-planar in both states, but that disorder in the crystal gives rise to a statistical planarity; (ii) that there are small, but genuine, differences between the molecular conformations in solid and vapour, for the reason suggested above; (iii) that the molecules are coplanar in both states, but that the substituent groups in the vapour execute considerable out-of-plane vibrations, which are in opposite phase as between neighbours. None of the x-ray studies made hitherto is precise enough to exclude (i); but it seems unlikely that this effect alone could explain all the observed differences.

Two remarkable compounds, the molecules of which show severe overcrowding, are *m*- and *p*-xylylenes (XXV and XXVI), which have been analysed by three-dimensional methods with considerable accuracy by Brown (1953). The *m*-compound was first made by Pellegrin (1899), and his formulation was confirmed by Wilson Baker and his co-workers (1951). The molecule has a crystallographic

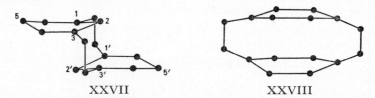

XXV   XXVI

centre of symmetry, and it proved to have the conformation suggested in XXVII. Carbon atoms 2 of the benzene rings (the points of attachment of the linking side-chains being 1 and 3) are about 2·69 Å apart. The distortion of the rings can be described either as a folding of each towards the other along the C(2) .... C(5) axis, or alternatively as a keel-to-keel presentation of two 'boat' forms. Each bond to the methylene groups makes an angle of about 15° with the mean plane of the benzene ring. These bonds and that between the two methylene groups do not deviate significantly from normal single bonds in length (C—C = 1·543 ± 0·013 Å), whilst the bonds in the rings are also normal after their kind (C—C = 1·386 ± 0·008 Å). (These limits are not formal e.s.d.-values, but are based on an averaging of the different bonds of either type.)

XXVII   XXVIII

The *para*-compound had been obtained as a solid of m.p. 285° amongst the products of pyrolysing *p*-xylene. The constitution was unknown, and it was solely by x-ray analysis that the molecule was shown to have the implausible-seeming formula XXVI. The crystal structure proved to be one of remarkable simplicity: there are two molecules, $C_{16}H_{16}$, in a cell of the space-group $P4_2/mnm$, and it follows that the molecule has the point-symmetry *mmm*, so that only 7 coordinates are needed to define the positions of the three carbon atoms constituting the asymmetric unit. Two of these must have identical *x*- and *y*-coordinates. In the refinement it was possible to locate the hydrogen atoms also. The conformation is sketched in XXVIII. The benzene rings are here folded away from one another along the line of the *para*-carbon atoms; or, in other words, the rings are each distorted to a 'boat' form, with a deck-to-deck presentation. Opposite

30

pairs of aromatic carbon atoms are separated by 2·83 or 3·09 Å. Again the C—C lengths are normal: 1·39–1·40 Å for the aromatic bonds, and 1·54–1·55 Å for the others.

In all the foregoing examples a molecule is pushed out of its ideally planar conformation because of intramolecular steric repulsions. An opposite situation would prevail in a molecule that was pulled out of the plane by intramolecular attractions. An example of this may be found in the analogue of nickel phthalocyanine (XXIX) prepared

XXIX

by Elvidge and Linstead (1952), which has a non-coplanar molecule in the solid state (Speakman, 1953). Phthalocyanine and its metal derivatives have coplanar molecules, and are usually isomorphous with each other (Robertson, 1935, 1936); and this is because the metal atom can be inserted without appreciably disturbing the shape of the molecule. But in a planar form of XXIX it seems likely that the pyridine nitrogen atoms would be about 4·8 Å apart, which is too far for the formation of dative bonds with the nickel atom (Ni—N $\approx$ 1·9 Å); and the warping of the structure has been tentatively attributed to the formation of such bonds.

Conformation of Fluorocarbon Chains

An interesting effect, which can be considered as akin to overcrowding, has been detected in straight-chain fluorocarbons by Bunn and Howells (1954). The normal conformation of hydrocarbon chains is that of a planar zig-zag (XXXc); but the chains in perfluorocetane ($C_{16}F_{34}$) and in poly-tetrafluoroethylene are twisted, so as to execute a half-turn (180°) in 13 CF_2-groups (XXXa, b). This difference is explained as the result of steric interaction which would otherwise occur between the fluorine atoms of alternate groups. In a planar carbon zig-zag, alternate atoms are 2·54 Å apart, and this distance would also separate hydrogen or fluorine atoms joined to these carbons. This separation exceeds the sum of the van der Waals radii of two hydrogen atoms ($\sim$ 2·4 Å), but is somewhat less than that of two fluorine atoms ($\sim$ 2·7 Å). The observed twist is substantially that required to maintain the necessary separation of the fluorine atoms.

31

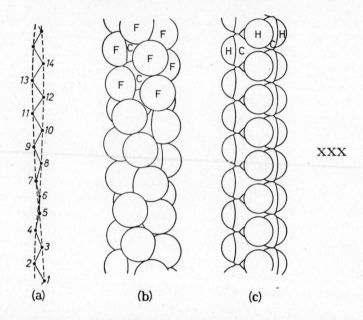

XXX

(a)   (b)   (c)

SOME X-RAY ANALYSES OF STEREOCHEMICAL INTEREST

Polysulphur Chains

An x-ray analysis by Dunitz (1956) has revealed the structure of the anion in sodium dithionite, $Na_2S_2O_4$, which had been the subject of much speculation. The ion can be represented as $[O_2S—SO_2]^{2-}$; the distribution of valencies round each sulphur atom is pyramidal, so that the structure can be likened to a tent (XXXI), with the sulphur atoms (S—S = $2·389 \pm 0·010$ Å) along the ridge, and the four oxygen atoms (S—O = $1·507 \pm 0·017$ Å) at the four corners, roughly in the same plane at 'ground level'.

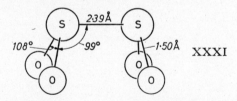

XXXI

In its elementary forms, as in its compounds, sulphur has a marked propensity for forming chains of atoms. A great many substances involving this structural feature, or with some of the sulphur atoms replaced by those of Group VI *B* elements, have been studied crystallographically (*cf* Speakman, 1954). The S—S—S angle is always within a few degrees of 105°. Unlike the polycarbon chain, the polysulphur chain when it comprises more than three atoms is never planar nor is it ever branched. Whereas the energy barriers hindering free rotation about the C—C bond are so situated as to favour a dihedral angle (*i.e.* the angle between the planes of C(1)—C(2)—C(3) and of C(2)—C(3)—C(4)) of 60°, or preferably 180°, those for S—S bonds favour a dihedral angle of about 90°. As with oxygen in H_2O_2, this can be attributed to the repulsion between the unshared electrons of the $p\pi$-orbitals on each atom; and Pauling (1949) has estimated that the barrier hindering free rotation should in the case of sulphur have a height of about 5 kcal.mole^{-1}. Observed values of the S—S—S—S dihedral angle are generally about 90°, but it is not surprising to find them ranging over 20° on either side. For further discussion of related systems see also Chapter 8.

As Foss (1953) has pointed out, a chain of five sulphur atoms should therefore exist in two stable conformations: in the *cis*-form the two terminal S—S bonds are on the same side of the plane defined by the central three atoms; in the *trans*-form they are on opposite sides. Provided it is regular in its bond-lengths and angles, the *cis*-form possesses a plane of symmetry; and it can be regarded as a segment of the annular S_8 molecule in orthorhombic sulphur. The details of this structure have been redetermined with high precision by Abrahams (1955). The *trans*-form possesses a two-fold axis of symmetry, and it constitutes a helix which is dissymmetric and so can be of either hand; it can be regarded as a section of the extended helices in plastic sulphur, or of the corresponding ones in hexagonal selenium or in tellurium. Pentathionates and related compounds exemplify both types of chain. Barium pentathionate, $Ba(S_5O_6).2H_2O$, studied by Foss and Zachariasen (1954), has four stoicheiometric molecules in a unit cell of space-group P*nma*; the anion must therefore have a plane of symmetry, and must contain a *cis*-chain, as is borne out by the detailed analysis. On the other hand, Dawson, Mathieson and Robertson (1948) showed that sulphur diphenylthiosulphonate, Ph.SO_2.S.S.S. SO_2.Ph, has four molecules in a unit cell belonging to the enantiomorphous pair of space-groups, $P4_12_12$ and $P4_32_12$; it follows that the molecule must possess a two-fold axis of symmetry, and must embody a *trans*-chain. It also follows that spontaneous resolution must occur on crystallization, any individual crystal containing only *d*- or *l*-isomerides. The inherent difference in energy between *cis*- and *trans*-varieties of the same chain is likely to be small, so that it is not contrary to expectation to find that the same anion can assume either form in different salts. The anion in caesium hexasulphide (Abrahams and Grison, 1953) has the helical-chain form.

Olefin Complexes of Metallic Salts

Zeise's salt, of composition KCl.$PtCl_2$.C_2H_4.H_2O, has been known for over 120 years, and numerous other olefin complexes have been discovered subsequently. Werner formulated them as coordination

33

compounds (*e.g.* $K[PtCl_3(C_2H_4)].H_2O$), and there has been much speculation as to the mode of attachment of the olefin molecule (for a summary see Chatt, 1949). The structure proposed by Chatt and Duncanson (1953), and justified by infra-red evidence in particular, has now been confirmed by x-ray work (Wunderlich and Mellor, 1954, 1955), though at the moment only a preliminary account is available. The chlorine atoms occupy three corners of a square, at whose centre is the platinum atom; the distance between platinum and chlorine is 2·3–2·4 Å, though the locating of a light atom near to one so heavy as platinum cannot be accurate. The ethylene molecule is in the ' side-on ' position, with its centre at the fourth corner of the square and the C—C bond (~ 1.5 Å) perpendicular to its plane. The distance between platinum and carbon is approximately 2·2 Å. Following a suggestion by Dewar (1951), Chatt and Duncanson interpreted the bonding as follows : a σ-type bond results from overlap between the π-orbital of the olefin and the dsp^2-hybridized orbital of the platinum, the former acting as donor ; a π-type bond is also formed by overlap of the anti-bonding $\pi*2p$-orbital of the ethylene carbon atoms and two suitably directed dp-hybridized orbitals of the platinum, the latter now acting as donor. The cooperation of these two effects gives the complex its considerable stability ; and the two-way coordination avoids the accumulation of excessive charge on the ethylene.

Trichloromercury Oxonium Chloride

The basic mercuric chloride of composition $2HgCl_2.HgO$, has been known for many years, and its crystal structure has now been analysed by two independent groups of workers (Weiss *et al.*, 1953 ; Šćavničar and Grdenić, 1955), whose findings are in excellent agreement. The crystals belong to the cubic space-group $P2_13$, with two formula-units per cell. It follows that the oxygen atom and one chlorine must each be in a special position on a cube diagonal, with trigonal environment. In fact the compound proves to be an oxonium salt of formula XXXII.

XXXII

The atoms O—Hg—Cl are collinear, or nearly so, with the bonds O—Hg and Hg—Cl = 2·06 and 2·39 Å respectively, according to the former group of workers, and 2·03 and 2·28 Å according to the latter.

Both groups agree in finding the whole cation to be coplanar, though this is not a crystallographic requirement. An oxonium ion would be expected to have a pyramidal structure; notable amongst the evidence in favour of this expectation is the infra-red spectroscopic work of Ferriso and Hornig (1955) on the hydrates of the halogen hydrides at −195°C. For this reason the Jugoslav workers suggest that the O—Hg bonding may really be ionic, though the interatomic distance observed is more appropriate to a covalency; whilst the German workers think that the oxygen atom may be oscillating between positions on either side of the plane. However the precise location of an oxygen atom near the centre of gravity of three mercury atoms is difficult. Therefore, although the German group tried the effect of moving the oxygen atom through 0·4 Å to a position in accord with a more orthodox arrangement of the oxygen valencies, and found that this gave a decidedly inferior agreement between observed and calculated intensities, it may still be possible that the oxygen position deduced is a spurious one occasioned by its heavy environment.

Structure of a Mesoionic Compound

Bryden (1955) has studied the mesoionic compound produced by methylating 2-methyl-5-aminotetrazole. The substance gives a hydrochloride and a hydrobromide, and the structure could therefore be determined by the method of isomorphous replacement. It is not possible to represent a molecule of this type by any single bonddiagram, but the structure of the cation can be conventionally shown

$$CH_3—N \underset{N—N—CH_3}{\overset{N—C=\overset{+}{N}H_2}{\Big|}}$$

XXXIII

by XXXIII. The positions found for the atoms preclude the presence of any cross-linkage, and the bond-lengths between ring atoms (viz. N—N = 1·35, 1·30, 1·31 Å, and C—N = 1·36, 1·38 Å) imply much resonance stabilization. The exocyclic C—N bond is short (1·29 Å), and the position of this nitrogen atom in relation to the neighbouring halide ions indicates that the proton has been accepted here, though hydrogens were not explicitly located in this analysis.

The writer is indebted to Professor J. M. Robertson, F.R.S., Dr. T. H. Goodwin and Dr. S. C. Abrahams for helpful discussions, and to the last-named for access to his manuscript of a review article on the stereochemistry of oxygen, sulphur, and the elements of Group VI B (Abrahams, 1956).

REFERENCES

Abd El Rahim, A.M. and Carlisle, C. H. (1954) *Chem. & Ind.* 279
Abrahams, S. C. (1955) *Acta cryst., Cop.* **8**, 661; (1956) *Quart. Rev. chem. Soc., Lond.* **10**, 407
— and Grison, E. (1953) *Acta cryst., Cop.* **6**, 206
— and Robertson, J. M. (1948) *ibid* **1**, 252; (1956) *ibid* **9**, 966
Ahmed, F. R. and Cruickshank, D. W. J. (1953) *ibid* **6**, 385
Albrecht, G., Schnakenberg, G. W., Dunn, M. S. and McCullough, J. D. (1943) *J. phys. Chem.* **47**, 27
Andrew, E. R. (1950) *J. chem. Phys.* **18**, 607
Bacon, G. E. (1955) *Neutron Diffraction*, Oxford University Press
— and Curry, N. A. (1956) *Acta cryst., Cop.* **9**, 82
— and Pease, R. S. (1953) *Proc. roy. Soc.* **A220**, 397; (1955) *ibid* **A230**, 359
Baker, W. McOmie, J. F. W. and Norman, J. M. (1951) *J. chem. Soc.* 1114
Bastiansen, O. (1949) *Acta chem. Scand.* **3**, 408
— and Hassel, O. (1947) *ibid* **1**, 489
Beevers, C. A. and Lipson, H. (1935) *Proc. roy. Soc.* **A148**, 664
Bell, F. and Waring, D. H. (1949) *J. chem. Soc.* 2689
Bergmann, E. D., Fischer, E. and Pullman, B. (1951) *J. Chim. phys.* **48**, 356
Bernal, J. D. (1932) *Chem. & Ind.* **51**, 259; 466
Bijvoet, J. M. (1949) *Proc. Acad. Sci. Amst.* **52**, 152; (1955) *Endeavour* **14**, 71
Brockway, L. O. and Robertson, J. M. (1939) *J. chem. Soc.* 1324
Bommel, A. J. van (1953) *Proc. Acad. Sci. Amst.* **56B**, 268
Brown, C. J. (1953) *J. chem. Soc.* 3265; 3278
— Peiser, H. S. and Turner-Jones, A. (1949) *Acta cryst., Camb.* **2**, 167
Bryden, J. H. (1955) *ibid* **8**, 211
Bunn, C. W. and Howells, E. R. (1954) *Nature, Lond.* **174**, 549
Cahn, R. S., Ingold, C. K. and Prelog, V. (1956) *Experientia* **12**, 81
Campbell, I. G. M. (1953) *Annu. Rep. Progr. Chem.* **50**, 152
Carlisle, C. H. and Crowfoot, D. (1941) *J. chem. Soc.* 6
Chatt, J. (1949) *ibid* 3340
— and Duncanson, L. A. (1953) *ibid* 2939
Clar, E., Kelly, W., Robertson, J. M. and Rossmann, M. G. (1956) *ibid* 3878
Coulson, C. A. and Senent, S. (1955) *ibid* 1819
Cowley, J. M. (1953) *Acta cryst., Cop.* **6**, 522
Cox, E. G., Cruickshank, D. W. J. and Smith, J. A. S. (1955) *Nature, Lond.* **175**, 766
— Pinkard, F. W., Wardlaw, W. and Webster, K. C. (1935) *J. chem. Soc.* 459
— and Smith, J. A. S. (1954) *Nature, Lond.* **173**, 75
Cruickshank, D. W. J. (1949) *Acta cryst., Camb.* **2**, 65, 154; (1956) *ibid* **9**, 915
Davies, M. and Thomas, W. J. O. (1951) *J. chem. Soc.* 2858
Dawson, I. M., Mathieson, A. McL. and Robertson, J. M. (1948) *ibid* 322
Dewar, M. J. S. (1951) *Bull. Soc. chim. Fr.* **18C**, 79
Donaldson, D. M. and Robertson, J. M. (1953) *J. chem. Soc.* 17
Dunitz, J. D. (1956) *Acta cryst., Cop.* **9**, 579
Elvidge, J. A. and Linstead, R. P. (1952) *J. chem. Soc.* 5008
Ferriso, C. C. and Hornig, D. F. (1955) *J. chem. Phys.* **23**, 1464
Foss, O. (1953) *Acta chem. Scand.* **7**, 1221
— and Zachariasen, H. (1954) *ibid* **8**, 473
Fridrichsons, J. and Mathieson, A. McL. (1955) *Acta cryst., Cop.* **8**, 761
Grenville-Wells, H. J. and Lonsdale, K. (1954) *Nature, Lond.* **173**, 1145
Hägg, G. (1944) *Svedberg Anniversary Volume*, pp. 140–154, Stockholm, Almqvist and Wiksells

Hampson, G. C. and Robertson, J. M. (1941) *J. chem. Soc.* 409
Hargreaves, A. (1943) *Nature, Lond.* **152,** 600
Harnik, E., Herbstein, F. H., Schmidt, G. M. J. and Hirshfeld, F. L. (1954) *J. chem. Soc.* 3288
— and Schmidt, G. M. J. (1954) *ibid* 3295
Hendricks, S. B. (1933) *Z. Kristallogr.* **84,** 85
Herbstein, F. H. and Schmidt, G. M. J. (1954a) *J. chem. Soc.* 3302 ; (1954b) 3314
Hine, R. and Rogers, D. (1956) *Chem. & Ind.* 1428
Hirshfeld, F. L. and Schmidt, G. M. J. (1956) *Acta cryst., Cop.* **9,** 233
Hodgkin, D. C., Pickworth, J., Robertson, J. H., Trueblood, K. N., Prosen, R.J. and White, J. G. (1955) *Nature, Lond.* **176,** 325 (see also *ibid* **178,** 64)
Hughes, E. W. (1941) *J. Amer. chem. Soc.* **63,** 1737
Jeffrey, G. A. and Cruickshank, D. W. J. (1953) *Quart. Rev. chem. Soc.* **7,** 335
Klug, A. (1947) *Nature, Lond.* **160,** 570
Lipscomb, W. N. (1950) *Rev. sci. Instrum.* **21,** 396
Lipson, H. and Cochran, W. (1953) *Determination of Crystal Structures,* p. 207, London, Bell
Lonsdale, K. (1931) *Proc. roy. Soc.* **A133,** 536
McCasland, G. E. and Proskow, S. (1955) *J. Amer. chem. Soc.* **77,** 4688
McClure, D. S. and Schnepp, O. (1955) *Report, Off. Nav. Res., Phys. Branch,* N6–ori–211–III
McIntosh, A. O., Robertson, J. M. and Vand, V. (1954) *J. chem. Soc.* 1661
McKeown, P. J. A., Ubbelohde, A. R. and Woodward, I. (1951) *Acta cryst., Camb.* **4,** 391
Mathieson, A. McL. (1955) *Rev. Pure appl. Chem. Aust.* **5,** 113 ; (1956) *Acta cryst., Cop.* **9,** 317
Merkel, E. and Wiegand, C. (1948) *Z. Naturforsch.* **3b,** 93
Merritt, L. L. jr., Guare, C. and Lessor, A. E. jr. (1956) *Acta cryst., Cop.* **9,** 253
Newman, M. S., Lutz, W. B. and Lednicer, D. (1955) *J. Amer. chem. Soc.* **77,** 3420
Nowacki, W. (1942) *Helv. chim. Acta* **25,** 863 [See also : *ibid* (1951) **34,** 1957, and Part I of *Crystal Data* by J. D. H. Donnay and W. Nowacki (1954), Geolog. Soc. of America]
Nyburg, S. C. (1954) *Acta cryst., Cop.* **7,** 779
Pauling, L. (1935) *J. Amer. chem. Soc.* **57,** 2680 ; (1949) *Proc. nat. Acad. Sci., Wash.* **35,** 495
— and Shappell, M. D. (1930) *Z. Kristallogr.* **75,** 128
Peerdeman, A. F. (1956) *Acta cryst., Cop.* **9,** 824
— van Bommel, A. J. and Bijvoet, J. M. (1951) *Proc. Acad. Sci. Amst.* **B54,** 16 [See also : (1951) *Nature, Lond.* **168,** 271]
Pellegrin, M. (1899) *Rec. trav. chim. Pays-Bas* **18,** 457
Peterson, S. W. and Levy, H. A. (1952) *J. chem. Phys.* **20,** 704. [See also *Acta cryst., Cop.* **10,** (1957) 70]
Phillips, D. C. (1956) *Acta cryst., Cop.* **9,** 237
Pinnock, P. R., Taylor, C. A. and Lipson, H. (1956) *ibid* **9,** 173
Pinsker, Z. G. (1953) *Electron Diffraction* (Trans. by Spink and Feigl) London, Butterworths
Powell, H. M. (1954) *J. chem. Soc.* 2658 (includes other references)
Pré, S. du and Mendel, H. (1955) *Acta cryst., Cop.* **8,** 311
Pringle, G. E. (1954) *ibid* **7,** 716
Robertson, J. M. (1935) *J. chem. Soc.* 615 ; (1936) *ibid* 1195
— and Woodward, I. (1940) *ibid* 36
Robinson, Sir Robert and Teuber, H. J. (1954) *Chem. & Ind.* 783
Rogers, D. (1950) *Acta cryst., Camb.* **3,** 455
Rollett, J. S. (1955) *ibid* **8,** 487

Saito, Y., Nakatsu, K., Shiro, M. and Kuroya, H. (1955) *ibid* **8**, 729

Ščavničar, S. and Grdenić, D. (1955) *ibid* **8**, 275

Skinner, J. M., Stewart, G. M. D. and Speakman, J. C. (1954) *J. chem. Soc.* 180

Smith, J. A. S. (1953) *Quart. Rev. chem. Soc., Lond.* **7**, 279 (see also Richards, R. E. (1956) **10**, 480)

Speakman, J. C. (1948) *Nature, Lond.* **162**, 695; (1949) *J. chem. Soc.* 3357; (1953) *Acta cryst., Cop.* **6**, 784; (1954) *Annu. Rep. Progr. Chem.* **51**, 372; (1956) *ibid* **53**, in the Press

Stoicheff, B. P. and Herzberg, G. (1955) *Nature, Lond.* **175**, 79

Toussaint, J. (1948) *Acta cryst., Camb.* **1**, 43

Trommel, J. and Bijvoet, J. M. (1954) *ibid* **7**, 703

Vainshtein (Weinstein; Vajnštejn), B. K. and Pinsker, Z. G. (1954) *Trudy Inst. Kristall. Akad. Nauk, S.S.S.R.*, No. 10, 62

Vand, V. and Pepinsky, R. (1954) *Acta cryst., Cop.* **7**, 595

Vos, A. and Wiebenga, E. H. (1955) *ibid* **8**, 217; (1956) **9**, 92

Weiss, A., Nagorsen, G. and Weiss, Al. (1953) *Z. anorg. Chem.* **274**, 151

Wheatley, P. J. (1954) *Acta cryst., Cop.* **7**, 68

Wheland, G. W. (1949) *Advanced Organic Chemistry*, pp. 147–151, New York, Wiley

Wilson, A. J. C. (1949) *Acta cryst., Camb.* **2**, 318

Wollan, E. O., Davidson, W. L. and Shull, C. G. (1949) *Phys. Rev.* **75**, 1348

Woodward, P. (1955) *Chem. & Ind.* 1599

Wunderlich, J. A. and Mellor, D. P. (1954) *Acta cryst., Cop.* **7**, 130; (1955) **8**, 57

Zachariasen, W. H. (1954a) *ibid* **7**, 305; (1954b) *ibid* **7**, 783, 788, 792

2

THE STEREOCHEMISTRY OF HOMOLYTIC PROCESSES

Gareth H. Williams

THE existence of organic free radicals was experimentally demonstrated by Gomberg (1900) who first enunciated the hypothesis that an organic compound (in the first instance, hexaphenylethane) might exist in solution in equilibrium with the uncharged particles, or free radicals (in this case triphenylmethyl radicals) which were formed from it by dissociation. The idea of an anomalous valency for carbon was not at that time a popular one, but the accumulation of facts, from many fields, has resulted in the establishment of the concept.

Ingold (1938) distinguished between two modes of bond-fission, which were termed 'heterolysis' and 'homolysis':

$$\text{Heterolysis} \quad A : B \longrightarrow A :^- + B^+$$

$$\text{Homolysis} \quad A : B \longrightarrow A \cdot + B \cdot$$

where A and B are atoms or groups of atoms. The reaction of homolysis is characterized by the production of neutral fragments each possessing an odd, unpaired electron. The term 'free radical' is used in this sense and consequently may include some stable, more particularly inorganic, molecules *e.g.* nitric oxide.

Since more energy is required to separate the charged particles resulting from heterolytic fission of a bond than the neutral fragments resulting from the corresponding homolytic fission, it might be considered that the latter process should be favoured energetically, and in the gas phase this is certainly true. However, for the majority of reactions in solution, particularly with solvents of high dielectric constant, heterolytic fission predominates, because the solvation of the resulting ions results in an energetic advantage being given to this mode of fission. In solution, therefore, homolytic reaction is the exception rather than the rule. Nevertheless, homolytic mechanisms have now been established for a wide variety of organic reactions, and the study of these reactions has become a significant part of organic chemistry.

In this chapter some steric aspects of homolytic processes will be considered, and inasmuch as the stability of a radical is relevant to a consideration of its stereochemical properties, it is necessary to discuss briefly the meaning of the concept of stability as applied to free radicals.

Organic free radicals have been divided into two classes: those of long life, like the triarylmethyls studied by Gomberg, which are stabilized by resonance, and those of short life, like phenyl and methyl, which are not so stabilized, and make their appearance only as labile intermediates in reactions. The inference that short-lived free radicals are unstable is, however, erroneous; indeed, the contrary is the case. The reason why they cannot be prepared in large quantity is not that their molecules break down—and there is no doubt that a single radical completely isolated from all contact with other molecules would, except in a few special cases, remain unchanged indefinitely. The reason is instead that short-lived free radicals are so extraordinarily reactive that each entity undergoes some sort of chemical change in an attempt to satisfy its normal valency requirements before it has made a large number of collisions with other molecules. Strictly speaking, therefore, the term ' short-lived ', when applied in description of a free radical, means nothing unless the environmental conditions are also stated. However, in practice, the reactivity of most short-lived free radicals is so great that some reaction always occurs within a very few collisions.

A number of stereochemical problems arise in free-radical chemistry, and some of the more important of these will be considered in this chapter. For many years, interest has been aroused in the configuration of stable free radicals of the triarylmethyl type, and, more recently, in the configuration of short-lived free radical intermediates in homolytic reactions. The steric orientation of homolytic addition to ethylenic double bonds, and the allied problem of free radical-induced isomerization of cis- and trans-ethylenic systems, have recently been the the subjects of a good deal of both experimental and theoretical work. Finally, the various kinetic steric effects of steric hindrance, steric acceleration, and steric inhibition of resonance, which are exhibited in homolytic reactions, will be briefly considered.

THE CONFIGURATION OF FREE RADICALS

Stable Free Radicals

The stereochemical configuration of a carbon atom which forms three single bonds and possesses, in addition, one unpaired electron (I) may be thought to be either pyramidal, or planar. The pyramidal configuration, with the three groups R, R', and R'' occupying three apices of a tetrahedron, the fourth apex being occupied by the unpaired electron, presupposes that the unpaired electron has the ability to maintain the molecule in the tetrahedral configuration, and if this configuration is optically stable, enantiomorphic forms of the free radical are possible.

40

I

On the other hand, if the radical I assumes a completely planar configuration, it must possess a plane of symmetry, and the existence of enantiomorphic forms is precluded, provided, of course, that none of the groups R, R′, and R″ is itself asymmetric. No free radical of this type has yet been resolved into optical isomerides, but this is no proof that such resolution is impossible in principle, especially in view of the experimental difficulties encountered in studies of free radicals. Nevertheless, it is commonly assumed that the planar configuration is the most stable one for such a free radical. Karagounis (1951) has shown that the infra-red spectrum of triphenylmethyl is consistent with such a structure. The spectra of triphenylmethane in carbon tetrachloride and hexane solution, and of hexaphenylethane in carbon tetrachloride and carbon disulphide, were taken over the range 650–3500 cm^{-1}. By measuring the spectrum of hexaphenylethane at different dilutions, it was found possible to assign 29 bands to vibrations of the triphenylmethyl radical. Comparison of this observed spectrum of triphenylmethyl with vibration frequencies calculated on the basis of planar and pyramidal configurations led to the conclusion that triphenylmethyl was most probably of a planar configuration.

This assumption is supported by the observation that loss of configuration takes place whenever such free radicals are formed. Thus, for example, Wallis and Adams (1933) allowed triphenylmethyl chloride to react with mercury in the presence of (−)-p-diphenylyl-α-naphthylphenylmethylthioglycollic acid (II). The triphenylmethyl

radicals formed were shown to react slowly with II, liberating p-diphenylyl-α-naphthylphenylmethyl radicals. The reaction was accompanied by a change in colour, and by the gradual decrease of the optical rotation to zero. The peroxides which were formed on the admission of air were also found to be optically inactive, and although the reaction did not go to completion, but resulted in the establishment of an equilibrium, the starting material (II) which remained at the end of the reaction was also optically inactive. Thus the conclusion is inescapable that the triarylmethyl radicals derived from II lose configuration on liberation, and that on reformation of II, the (+) and (−) forms are obtained in equal amounts.

An attempt to resolve the *p*-diphenylyl-α-naphthylphenylmethyl radical into its optical antipodes was made by Karagounis (1949). Chromatographic adsorption using D-lactose, sucrose, (−)-silica, (+)-sodium chlorate, and alumina coated with D-alanine as adsorbents was employed. Polarimetric analysis of the adsorbate and the eluate showed that no resolution had taken place.

Further confirmation of the planar configuration is provided by the demonstration by Karagounis and Jannakopoulos (1940) that both triphenylmethyl and tri-*p*-diphenylylmethyl radicals have no dipole moment.

The planar configuration of triarylmethyl radicals is also consistent with theoretical explanations of the great stability of these radicals. Thus it has been pointed out (Wheland, 1949) that stable free radicals of the type of triphenylmethyl would be expected to be completely planar, since all the resonating structures, *e.g.* III–V, can be free of strain at the same time only if the three phenyl groups are coplanar with one another and with the central carbon atom. This author has,

III   IV   V

however, also pointed out that such complete planarity is inconsistent with the molecular dimensions, some interference between the *ortho*-hydrogen atoms of neighbouring phenyl groups being unavoidable. Complete planarity is therefore impossible for steric reasons, and it was suggested that the departure from planarity which appears to be necessary takes the form of rotation of each of the phenyl groups about the axis of the bond joining it to the extra-nuclear carbon atom. The structure is then analogous to a three-bladed propeller, or windmill. This type of structure was also advocated by Lewis and Calvin (1939). Calculations using the molecular-orbital method (Samoïlov and Dyatkina, 1948) of the energy of interaction between the nearest hydrogen atoms in the triphenylmethyl radical have shown that the aromatic nuclei should lie at an angle of about 30° to the plane of the three central bonds, thus affording theoretical justification for the 'windmill' configuration. Lewis and Calvin (1939) also predicted that molecules of this type should exist in two isomeric forms, which they termed the 'symmetrical helix' and 'distorted helix' configurations. The symmetrical helix form is strictly analogous to a three-bladed propeller, and the distorted helix is analogous to a propeller in which the direction of inclination of one of the blades to the plane of the structure is opposite to that of the other two. In order to demonstrate the existence of these two isomeric forms in triarylmethyl carbonium ions, the spectrum of the crystal-violet cation was measured in a number of solvents (Lewis, Magel and Lipkin, 1942). All the spectra showed two particular absorption bands which were called A and B. In the ethanolic solution it was found that the relative height of band B decreased with diminishing temperature, and thus it was concluded that the two bands belong to isomers of the crystal violet cation (VI and VII), of which VII has the higher energy by 580 cal.mole^{-1}. Thus the more stable form (VI) is the symmetrical

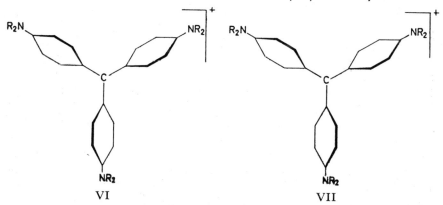

VI   VII

helix, and the less stable (VII) the distorted helix configuration. The necessary restriction to the rotation of the aromatic rings, which, if free, would allow interconversion of the two forms, was considered to be due to the steric interference of the adjacent *ortho*-hydrogen atoms. The force of repulsion arising from this interference was thought to be balanced by the force opposing free rotation, which, in turn, may arise from the partial double-bond character of the bonds joining the aromatic rings to the extra-nuclear carbon atom. These two isomers are not optical antipodes, but the last-named authors pointed out that molecules in either of these configurations should, given the necessary conditions for asymmetry, exist in enantiomorphic forms. The activation energy for interconversion of these two forms was thought to be only of the order of 2 or 3 kcal.mole^{-1}, since interconversion is rapid in ethanol even at 114°K.

A similar demonstration is reported by the same authors of the existence of two forms of the cation of malachite green. In this instance a single absorption band was found to be split into two bands when the temperature was reduced to 114°K. Thus, in this instance also, two forms appear to be capable of existence, though, presumably owing to a lower activation energy for their interconversion, they can be distinguished only at low temperatures.

The absorption spectrum of the triphenylmethyl radical was also investigated with the object of demonstrating the existence of this type of isomerism (Lewis, Lipkin and Magel, 1944). These workers did not, however, succeed in finding direct evidence for the existence of 'windmill isomerism' in this molecule.

From the evidence discussed above, it appears that the 'windmill' configuration is the most likely one for triarylmethyl radicals. The existence of a 'distorted helix' structure in the free radicals, while feasible on theoretical grounds, does not appear to have been demonstrated experimentally. However, as has been shown (Lewis, Magel and Lipkin, 1942), a free radical of the type of structure I above, in which all three aryl groups are different, and which exists in the symmetrical-helix configuration, possesses no element of symmetry. Such a radical should, therefore, exist in two enantiomorphic forms, and optical resolution is possible in principle, though, in practice, the ready interconversion of the two forms (racemization) may frustrate attempts at experimental demonstration. There seems, however, to be no reason why such attempts might not be successful if a radical in which sufficiently bulky groups were placed in the *ortho*-positions were used. This may, indeed, be the explanation of the results of Karagounis and Drikos (1933, 1934) which are difficult to accommodate on the basis of a completely planar configuration for these radicals. These workers studied the influence of chlorine on the *p*-diphenylyl-α-naphthylphenylmethyl radical (VIII) under the influence of circularly polarized light at two different wavelengths (4350 Å and 5890 Å). The reaction involves the attack of atomic chlorine on the radical VIII, producing the corresponding chloride IX. Determination of the optical rotation of the solution at various intervals of time showed that the initially inactive solution developed *dextro-* or *laevo-*rotation (depending on the direction of polarization of the light used) to a maximum of about 0·08°, reached after about 1 hour. The rotation then decreased until at the completion of the reaction the solution was again inactive. It was also found that the circularly polarized light had no effect on the free radicals themselves. This asymmetric synthesis is of interest, since it is the only such study of free radicals which is reported in the literature.

The original interpretation placed upon these results was that they indicated that the groups in triarylmethyl radicals are probably not planar. In view of the more modern concept of windmill configuration,

VIII   IX

as discussed above, it is possible that the molecular asymmetry arising from such a structure may be responsible for the preferential production of one isomer of IX rather than the other under the influence of the circularly polarized light.

Free-radical Intermediates (Free Radicals of Short Life)

As has been stated above, the most stable configuration of free radicals containing trivalent carbon appears to be a completely planar one. Thus, if a free-radical intermediate attains this most stable configuration before further reaction, and provided no other sources of asymmetry (such as restricted rotation of the groups R, R′ and R″ in formula I) exist, then inactive products would always be expected to be formed. It is possible, however, in principle, that owing to the extreme reactivity of some radicals, further reaction of the radicals may take place at a rate comparable with that of racemization, and in these circumstances a greater or lesser amount of activity may be retained in the products of reactions involving optically active free-radical intermediates.

If, however, racemic starting materials are used, or if the radicals are generated from materials which are not optically active, then active products would not be expected to be formed, and no conclusions concerning the optical stability or configuration of the radicals can be drawn from such experiments. A number of experiments of this type are described in the literature, and the following examples are given.

The reaction of acetyl peroxide with chloroacetic acid and methyl chloroacetate has been studied by Kharasch, Jensen and Urry (1945). Acetyl peroxide gives methyl radicals by homolysis and subsequent decarboxylation of the acetyloxy radicals produced. The methyl radicals then attack the acid or ester, removing a hydrogen atom from the α-carbon atom, and the resulting free radicals dimerize to give dichlorosuccinic acid (or its dimethyl ester) thus:

$$CH_3 \cdot CO \cdot O \cdot O \cdot CO \cdot CH_3 \longrightarrow 2CH_3 \cdot CO \cdot O \cdot$$
$$CH_3 \cdot CO \cdot O \cdot \longrightarrow CH_3 \cdot + CO_2$$
$$CH_3 \cdot + ClCH_2CO_2H \longrightarrow CH_4 + Cl \cdot \dot{C}H \cdot CO_2H$$
$$2Cl \cdot \dot{C}H \cdot CO_2H \longrightarrow \begin{array}{c} ClCHCO_2H \\ | \\ ClCHCO_2H \end{array}$$

Side-reactions also take place, yielding more complex products which are, however, unimportant in the present context. It was found that the dichlorosuccinic acid and the dimethyl dichlorosuccinate isolated both contained approximately equal amounts of the racemic and *meso* isomers. This does not necessarily mean that the radicals are inactive because they exist in a planar configuration, since the same result would be obtained if the radicals were optically stable in the pyramidal (or tetrahedral) configuration, for the $(+)$ and $(-)$ isomers of the radicals must have been produced in equal amounts.

A similar result was obtained by Hey, Pengilly and Williams (1956), who studied the reaction of benzoyl peroxide with ethylbenzene. Phenyl radicals are produced by homolysis and decarboxylation in a manner analogous to the production of methyl radicals from acetyl peroxide, and attack both the nucleus and the side-chain of ethylbenzene. The nuclear reaction is that of substitution, but the side-chain reaction takes the form of hydrogen-abstraction from the α-carbon atom, followed by dimerization of the radicals so produced :

$$C_6H_5 \cdot + C_6H_5CH_2CH_3 \longrightarrow C_6H_6 + C_6H_5\dot{C}HCH_3$$
$$2C_6H_5\dot{C}HCH_3 \longrightarrow \begin{array}{c} C_6H_5CH \cdot CH \cdot C_6H_5 \\ | \quad\quad | \\ CH_3 \;\; CH_3 \end{array}$$

From this reaction, the racemic and *meso* forms of 2 : 3-diphenylbutane were isolated in equal amounts.

The decomposition of both diastereoisomeric forms (racemic and *meso*) of 2 : 2′-azobis-2 : 4-dimethylvaleronitrile (X) in benzene solution was studied by Overberger and Berenbaum (1951b). The reaction proceeds as follows :

$$(CH_3)_2CHCH_2\underset{\underset{CN}{|}}{\overset{\overset{CH_3}{|}}{C}} \cdot N : N \cdot \underset{\underset{CN}{|}}{\overset{\overset{CH_3}{|}}{C}}CH_2CH(CH_3)_2 \longrightarrow 2(CH_3)_2CHCH_2\underset{\underset{CN}{|}}{\overset{\overset{CH_3}{|}}{C}} \cdot + N_2$$

X   XI

$$2(CH_3)_2CHCH_2\underset{\underset{CN}{|}}{\overset{\overset{CH_3}{|}}{C}} \cdot \longrightarrow (CH_3)_2CHCH_2\underset{\underset{CN}{|}}{\overset{\overset{CH_3}{|}}{C}}-\underset{\underset{CN}{|}}{\overset{\overset{CH_3}{|}}{C}} \cdot CH_2CH(CH_3)_2$$

XII

46

The product (XII) isolated consisted of a mixture of the racemic and *meso* forms, and the same mixture was obtained from both diastereo-isomeric forms of X. The authors concluded that the radicals (XI) exist in a relatively free state in solution, and that they assume a planar configuration. However, as has been pointed out by Haines and Waters (1955), the second conclusion is not valid, for if the homolyses of both the *meso*- and the racemic forms of the azo-nitrile liberated enantiomorphous (+)- and (−)-radicals, then at all times during the decomposition both these would be present in equivalent amounts from each starting material and would, by random combination, necessarily yield 50 per cent each of the *meso*- and the racemic dimer (XII). A similar result was, in fact, obtained by Haines and Waters, who studied the decomposition of 4 : 4′-azobis-4-cyanopentanoic acid (XIII). Similar mixtures of the racemic and *meso*- forms of the product 4 : 5-dicyano-4 : 5-dimethyloctane-1 : 8-dioic acid (XIV) were obtained from both forms of XIII.

$$[:N \cdot CMe(CN) \cdot CH_2 \cdot CH_2 \cdot CO_2H]_2 \longrightarrow [\cdot CMe(CN) \cdot CH_2 \cdot CH_2 \cdot CO_2H]_2 + N_2$$

XIII   XIV

In all the experiments described above, both enantiomorphous forms of the free radicals concerned were generated in equal amounts, and consequently no active products could be obtained. A number of experiments have, however, been described in which, by the use of optically active starting materials, free radicals have been generated in forms which must initially have been optically active. In such circumstances, as already stated, activity may be retained in the products if the rate of any subsequent reaction of the radicals is comparable with the rate at which they undergo racemization or assume a planar configuration. This situation, however, seems to be extremely difficult to attain, because in the majority of the cases recorded in the literature, complete racemization has been found to take place whenever free radicals have been formed.

A number of different reactions which may involve free radicals have been studied from this point of view. The electrolysis of potassium (−)-ethylmethylacetate was found by Wallis and Adams (1933) to produce optically inactive 3 : 4-dimethylhexane. This is consistent with the assumptions that *sec.*-butyl radicals are intermediate in the reaction, and that these radicals are not sufficiently optically stable to retain their asymmetry during the short period of time for which they exist in the free state in solution. Wallis and Adams also investigated the production of 3 : 4-dimethylhexane by the action of sodium on (+)-2-bromobutane :

$$2C_2H_5CHBr + 2Na \longrightarrow C_2H_5CH \cdot CHC_2H_5$$
$$\quad\quad | \quad\quad\quad\quad\quad\quad\quad\quad\quad | \quad |$$
$$\quad CH_3 \quad\quad\quad\quad\quad\quad\quad CH_3 \, CH_3$$

Once again inactive 3 : 4-dimethylhexane was obtained. The products of both these reactions presumably consisted of a mixture of the racemic and *meso*- forms, although this possibility was not investigated. The same workers investigated another Wurtz reaction, namely that of $(-)$-α-bromodibenzyl with sodium, giving, once again, optically inactive 1 : 2 : 3 : 4-tetraphenylbutane:

$$2C_6H_5CH \cdot CH_2C_6H_5 + 2Na \longrightarrow C_6H_5CH_2CH—CHCH_2C_6H_5$$
$$\underset{Br}{|} \qquad\qquad \underset{C_6H_5}{|} \; \underset{C_6H_5}{|}$$

Racemization must have occurred at some intermediate stage since both reactants and products were optically stable. These results are therefore consistent with the hypothesis that free radicals are formed as intermediates in the Wurtz reaction. On the other hand, Ott (1928) obtained optically active $(+)$-2 : 3-diphenylbutane, together with some of the *meso*- form of this hydrocarbon, by the action of sodium on $(-)$-1-phenylethyl chloride:

$$2C_6H_5CH(CH_3)Cl + 2Na \longrightarrow C_6H_5CH(CH_3)CH(CH_3)C_6H_5$$

The unreacted 1-phenylethyl chloride which was recovered at the end of the reaction was found to have been racemized to some extent. This result points to a mechanism which does not involve free radicals, but possibly a reaction, which may well be heterolytic in character, between the active alkyl chloride and sodium to give $C_6H_5CH(CH_3)Na$, followed by the reaction:

$$C_6H_5CH(CH_3)Cl + C_6H_5CH(CH_3)Na \longrightarrow C_6H_5CH(CH_3)CH(CH_3)C_6H_5 + NaCl$$

It has been suggested by Tarbell and Weiss (1939) that the racemization of the unchanged chloride observed by Ott may be due to an 'exchange' reaction of the sodium and chlorine atoms of different molecules:

$$C_6H_5CHCH_3 + C_6H_5CHCH_3 \longrightarrow C_6H_5CHCH_3 + C_6H_5CHCH_3$$
$$\underset{Na}{|} \qquad \underset{Cl}{|} \qquad\qquad \underset{Cl}{|} \qquad \underset{Na}{|}$$
$$(\pm) \qquad (-) \qquad\qquad (\pm) \qquad (\pm)$$

Some evidence, not based on measurements of optical activity, has recently been adduced, notably by Kharasch, Holton and Nudenberg (1955) and Bryce-Smith (1956), for the presence of free radicals during Wurtz reactions in solution. The latter author, however, has drawn attention to the complex nature of the reaction and the possibility of competition between homolytic and heterolytic modes of reaction, which may well lead to different optical consequences when active halides are employed. Experiments with *n*- and *sec.*-butyl halides and sodium and potassium indicated that in these reactions, at least, the homolytic reaction was only of very minor significance, although it is more important when lithium is used. Thus it seems likely that many

Wurtz reactions with sodium and potassium are heterolytic, and that it is dangerous to ascribe the racemizations observed by Wallis and Adams to the formation of free radicals until the homolytic or heterolytic character of these reactions has been determined. Racemization could arise from heterolytic reaction of the carbanion of the metal alkyl with the halide if this reaction proceeded by the S_N1 mechanism, for configuration would be lost in the carbanion and in the carbonium ion derived from the halide. Again, in this mechanism some measure of activity might be retained. On the other hand, if this reaction were of the S_N2 type, Walden inversion should take place. It appears, therefore, that the loss of configuration which accompanies some Wurtz reactions is not an unequivocal demonstration of the participation of free radicals in these reactions.

Loss of configuration has also been found to take place when Grignard reagents and alkyl-lithium compounds are formed from alkyl halides. Pickard and Kenyon (1911) first demonstrated this in the preparation of the Grignard reagent from (—)-2-iodobutane. Schwartz and Johnson (1931), and Porter (1935), carried out a similar demonstration with (+)-2-bromo-octane, and Tarbell and Weiss (1939) showed that activity was lost when the lithium compound was prepared from (+)-2-chloro-octane. These experiments support the view that in these reactions free radicals, which are optically inactive, are formed as intermediates. Kharasch, Holton and Nudenberg (1954) have isolated products derived from the attack of free radicals on isoprene from reactions between alkyl halides and magnesium in the presence of isoprene, and have drawn the conclusion from this evidence that free alkyl radicals are probably formed in this reaction, although these authors have pointed out that their evidence is not wholly convincing. In the 'lithium-Wurtz' reactions, as stated above, Bryce-Smith (1956) has shown that the homolytic reaction is of considerably greater importance than in Wurtz reactions with sodium and potassium.

The photochemical or peroxide-catalysed chlorination of hydrocarbons is undoubtedly a homolytic reaction. The chlorination of (+)-1-chloro-2-methylbutane (XV) was investigated by Brown, Kharasch and Chao (1940), and the 1 : 2-dichloro-2-methylbutane (XVI) formed was found, when separated from the other chlorinated compounds which were formed simultaneously, to be completely racemic. This was taken as evidence that the radical XVII was formed as an intermediate, and that the reaction proceeds by the

$$Cl \cdot CH_2 \cdot CH \cdot CH_2 \cdot CH_3 \qquad Cl \cdot CH_2 \cdot \overset{\displaystyle Cl}{\underset{\displaystyle CH_3}{\overset{|}{\underset{|}{C}}} \cdot CH_2 \cdot CH_3 \qquad Cl \cdot CH_2 \cdot \overset{\displaystyle \cdot}{\underset{\displaystyle CH_3}{\overset{}{\underset{|}{C}}} \cdot CH_2 \cdot CH_3$$

Cl·CH₂·CH·CH₂·CH₃	Cl	
	CH₃	CH₃

XV   XVI   XVII

49

chain-mechanism (a) below, rather than by a direct replacement of the hydrogen atom by chlorine [mechanism (b)], since the latter mechanism should give rise to Walden inversion rather than to the observed racemization.

(a) $\qquad$ Cl·+RH $\longrightarrow$ HCl+R·

$\qquad$ R·+Cl$_2$ $\longrightarrow$ RCl+Cl·

(b) $\qquad$ Cl·+RH $\longrightarrow$ RCl+H·

$\qquad$ H·+Cl$_2$ $\longrightarrow$ HCl+Cl·

Conversely, the retention of activity without Walden inversion in the formation of *sec.*-butyl ethylmethylacetate during the decomposition of ethylmethylacetyl peroxide has been taken by Kharasch, Kuderna and Nudenberg (1954) as an indication that this reaction does not involve free radicals, but that the loss of carbon dioxide by the peroxide is an intramolecular process:

$$\underset{[\alpha]_D^{20}+34°}{\overset{\displaystyle CH_3}{\underset{\displaystyle C_2H_5}{\diagdown\diagup}}CH\cdot CO\cdot O\cdot O\cdot CO\cdot CH\overset{\displaystyle CH_3}{\underset{\displaystyle C_2H_5}{\diagup\diagdown}}} \longrightarrow \underset{[\alpha]_D^{24}+27°}{\overset{\displaystyle CH_3}{\underset{\displaystyle C_2H_5}{\diagdown\diagup}}CH\cdot CO\cdot O\cdot CH\overset{\displaystyle CH_3}{\underset{\displaystyle C_2H_5}{\diagup\diagdown}}} +CO_2$$

Hydrolysis of the ester with potassium hydroxide gave *sec.*-butyl alcohol ($[\alpha]_D^{25}+10.2°$) and ethylmethylacetic acid ($[\alpha]_D^{25}+10°$). The correlation between the configurations of these two substances being already established (for a review with references, see Mills and Klyne, 1954), it thus became apparent that replacement of ·CO·O·OR by OR at C* occurred without inversion.

However, one or two examples have been reported of the retention of a small amount of optical activity by free-radical intermediates. Kharasch, Kuderna and Urry (1949) have shown that when acetyl peroxide is allowed to react with (+)-ethylmethylacetic acid (XVIII),

$$\underset{XVIII}{\overset{\displaystyle C_2H_5\cdot CH\cdot CO_2H}{\underset{\displaystyle CH_3}{|}}} \qquad \underset{XIX}{\overset{\displaystyle C_2H_5\cdot \overset{\displaystyle \cdot}{C}\cdot CO_2H}{\underset{\displaystyle CH_3}{|}}} \qquad \underset{XX}{\overset{\displaystyle CO_2H \quad CO_2H}{\overset{\displaystyle | \qquad |}{\underset{\displaystyle CH_3 \quad CH_3}{\underset{\displaystyle | \qquad |}{C_2H_5\cdot C \!-\!\!-\!\!-\! C\cdot C_2H_5}}}}}$$

the diethyldimethylsuccinic acid (XX) produced by the dimerization of the radical (XIX) is slightly, but definitely, dextrorotatory.

Again, in the addition of ethyl $(-)$-α-bromopropionate (XXI) to oct-1-ene under the influence of a trace of acetyl peroxide, Kharasch and Skell (1949) have shown that the adduct (XXIII) has a small but definite laevorotation. In these cases, therefore, it seems that the rate of

$$CH_3 \cdot CHBr \cdot CO_2Et \qquad CH_3 \cdot \overset{\cdot}{C}H \cdot CO_2Et \qquad \begin{matrix} CH_2 \cdot CHBr\text{--}nC_6H_{13} \\ | \\ CH_3 \cdot CH \cdot CO_2Et \end{matrix}$$

$$\text{XXI} \qquad\qquad\qquad \text{XXII} \qquad\qquad\qquad \text{XXIII}$$

racemization of the intermediate radicals (XIX) and (XXII) is not overwhelmingly greater than the rate of their dimerization or addition to an olefin.

The partial racemization of optically active aryl radicals has been used recently by de Tar and Howard (1955) to confirm their intervention in reactions of homolytic arylation. The reactions studied were those of the optically active forms of the diacyl peroxide of 2-methyl-6-nitrodiphenyl-2'-carboxylic acid (XXIV) with carbon tetrachloride, bromotrichloromethane, and benzene, and of the diazonium chloride and fluoborate of 2'-amino-2-methyl-6-nitrodiphenyl (XXV) with benzene and sodium hydroxide (Gomberg reaction). The product of the reactions of XXIV and XXV with benzene was 2-methyl-6-nitro-2'-phenyldiphenyl (XXVI). In the reaction with carbon tetrachloride, a chlorine atom, and, in that with bromotrichloromethane, a bromine atom was found to enter the nucleus at the 2'-position.

$$\text{XXIV} \qquad\qquad\qquad \text{XXV} \qquad\qquad\qquad \text{XXVI}$$

All these reactions were found to result in partial racemization, and this must have taken place in the intermediate free aryl radical (XXVII), since all the reactants and products were optically stable

$$\text{XXVII}$$

under the conditions of the reaction. The removal of the groups attached to the 2'-position provides the only means whereby rotation of the aryl groups may become unrestricted, and hence it was concluded that the radical XXVII is an intermediate in these reactions.

Moreover, the fact that only partial racemization is observed indicates that the racemization of the radical XXVII by rotation of the aryl groups is a process requiring activation and that its rate is comparable with the rates of substitution of bromine, chlorine, and phenyl at the 2′-position.

THE STEREOCHEMISTRY OF FREE-RADICAL ADDITION REACTIONS

The free-radical addition reactions of olefinic systems have been the subject of a number of comprehensive reviews, the most recent being that of Cadogan and Hey (1954). A discussion of the evidence on which mechanisms have been advanced for these reactions is outside the scope of this chapter, and indeed, this subject has been adequately covered in earlier reviews. However, the following generalized scheme for the radical-chain addition of an addendum XY to an olefin $R \cdot CH : CH_2$ under free-radical or photochemical initiation to give the 1 : 1 adduct, is included for reference:

$$R' \cdot + XY \longrightarrow R'X + Y \cdot$$

Initiation $\qquad or \: XY \xrightarrow{h\nu} X \cdot + Y \cdot$

$$Y \cdot + R \cdot CH : CH_2 \longrightarrow R \cdot \overset{\bullet}{C}H \cdot CH_2 Y$$

Chain-transfer $\qquad R \cdot \overset{\bullet}{C}H \cdot CH_2 \cdot Y + XY \longrightarrow R \cdot CHX \cdot CH_2 Y + Y \cdot$

The homolytic addition of hydrogen halides to simple non-cyclic olefins is not stereospecific because the addition of atomic halogens is reversible. Thus bromine atoms have been shown by Derbyshire and Waters (1949) to catalyse the isomerization of maleic to fumaric acid by reversible addition, to give the radical XXVIII in which free rotation of the groups is possible. Bromine atoms have also been shown to catalyse the *cis-trans* isomerization of stilbene (Kharasch, Mansfield and Mayo, 1937), $\alpha\alpha'$-dichlorostilbene (Taylor and Murray, 1938), and 2-bromobutene (Lepingle, 1926). The *cis-trans* isomerization of diiodoethylene has been shown by Noyes, Dickinson and Schomaker (1945) to be catalysed by iodine atoms by a similar mechanism of reversible addition. The homolytic addition of bromotrichloromethane to *cis*- and *trans*-but-2-ene has been shown by Skell and Woodworth (1955) to give rise to isomerization of the olefin, and the addition of vinyl acetate to *cis*- and *trans*-dichloroethylene has been shown by Mayo and Wilzbach (1949) to give a similar result.

XXVIII $\qquad\qquad\qquad\qquad$ XXIX

Investigations of the stereochemistry of free-radical addition must therefore be carried out with cyclic olefins, for only in such systems are *cis-trans* isomerizations impossible and the resulting complications avoided. The additions of various reagents to cyclic olefins have been studied, and in almost all cases predominantly *trans*-addition has been found to take place. The results of Kharasch and Friedlander (1949), as interpreted by Fawcett (1950), indicate that *trans*-addition takes place in the radical-chain addition of bromotrichloromethane to *cyclo*hexene and *bicyclo*-[2 : 2 : 1]-hept-2-ene (norbornylene, XXIX), although more recently some doubt has been cast on the validity of this conclusion (Cristol and Hause, 1952 ; Cristol and Brindell, 1954). Cristol and Brindell (1954) have also shown that the addition of *p*-thiocresol to norbornylene gives pure *exo*-norbornyl *p*-tolyl sulphide (XXX). Neither the *endo*-isomer (XXXI), nor the product of Wagner–Meerwein rearrangement, 7-*p*-tolylthionorcamphane (XXXII), was found. These authors have pointed out that these results can be interpreted adequately without the postulate of mesomeric or bridged free-radical intermediates.

XXX	XXXI	XXXII

$$[X = SC_6H_4CH_3(p)]$$

Cristol and Brindell (1955) have shown that *trans*-addition of toluene-*p*-sulphenyl chloride to norbornylene takes place. Goering, Abell and Aycock (1952) have shown that the free-radical addition of hydrogen bromide to 1-bromo*cyclo*hexene gives exclusively *cis*-1 : 2-dibromo*cyclo*hexane, indicating the occurrence of *trans*-addition. Since the product is probably the thermodynamically less stable isomer [*cf* Barton (1953)] the possibility that *cis*-addition to give the *trans*-isomer first takes place, followed by *trans* ⟶ *cis*-isomerization, is eliminated. 1-Methyl*cyclo*hexene also undergoes *trans*-addition of hydrogen bromide to give *cis*-1-bromo-2-methyl*cyclo*hexane :

where X = CH₃ or Br

It is noteworthy that 1-methyl*cyclo*hexene exhibits the rare property of undergoing heterolytic and homolytic addition reactions at comparable rates. The relative importance of the two mechanisms varies with conditions, for the reaction with hydrogen bromide is exclusively heterolytic at −80° and exclusively homolytic at +35°. The homolytic addition of hydrogen bromide to 3-bromo*cyclo*hexene has been investigated by Kharasch, Sallo and Nudenberg (1956), and shown to give substantially pure *trans*-1 : 3-dibromo*cyclo*hexane, indicating *trans*-addition. The same result was obtained by these workers for the addition of bromine to *cyclo*hexene, which gave *trans*-1 : 2-dibromo-*cyclo*hexane.

Goering and Sims (1955) investigated the addition of hydrogen bromide to 1-chloro*cyclo*hexene under irradiation by ultra-violet light. The reaction was shown to be homolytic by the orientation of the addition, which is opposite to that predicted by the Markownikoff rule, and by the fact that no reaction took place in the dark. The product was shown by various methods, including dipole-moment measurements (Bender, Flowers and Goering, 1955), to be *cis*-1-bromo-2-chloro*cyclo*hexane, indicating that *trans*-addition had taken place. The amount of *cis*-addition was estimated to be not more than 0·3 per cent. The homolytic additions of hydrogen sulphide, thiophenol and thiolacetic acid to 1-chloro*cyclo*hexene under irradiation with ultra-violet light were investigated by Goering, Relyea and Larsen (1956). Once again predominantly *trans*-addition was found, although, particularly with thiolacetic acid, appreciable amounts of *cis*-addition occurred. The proportion of *cis*-addition was also found to be dependent upon the relative concentrations of the addendum and 1-chloro*cyclo*hexene. These workers' results are summarized in TABLE 1. Once again the products of *trans*-addition are thermo-

TABLE 1. STERIC ORIENTATION OF ADDITION TO 1-CHLORO*cyclo*HEXENE
(Goering, Relyea and Larsen, 1956)

Addendum	Mole Ratio ([Addendum]/[Substrate])	% *trans*-Adduct (*cis*-addition)
H_2S	1	14
	18	10
	56	7·5
C_6H_5SH	1	5·2
	18	0·9
$CH_3CO·SH$	1	34
	18	27

dynamically the less stable, and control experiments were performed which showed that no interconversion of the *cis*- and *trans*-adducts took place under the reaction conditions. Thus the nature of the product must have been determined solely by kinetic control.

The light-catalysed homolytic addition of thiolacetic acid to 1-methyl*cyclo*pentene and 1-methyl*cyclo*hexene has been investigated by

Bordwell and Hewett (1954). The adduct obtained with 1-methyl-*cyclo*pentene gave on hydrolysis a mixture of 75 per cent of *cis*-2-methyl*cyclo*hexanethiol with 25 per cent of the *trans*-isomer, indicating 75 per cent of *trans*- and 25 per cent *cis*-addition. With 1-methyl-*cyclo*hexene, 85 per cent of *trans*- and 15 per cent *cis*-addition were shown to take place. Appreciable amounts of *cis*-addition have also been found by Berson and Swidler (1953) to take place in the (probably homolytic) addition of bromine to 3 : 6-epoxy*cyclo*hex-4-ene-*exo-cis*-1 : 2-dicarboxylic anhydride (*exo-cis*-3 : 6-endoxo-Δ^4-tetrahydrophthalic anhydride) (XXXIII).

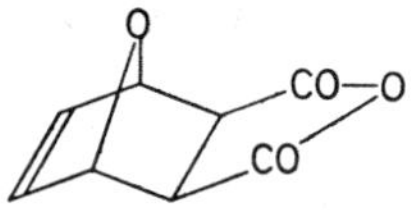

| XXXIII | XXXIV | XXXV |

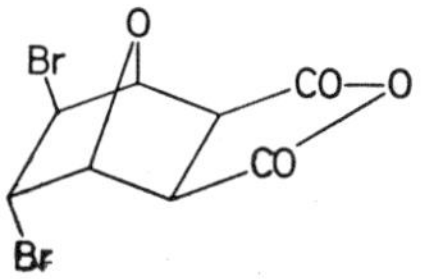

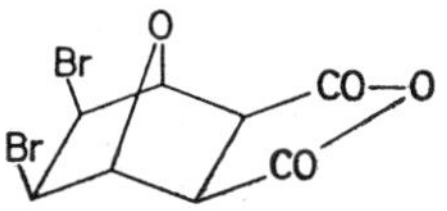

Two dibromides are produced, one of which is the racemic *trans*-dibromide (XXXIV), and the other a *meso*-compound which must therefore be the *cis*-adduct, and probably has the *exo*-configuration (XXXV).

The predominance of *trans*-addition in these homolytic addition reactions has given rise to a good deal of theoretical speculation. Goering, Abell and Aycock (1952) suggested that the intermediate radical in hydrogen bromide addition is a bridged structure represented by XXXVI, in which the bromine atom is situated centrally between

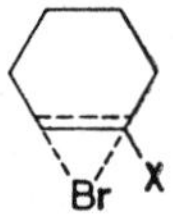

XXXVI

carbon atoms 1 and 2. This structure could arise by resonance among the canonical forms represented by XXXVII (a)–(e). Such an

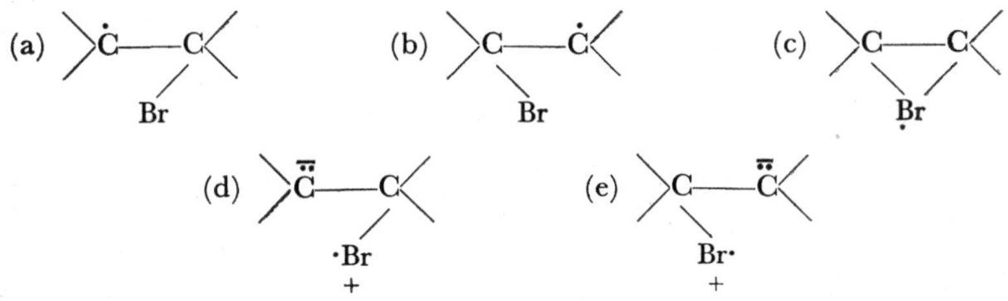

XXXVII

intermediate should react with hydrogen bromide in the direction remote from the bromine atom. Bridged bromonium ions which are sterically analogous to XXXVI have been postulated as intermediates in heterolytic bromine-addition (Ziegler and Shabica, 1952). However, it has also been pointed out (Goering and Sims, 1955; Cristol and Brindell, 1954) that the postulate of such mesomeric radicals is not necessary to explain the stereospecificity of the reactions and, indeed, it is difficult to explain the occurrence of any *cis*-addition on this basis. Berson and Swidler (1953), for example, found it necessary to postulate a different type of mesomeric radical in order to explain the *cis*-addition observed by them. Goering and Sims (1955) have also considered the possible formation of a π-complex between the olefin and the addendum, which again should lead to *trans*-addition. Thus, for the addition of hydrogen bromide to a 1-substituted *cyclo*hexene, the following mechanism is suggested:

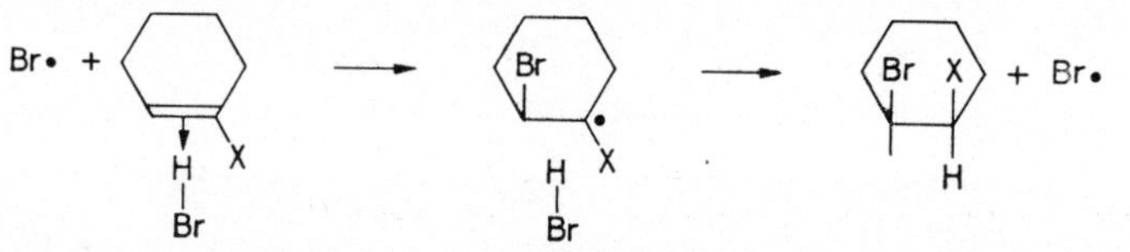

The existence of such π-complexes in solutions of hydrogen halides in olefins has been postulated by Brown and Brady (1952). However, the reaction was shown still to be highly stereospecific even in the presence of large quantities of ether, which would be expected to prevent the formation of π-complexes with the olefin by virtue of its own great affinity for hydrogen halides. The stereospecificity of the addition therefore appears to be not necessarily dependent on the possible formation of π-complexes.

The most cogent argument against these intermediates, however, is that it is possible to accommodate the results of these investigations on the basis of a simple free-radical intermediate. Apart from the intermediates mentioned above, Goering and Sims (1955) have pointed out that in the addition of hydrogen bromide to substituted *cyclo*hexenes, for example, the intermediates XXXVIII and XXXIX, in which the bromine atom takes up the axial and equatorial conformations, respectively, are possible. Of these two intermediates,

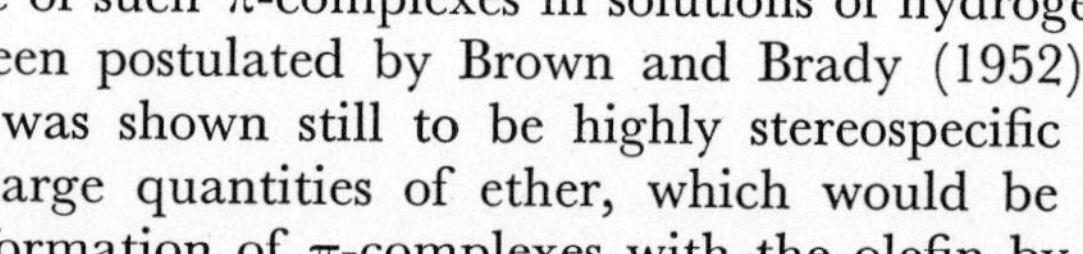

XXXVIII (axial)   XXXIX (equatorial)

XXXVIII is consistent with the stereospecificity of the addition, because approach to it of a hydrogen bromide molecule from the side remote from the bromine atom is sterically favoured. The intermediate XXXIX is not so favoured, since no such advantage exists to approach from either side of the molecule. The prediction of the relative stability of XXXVIII and XXXIX is not possible with any degree of certainty because, as pointed out by Corey (1953), who discussed the stability of 1 : 2-disubstituted *cyclo*hexane derivatives, the effects of dipole and steric interactions may work in opposite directions. However, as pointed out by Noyes, Dickinson and Schomaker (1945), it seems likely that the initial approach of the bromine atom should be in the direction leading to the formation of XXXVIII, since such a direction of approach would lead to the greater interaction with the p_z orbitals of the double-bond. Goering, Relyea and Larsen (1956) therefore considered that the conformation of the free radical intermediate initially formed is that represented by XXXVIII, and that this may subsequently be converted into XXXIX. The reaction between an addendum HY and 1-substituted *cyclo*hexene may then be represented as follows :

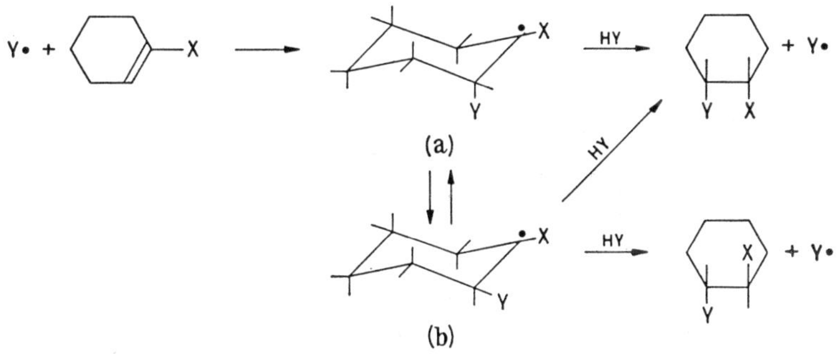

Intermediate (a) above (*cf* XXXVIII) leads to specifically *trans*-addition, while (b) (*cf* XXXIX) leads to both *cis*- and *trans*-addition, for the reasons already stated. Thus, if it can be assumed that (a) is formed first, the degree of stereospecificity would be expected to be dependent on the rate of the subsequent chain-transfer stage. Hence short life of the intermediate radical is expected to favour stereospecificity. This is consistent with the increase in stereospecificity with concentration of the addendum observed by Goering, Relyea and Larsen (1956), since the rate of the chain-transfer step must increase, and the life of the intermediate radical decrease with increasing concentration of the addendum.

KINETIC STERIC EFFECTS

Steric Hindrance

The kinetic phenomena associated with the occurrence of steric hindrance are usually most clearly observed in reactions of substitution by mechanisms in which an increase in the number of covalent bonds formed by the atom at which substitution is effected accompanies the formation of the transition state. Thus, in the field of heterolytic reactions, steric hindrance is observed in S_N2 substitution reactions at a saturated carbon atom, and in aromatic substitution reactions. Free radicals, however, do not effect simple substitution reactions at saturated carbon atoms, the preferred reaction at such sites being that of hydrogen- or halogen-abstraction. These reactions are therefore not susceptible to steric hindrance. In the field of homolytic aromatic substitution, however, effects attributed to steric hindrance have been observed by several workers.

TABLE 2.   NITRATION AND PHENYLATION OF ALKYLBENZENES

All values are % of product formed

		PhMe	PhEt	PhPr^i	PhBu^t
Nitration^a	ortho-	57	55	30	11·8
	meta-	3	0	7·7	8·7
	para-	40	45	62·3	79·5
Phenylation^b	2-	66·5	53	31	24
	3-	19·2	28	42	49
	4-	14·3	19	27	27

a Ingold (1953); Brown and Bonner (1954), cf also Chapter 3.
b Cadogan, Hey and Williams (1954); Hey, Pengilly and Williams (1956).

Hey, Pengilly and Williams (1956), and Cadogan, Hey and Williams (1954) have investigated the reaction of phenyl radicals with toluene, ethylbenzene, isopropylbenzene, and tert.-butylbenzene. The radicals may react with the nuclei and the side-chains of these hydrocarbons, and the nuclear reaction is that of phenylation. The proportions of 2-, 3-, and 4-alkyldiphenyl formed in the phenylation reaction were measured, and the sharp reduction in the amount of the 2-isomer formed with isopropylbenzene and tert.-butylbenzene was attributed to steric hindrance to substitution at a position ortho- to the bulky isopropyl and tert.-butyl groups. The results are given in TABLE 2, together with the proportions of isomers formed in the nitration of these hydrocarbons, where closely analogous steric effects on the proportion of the 2-isomer were observed. In both reactions the characteristic patterns of electrophilic and homolytic substitution, respectively, were shown by toluene and ethylbenzene, while in both reactions the proportion of the ortho-(2-) isomer is drastically reduced when substitution is effected in the nuclei of isopropylbenzene and *tert.*-butylbenzene. Anomalously low percentages of the *ortho*-(2-) isomer in homolytic arylation reactions have also been reported with benzotrichloride (Dannley and Sternfeld, 1954), benzotrifluoride (Dannley and Sternfeld, 1954; Rondestvedt and Blanchard, 1956), and trimethylphenylsilane (Rondestvedt and Blanchard, 1956). These effects have also been attributed to the steric difficulty of substitution at a position adjacent to a bulky group, although, as Rondestvedt and Blanchard (1956) have pointed out, this explanation is not entirely satisfactory for benzotrifluoride, since the trifluoromethyl group is comparable in size with methyl.

The possible influence of steric hindrance in homolytic addition reactions of olefins in determining (a) the relative reactivity of various olefins and (b) the orientation of the addition has been discussed recently by Mayo and Walling (1950) and Cadogan and Hey (1954). In all cases of free-radical addition to olefins of the type $R \cdot CH : CH_2$ so far investigated, the point of initial attack has been exclusively at the terminal methylene group, and three theories have been considered to account for this orientation :

(i) Waters (1946) has suggested that free halogen atoms (in halogen and hydrogen halide addition, for example) are electrophilic in character, and thus attack the point of highest electron density. A generalization of this theory to include all free radicals has sometimes been assumed.

(ii) The importance of steric factors in determining the point of attack has been emphasized by Mayo and Walling (1950).

(iii) Mayo and Walling (1940) have pointed out that the point of attack should also depend upon the relative stability of the two radicals which may be formed by the initial addition of the attacking radical to the olefin.

The first of these theories can probably be discounted in view of the fact that the direction of addition to olefins of the type $R \cdot CH : CH_2$ appears to be independent of the polar nature of R, the initial attack being on the terminal carbon atom whatever the direction of polarization of the double bond (see, for example, Haszeldine and Steele, 1953; Haszeldine, 1952).

Of the remaining two theories, neither alone seems able to give a complete explanation of all the observed facts. As a result of a detailed consideration of the relevant experimental data, Cadogan and Hey (1954) have concluded that the main factor influencing the direction of addition of a free radical $X \cdot$ to olefins $R \cdot CH : CH_2$ appears to be the relative stabilities of the intermediate radicals $R \cdot \dot{C}H \cdot CH_2 \cdot X$ and $R \cdot CHX \cdot CH_2 \cdot$. Haszeldine (1953) has postulated that radical stability decreases as the number of hydrogen atoms attached directly to the carbon atom carrying the unpaired electron is increased, and so, for decreasing radical - stability, tertiary ($\geqslant$C·) > secondary (>CH·) > primary (–CH$_2$·), where the terms primary, secondary and tertiary indicate the number of atoms other than hydrogen which are attached to the carbon atom formally carrying the unpaired electron. It appears that such a rationalization is consistent with the known data concerning the orientation of free-radical addition.

However, the influence of steric factors is not ruled out by this interpretation, and some results concerning the relative reactivity of various olefins seem to be best explained on the basis of steric effects. The copolymerization of chlorinated ethylenes with styrene, vinyl acetate and acrylonitrile has been studied by Alfrey and Greenberg (1948) and by Doak (1948). These workers have shown that, whereas the reactivity of vinyl chloride is increased by substitution of a further chlorine atom at the 1-position, it is decreased by substitution of one or two chlorine atoms at the 2-position. Since the initial attack is at C-2, this decrease in reactivity was attributed to steric hindrance. Another reaction in which steric influences may be operative is that of the addition of bromotrichloromethane to β-methylstyrene (Kharasch and Sage, 1949). It was shown that β-methylstyrene is very much less reactive than styrene, whereas Kharasch, Simon and Nudenberg (1953) have shown that α-methylstyrene is about four times more reactive than styrene. It is understandable that the methyl group in α-methylstyrene might increase the stability of the intermediate radical by hyperconjugation, but there seems no reason why a β-methyl group should cause any marked decrease in the stability of this radical. It is possible, therefore, that this decrease in reactivity may be due to the steric effect of the methyl group at the position which is the site of the initial attack.

It must be emphasized that the approach to the problem of the influence of substituent groups on homolytic addition reactions has so far been solely empirical, and that much more work must be done before the importance of the various factors can be accurately assessed.

Steric Acceleration

The possibility exists that in sufficiently crowded molecules, where the reaction centres are surrounded by bulky groups, steric strains present in the original molecule may be relieved by homolytic dissociation. Such a circumstance may give rise to steric acceleration of the dissociation in a manner analogous to that found in the unimolecular heterolysis of certain halides (for a review, see de la Mare, 1954). Differences in the rates and activation energies for the homolytic decomposition of azobis-*iso*butyronitrile (XL, R = CH$_3$) and its homologues (XL, R = C$_2$H$_5$, n-C$_3$H$_7$, *iso*-C$_3$H$_7$, n-C$_4$H$_9$, *iso*-C$_4$H$_9$ and *cyclo*-C$_6$H$_{11}$) in toluene were thus attributed by Overberger, O'Shaughnessy and Shalit (1949) to steric acceleration.

$$
\begin{array}{ccc}
\underset{|}{\overset{CH_3}{|}} & \underset{|}{\overset{CH_3}{|}} & \underset{|}{\overset{CH_3}{|}} \ \underset{|}{\overset{CH_3}{|}} \\
R-C-N=N-C-R & \longrightarrow & R-C---C-R+N_2 \\
\underset{}{\overset{|}{CN}} & \underset{}{\overset{|}{CN}} & \underset{}{\overset{|}{CN}} \ \underset{}{\overset{|}{CN}}
\end{array}
$$

XL

The differences were correlated with the amount of steric interference of the two groups R as determined by inspection of Fischer-Hirschfelder models. Subsequently, Overberger and Biletch (1951) showed, by measuring the rates of decomposition of 2 : 2′-azobis-2-benzylpropionitrile (XL, $R = C_6H_5CH_2$) and the corresponding p-nitro- and p-chloro- compounds, that the p-substituents exerted very little polar effect on the reaction-rate, and that the steric effect of the benzyl group was about equal to that of the methyl group in azobis-*iso*-butyronitrile. Overberger and Berenbaum (1951a) separated the racemic and *meso* forms of three azonitriles of the type of XL (R = *cyclo*Pr, *iso*Bu, and *tert*.Bu) and showed that there was little difference in the rate of decomposition of the two diastereoisomers, and that this was consistent with the amounts of steric strain predicted by examination of molecular models. It was also shown that the effect of steric strain was much greater in the case of (R = *iso*Bu) than with (R = *iso*Pr or *tert*.Bu), and that this was consistent with a prediction, from examination of models, that the steric interference is caused largely by β- rather than by α-chain-branching. The decomposition of azonitriles of the type of XL with (R = *cyclo*alkyl) was investigated by Overberger, Biletch, Finestone, Lilker and Herbert (1953). The differences in rate and activation energy encountered were considered to be due to the release of ring-strain occasioned by the change from a tetrahedral to a trigonal configuration of C–1 of the alicyclic ring (*cf* Brown, Brewster and Schechter, 1954) :

$$
\begin{array}{ccc}
\overset{CN}{\diagup} \ \overset{NC}{\diagdown} & & \overset{CN}{\diagup} \\
R \quad C-N=N-C \quad R & \longrightarrow & 2R \quad C\cdot \quad +N_2
\end{array}
$$

Steric Inhibition of Resonance

Considerable differences in reactivity exist between the *cis* and *trans* forms of olefins of the type RHC=CHR towards copolymerization with other olefins (*e.g.* styrene) (see, for example, Marvel and Schertz, 1943, 1944 ; Lewis and Mayo, 1948). This problem has been reviewed and discussed by Mayo and Walling (1950). If it is assumed that the intermediate free-radical formed by the initial addition of a radical to the olefin has a planar or an easily reversible pyramidal configuration, then the addition of the same reference radical to either the *cis* or the *trans* olefin should lead to the same intermediate radical.

61

This is certainly true in some cases: thus Mayo and Wilzbach (1949) have shown that *cis*- and *trans*-1:2-dichloroethylene give identical products with vinyl acetate. It follows, therefore, that in these instances, the less stable isomer of the pair should be the more reactive. In fact, the less stable *trans*-1:2-dichloroethylene is the more reactive, as predicted. The prediction, however, breaks down in a number of cases. Thus, maleonitrile and fumaronitrile show no difference in reactivity although fumaronitrile is more stable than maleonitrile. Again, with the dialkyl maleates and fumarates, it is the more stable fumarates which are the more reactive (Lewis and Mayo, 1948). It follows, therefore, that interconversion of the intermediate radicals cannot, in these instances, be simultaneous with addition. The differences in reactivity shown in these cases were ascribed by Mayo, Lewis and Walling (1947) to steric inhibition of resonance.

Considering diethyl fumarates, the intermediate radical resulting from addition of a reference radical R· may exist as a resonance hybrid of canonical forms including XLI–XLIV. The forms XLI–XLIII can make substantial contributions only if the oxygen atom

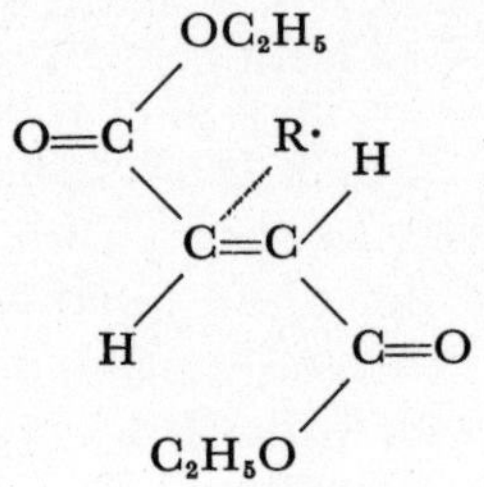

XLI

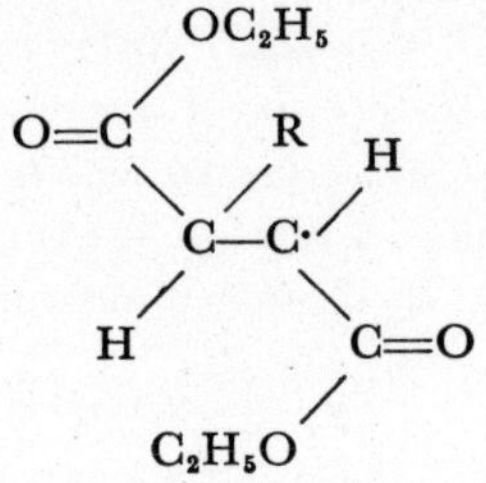

XLII

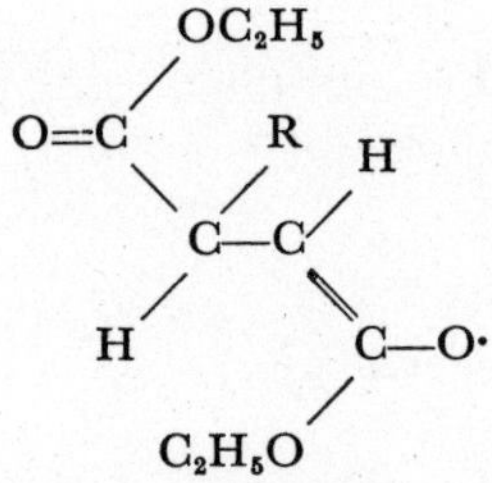

XLIII

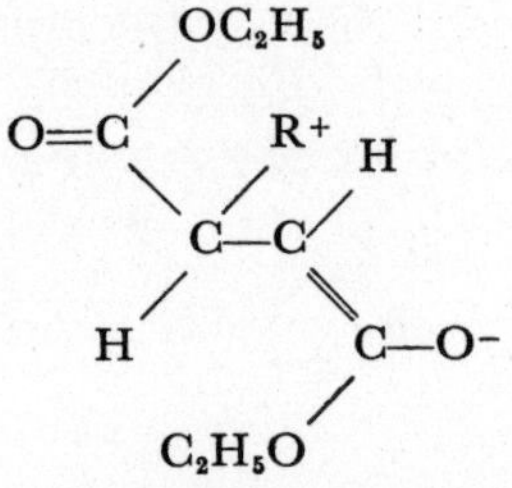

XLIV

of the carbonyl group involved lies in the same plane as the atoms attached to the doubly bound carbon atoms. It was shown by the use of molecular models that this requirement can be satisfied with the fumarates, but that the required configuration is sterically impossible with the maleates. Thus the transition state for addition to the fumarates would be expected to be favoured to this extent, and the effect may be large enough to reverse predictions made on the basis of the stabilities of the initial states. Forms such as XLIV, in

62

which R has donated an electron to the ester, may also contribute, and serve to increase the difference in reactivity between the stereochemical forms.

Other similar examples were discussed by Mayo and Walling (1950), and analogous explanations were offered for the observed differences in reactivity.

REFERENCES

Alfrey, T. and Greenberg, S. (1948) *J. Polymer Sci.* **3,** 297
Barton, D. H. R. (1953) *J. chem. Soc.* 1027
Bender, P., Flowers, D. L. and Goering, H. L. (1955) *J. Amer. chem. Soc.* **77,** 3463
Berson, J. A. and Swidler, R. (1953) *ibid* **75,** 4366
Bordwell, F. G. and Hewett, W. A. (1954) *Amer. chem. Soc. Abstracts,* 126th *Meeting* p. 6–O
Brown, H. C. and Bonner, W. H. (1954) *J. Amer. chem. Soc.* **76,** 605
— and Brady, J. D. (1952) *ibid* **74,** 3570
— Brewster, J. H. and Schechter, H. (1954) *ibid* **76,** 467
— Kharasch, M. S. and Chao, T. H. (1940) *ibid* **62,** 3455
Bryce-Smith, D. (1956) *J. chem. Soc.* 1603
Cadogan, J. I. G. and Hey, D. H. (1954) *Quart. Rev. chem. Soc., Lond.* **8,** 308
— — and Williams, G. H. (1954) *J. chem. Soc.* 3352
Corey, E. J. (1953) *J. Amer. chem. Soc.* **75,** 2301
Cristol, S. J. and Brindell, G. D. (1954) *ibid* **76,** 5699; (1955) *Amer. chem. Soc. Abstracts,* 127th *Meeting* p. 35–N
— and Hause, N. L. (1952) *J. Amer. chem. Soc.* **74,** 2193
Dannley, R. L. and Sternfeld, M. (1954) *ibid* **76,** 4543
Derbyshire, D. H. and Waters, W. A. (1949) *Trans. Faraday Soc.* **45,** 749
Doak, K. W. (1948) *J. Amer. chem. Soc.* **70,** 1525
Fawcett, F. S. (1950) *Chem. Rev.* **47,** 234
Goering, H. L., Abell, P. I. and Aycock, B. F. (1952) *J. Amer. chem. Soc.* **74,** 3588
— Relyea, D. I. and Larsen, D. W. (1956) *ibid* **78,** 348
— and Sims, L. L. (1955) *ibid* **77,** 3465
Gomberg, M. (1900) *Ber. dtsch. chem. Ges.* **33,** 3150
Haines, R. M. and Waters, W. A. (1955) *J. chem. Soc.* 4256
Haszeldine, R. N. (1952) *ibid* 2504, 3490; (1953) *ibid* 3565
— and Steele, B. R. (1953) *ibid* 1199
Hey, D. H., Pengilly, B. W. and Williams, G. H. (1956) *ibid* 1463
Ingold, C. K. (1938) *Trans. Faraday Soc.* **34,** 227; (1953) *Structure and Mechanism in Organic Chemistry,* New York, Cornell University Press, p. 258
Karagounis, G. (1949) *Helv. chim. acta* **32,** 1850; (1951) *ibid* **34,** 994
— and Drikos, G. (1933) *Naturwissenschaften* **21,** 697; *Nature, Lond.* **132,** 354; (1934) *Z. phys. Chem.* **26B,** 428
— and Jannakopoulos, T. (1940) *ibid* **47B,** 343
Kharasch, M. S. and Friedlander, H. N. (1949) *J. org. Chem.* **14,** 239
— Holton, P. G. and Nudenberg, W. (1954) *ibid* **19,** 1600; (1955) *ibid* **20,** 920
— Jensen, E. V. and Urry, W. H. (1945) *ibid* **10,** 386
— Kuderna, J. and Nudenberg, W. (1954) *ibid* **19,** 1283
— — and Urry, W. H. (1949) quoted by Wheland, G. W. (1949)
— Mansfield, J. V. and Mayo, F. R. (1937) *J. Amer. chem. Soc.* **59,** 1155
— and Sage, M. (1949) *J. org. Chem.* **14,** 537
— Sallo, J. and Nudenberg, W. (1956) *ibid* **21,** 129
— Simon, E. and Nudenberg, W. (1953) *ibid* **18,** 328

Kharasch, M. S. and Skell, P. S. (1949) quoted by Wheland, G. W. (1949)

Lepingle, M. (1926) *Bull. Soc. chim. Fr.* **39**, 741

Lewis, F. M. and Mayo, F. R. (1948) *J. Amer. chem. Soc.* **70**, 1533

Lewis, G. N. and Calvin, M. (1939) *Chem. Rev.* **25**, 342

— Magel, T. T. and Lipkin, D. (1942) *J. Amer. chem. Soc.* **64**, 1774; (1944) *ibid* **66**, 1579

de la Mare, P. B. D. (1954) in *Progress in Stereochemistry*, Vol. 1, Ed. W. Klyne, London, Butterworths, pp. 93 *et seq*

Marvel, C. S. and Schertz, G. L. (1943) *J. Amer. chem. Soc.* **65**, 2058; (1944) *ibid* **66**, 2135

Mayo, F. R., Lewis, F. M. and Walling, C. (1947) *Disc. Faraday Soc.* **2**, 285

— and Walling, C. (1940) *Chem. Rev.* **27**, 351; (1950) *ibid* **46**, 191

— and Wilzbach, K. E. (1949) *J. Amer. chem. Soc.* **71**, 1124

Noyes, R. M., Dickinson, R. G. and Schomaker, V. (1945) *ibid* **67**, 1319

Ott, E. (1928) *Ber. dtsch. chem. Ges.* **61**, 2124

Overberger, C. G. and Berenbaum, M. B. (1951a, b) *J. Amer. chem. Soc.* **73**, 2618, 4833

— and Biletch, H. (1951) *ibid* 4880

— — Finestone, A. B., Lilker, J. and Herbert, J. (1953) *ibid* **75**, 2078

— O'Shaughnessy, M. T. and Shalit, H. (1949) *ibid* **71**, 2661

Pickard, R. H. and Kenyon, J. (1911) *J. chem. Soc.* **99**, 65

Porter, C. W. (1935) *J. Amer. chem. Soc.* **57**, 1036

Rondestvedt, C. S. and Blanchard, H. S. (1956) *J. org. Chem.* **21**, 229

Samoilov, S. and Dyatkina, M. (1948) *Zhur. fiz. Khim.* **22**, 1294

Schwartz, A. M. and Johnson, J. R. (1931) *J. Amer. chem. Soc.* **53**, 1063

Skell, P. S. and Woodworth, R. C. (1955) *Amer. chem. Soc. Abstracts*, 127th *Meeting*, p. 26–N

de Tar, D. F and Howard, J. C. (1955) *J. Amer. chem. Soc.* **77**, 4393

Tarbell, D. S. and Weiss, M. (1939) *ibid* **61**, 1203

Taylor, T. W. J. and Murray, A. R. (1938) *J. chem. Soc.* 2078

Wallis, E. S. and Adams, F. H. (1933) *J. Amer. chem. Soc.* **55**, 3838

Waters, W. A. (1946) *The Chemistry of Free Radicals*, Oxford University Press, p. 182

Wheland, G. W. (1949) *Advanced Organic Chemistry*, New York, Wiley, pp. 713 *et seq*

Ziegler, J. B. and Shabica, A. C. (1952) *J. Amer. chem. Soc.* **74**, 4891

The author is indebted to Professor D. H. Hey, F.R.S., for reading and criticising this chapter.

3

THE STEREOCHEMISTRY OF DISPLACEMENTS AT UNSATURATED CENTRES

P. B. D. de la Mare

Terminology

IN aliphatic chemistry, use of the term 'substitution' to imply replacement of any group by any other is very general, particularly for reactions of organic molecules with nucleophilic reagents. This usage has consistently been carried over to describe, for example, nucleophilic displacement from aromatic systems of halogens, as halide ions, by other groups.

For reactions of electrophilic reagents with aromatic compounds, however, the term 'substitution' is sometimes taken to have the restricted meaning of replacement of hydrogen. Similarly, such terms as 'nitration' and 'halogenation' usually imply displacement of hydrogen, and this restricted sense has been adopted in this chapter. The terms replacement and displacement imply the more general process (*e.g.* the electrophilic displacement of *any* group, including hydrogen, by Br, NO_2 and so on). A systematic nomenclature for specific displacement reactions has been proposed by Bunnett (1954), and should always be used when ambiguity exists.

ELECTROPHILIC AROMATIC DISPLACEMENTS

General Considerations

The main patterns in electrophilic aromatic displacements are determined by the polar effects of the substituents. Discussions of the experimental evidence, and of the theories customarily invoked in explanation of these facts, are readily available (*cf* Ingold, 1953; Remick, 1949), and only such aspects as are needed in disentangling steric from polar effects in these reactions will be discussed here.

Many authors have considered that steric effects play a part, which may in some cases become predominant, in determining the rate of displacement, and the orientation, in some aromatic systems. Let us consider two examples. Holleman (1924) considered that the size of the reagent was important in determining the $o : p$-ratio in the reactions of substituted benzenes. He gave the values shown in TABLE 1 to demonstrate that the $\frac{1}{2}o : p$-ratio decreases with increasing size of the reagent, as the result of steric hindrance to the entry of the new group into the position *ortho*- to the directing substituent.

65

TABLE 1. $\frac{1}{2}o:p$-RATIOS IN ELECTROPHILIC DISPLACEMENTS

Directing substituent :	Me	Cl	Br	OH
Entering group :		$\frac{1}{2}o:p$-ratio		
Cl	0·69	0·35	0·37	0·50
NO$_2$	0·68	0·21	0·30	0·33
Br	0·33	0·06	0·08	0·05
SO$_3$H	0·26	0·00	0·00	—

It was assumed that the reagents involved in determining the above ratios increase in effective size in the order Cl< NO$_2$< Br< SO$_3$H. It will appear later that this is not wholly correct; the theory must be modified to take into account more detailed knowledge of the nature of the mechanisms of substitution.

Secondly, LeFevre (1933, 1934) considered that the size of the directing substituent might in some cases be important in determining orientation. He showed that, in the reactions of *p*-cymene with electrophilic reagents, the proportion of substitution *ortho*- to the *iso*propyl group was always less than that *ortho*- to the methyl group, as shown by the following figures :

Reaction of *p*-cymene :	Nitration	Bromination	Chlorination	Sulphonation
Substitution *ortho*- to the methyl group :	>70%	>54%	>59%	*c*. 80%

Two polar factors combine to make the interpretation of these observations uncertain in the absence of other information. First, especially for halogenation (*cf* de la Mare and Robertson, 1943 ; Berliner and Bondhus, 1946 ; Robertson, de la Mare and Swedlund, 1953), hyperconjugative electron-release, more powerful from the methyl than from the *iso*propyl group, could be responsible for the observed orientation. Secondly, even if the polar and steric effects combined to make activation of *ortho*-substitution by these two groups equal, the greater *meta*-activating power of the *iso*propyl than of the methyl group could give the observed sequence. Again, recent work (pp. 68–71) shows that the general principle discussed by LeFevre is correct, and applicable in part to these cases, but that details of the interpretation require modification.

The Nature of the Transition State

For any satisfactory qualitative demonstration, and still more for a quantitative demonstration of the importance of steric hindrance in a reaction, it is necessary to know the detailed mechanism of the rate-determining stage or stages, and thence to decide approximately the geometry both of the initial and of the transition state, in order to decide the magnitude of the steric forces that can be expected.

Details of the non-rate-determining stages may, of course, also be important in some cases. Of all aromatic displacement reactions, nitration has been the most fully investigated, and it is known that most nitrations involve attack on the aromatic nucleus by the nitronium ion (NO_2^+). The most probable geometry for the transition state in this and similar cases is that suggested by Cowdrey, Hughes, Ingold, Masterman and Scott (1937), shown in formula IA. The nitronium

IA   IB

ion approaches from above the aromatic nucleus, and displaces the hydrogen atom downwards. In the transition state, the partial bond between the nucleus and the nitro-group must become considerably developed, and the Ar—H bond must be only inconsiderably weakened, since deuterium or tritium is replaced at the same rate as hydrogen (cf Melander, 1950; Bonner, Bowyer and Gwyn Williams, 1953). Such a transition state, in which a canonical structure such as IB must be important, has approximately tetrahedral disposition of valencies at the carbon atom attacked, and accords with the fact that these reactions are considerably facilitated by the presence of con-jugative electron-releasing substituents ortho- or para- to the site of displacement, since the establishment of something approximating to a fully formed new bond in the transition state requires the availability of a full electron pair. This type of transition state was adopted by Wheland (1942) in his molecular-orbital treatment of aromatic substitution, as also by many later authors.

Comparison of Electrophilic Reagents

For satisfactory comparison with nitration, it is obviously desirable to choose a reagent which also reacts as a positive entity, since in this way differences resulting from polar influences will be minimized. Halogenation using acidified hypochlorous or hypobromous acid can be made to fulfil this condition, since under these circumstances the effective reagents can be shown to be the bare halogen cations, Cl^+ or Br^+, or the corresponding hydrated forms, $ClOH_2^+$ or $BrOH_2^+$ (cf Shilov and Kaniev, 1939; Derbyshire and Waters, 1951; de la Mare, Hughes and Vernon, 1950). It may be assumed that the transition state for displacement by these reagents will be very similar to that adopted in nitration. Kinetic measurements show that the kinetic form of the reaction is the same for all the compounds studied, so that not only the $\frac{1}{2}o:p$-ratios, but also the partial rate factors (*i.e.* the rates of reaction in the various positions in the nucleus, a single position in benzene being considered as unity) can be calculated.

In TABLE 2 are given values for the reaction of toluene with various reagents (de la Mare and Harvey, 1956; de la Mare, Harvey and Varma, unpublished; Cohn, Hughes, Jones and Peeling, 1952). In the absence of steric influences, the proportion of *ortho*-substitution should not change greatly with the reagent, provided that we are comparing, as we are here, reagents which all bear a full positive charge. Yet both chlorination and bromination give a substantially higher $\frac{1}{2}o$: p-ratio than does nitration. It is necessary, therefore, to consider whether steric effects should be greater in nitration by the nitronium

TABLE 2.   ELECTROPHILIC SUBSTITUTION IN TOLUENE DETERMINED BY
POSITIVELY CHARGED REAGENTS

Reagent and conditions :	ClOH, HClO$_4$ in water	BrOH, HClO$_4$ in aq. dioxan	HNO$_3$ in HOAc
Relative rate (PhH = 1) :	*c.* 60	36·2	24·5
%-*Ortho* :	74	70·3	56·5
%-*Meta* :	3	2·3	3·5
%-*Para* :	23	27·4	40·0
$\frac{1}{2}o$: p-ratio :	1·6	1·28	0·71
$\frac{1}{2}m$: p-ratio :	0·06	0·042	0·043
$RT \ln f_p^{Me}/f_o^{Me}$* :	−0·2	−0·11	0·14

* f_x^R = partial rate factor for substitution at the x-position in Ph.R.

ion than in bromination by Br$^+$ or BrOH$_2{}^+$. De la Mare and Harvey (1956) considered that this was indeed likely, on the basis of the probable geometry of the transition state, indicated in I. The nitronium ion is linear, but in reaction as an electrophilic reagent its shape must become distorted towards that of the nitro-group. Its final, most stable conformation is coplanar with the aromatic ring; and during the course of the reaction, while both the entering and the leaving group are still bound to the ring, non-bonding repulsions involving the leaving hydrogen atom must not become too large. For these reasons, the entering nitro-group will tend to maintain itself so that its oxygen atoms lie parallel with the aromatic ring, and hence its effective radius in the direction of the *o*-methyl group is likely to be greater than that of the spherical bromine atom.

Comparison of Directing Substituents

In a series of alkyl benzenes, the size of the directing substituent can be altered, without very considerably changing its polar character.

Cohn, Hughes, Jones and Peeling (1952) argued, on the basis of orientation and rates of nitration of *tert.*-butyl benzene as compared with toluene, that nitration *ortho*- to the *tert.*-butyl group is considerably hindered sterically. H. C. Brown and Bonner (1954) have provided orientation data for the nitration of ethyl and *iso*propylbenzene. The values are given in TABLE 3. There is no doubt that, whereas the

TABLE 3.   ORIENTATION IN THE NITRATION OF ALKYL BENZENES

Values are for nitration by nitric–sulphuric acid mixtures, except those in parentheses, which are for nitration in acetic acid

Compound :	Me.Ph		Et.Ph	Pr^i.Ph	Bu^t.Ph	
%-*Ortho* :	58·4	(56·5)	45·0	30·0	15·8	(12·0)
%-*Meta* :	4·4	(3·5)	6·5	7·7	11·5	(8·5)
%-*Para* :	37·2	(40·0)	48·5	62·3	72·7	(79·5)
$\frac{1}{2}o$: *p*-ratio :	0·78	(0·71)	0·46	0·24	0·11	(0·08)
$\frac{1}{2}m$: *p*-ratio :	0·059	(0·043)	0·067	0·062	0·079	(0·053)
$RT \ln f_p/f_o$ (kcal.mole^{-1}) :	0·11	(0·14)	0·34	0·62	0·96	(1·10)

$\frac{1}{2}m$: *p*-ratio remains substantially unchanged, or slightly increases, with increased *alpha*-branching in the alkyl group, the $\frac{1}{2}o$: *p*-ratio decreases regularly and considerably when this change is made.

Further test of the theory, that the entering bromine substituent, when supplied as a positively charged reagent, is smaller in effective radius than the entering nitro-group, can be obtained by comparing the bromination, by Br$^+$ or BrOH$_2^+$, with the nitration of *tert.*-butyl benzene. It would be predicted that the $\frac{1}{2}o$: *p*-ratio would decrease as the change was made from toluene to *tert.*-butyl benzene, but that it would decrease much less than for nitration. The experimental data are given in TABLE 4 (de la Mare and Harvey, 1957 ; Cohn, Hughes, Jones and Peeling, 1952).

TABLE 4.   ELECTROPHILIC SUBSTITUTION IN *tert.*-BUTYL BENZENE DETERMINED BY POSITIVELY CHARGED REAGENTS

Reagent and conditions :	BrOH, HClO$_4$ in aq. dioxan	HNO$_3$ in HOAc
Relative rate (PhH = 1) :	12·0	15·7
%-*Ortho* :	37·7	12·0
%-*Meta* :	7·2	8·5
%-*Para* :	53·2	79·5
$\frac{1}{2}o$: *p*-ratio :	0·36	0·075
$\frac{1}{2}m$: *p*-ratio :	0·068	0·053
$RT \ln f_p/f_o$ (kcal.mole^{-1}) :	0·45	1·10

It can be seen that the $\frac{1}{2}m : p$-ratio is not much affected by change in the reagent; but the $\frac{1}{2}o : p$-ratio is very considerably reduced when the reagent is changed from Br^+ to NO_2^+. It would be difficult to explain these differences other than in terms of steric hindrance; and the agreement with the qualitative predictions made above reinforces the view that the effective radius of the entering bromine is in this case less than that of the entering nitro-group.

It is of some interest to make approximate estimates, from the orientation data, of the magnitude of the steric forces involved in determining these ratios. The free energy of activation for *para*-bromination of toluene is greater than that of *ortho*-bromination by $(RT \ln f_p/f_o) = 0.11$ kcal.mole^{-1}. For nitration of toluene in acetic acid as solvent, the corresponding value is -0.14 kcal.mole^{-1}. If these rate-differences appear essentially in the energies of activation, and are determined predominantly by steric hindrance, it can be seen that in the case of the o-methyl substituent, there is about 0.25 kcal.mole^{-1} more steric hindrance for nitration than for bromination; about an extra 0.93 kcal.mole^{-1} accrues, in nitration, from the introduction of the *tert.*-butyl group in place of the methyl group.

A consequence of the theory just outlined is that, for nitration, any substituent the effective radius of which is as large as, or larger than, the methyl group will introduce some steric hindrance to *ortho*-substitution. Therefore, for example, it seems now quite certain that the decrease in $\frac{1}{2}o : p$-ratio for nitration in the series PhCH$_3$ (0.69), PhCH$_2$Cl (0.36), PhCHCl$_2$ (0.27), PhCCl$_3$ (0.12) (*cf* Holleman, 1914; Ingold and Shaw, 1949) can be attributed largely to steric hindrance (*cf* de la Mare, 1949).

Similarly, there must be appreciable steric hindrance to the nitration of bromobenzene and of iodobenzene, since the bromine atom is of similar size to, and the iodine atom is larger in effective radius than the methyl group. The $\frac{1}{2}o : p$-ratios for the nitration of the halogenobenzenes are: PhF, 0.07; PhCl, 0.21; PhBr, 0.31; PhI, 0.35 (Holleman, 1924). This sequence is opposite to that expected if steric effects alone determined these ratios, but it is not correct to deduce, as has been done for example by Ferguson (1955) that steric effects are here negligible. It is more correct to say that polar effects are differentially larger than steric effects.

Other bulky substituting agents must be subject to steric hindrance when introduced *ortho*- to bulky substituents. McGary, Okamoto, and Brown (1955; *cf* also Brown and McGary, 1955) have argued that chloromethylation, mercuration, and *iso*propylation fall into this category. In a recent paper, Brown and Smoot (1956) have argued that steric hindrance is small or absent in the *ortho*-nitration, and in certain other substitutions, of toluene. The present author regards the experimental facts as controverting this aspect of Brown and Smoot's theoretical treatment.

Molecular Halogenation

A rather different situation arises when one considers the reactions of molecular halogens. Chlorination and bromination, when carried out under the common preparative conditions using solutions of the halogen in a hydroxylic solvent, involve molecular halogen as the effective electrophilic reagent, as has been shown by a number of investigators (for summaries, see Robertson, de la Mare and Swedlund, 1953; Robertson, 1954). The same is probably true of substitutions in such solvents as carbon tetrachloride (*cf* Robertson *et al.*, 1949; Robertson, 1954). Under these conditions, the orientation of substitution in toluene is considerably different from that which is found with the positively charged reagents discussed above. TABLE 5 shows values for the chlorination and bromination of toluene (Gindraux, 1929; de la Mare, Harvey and Varma, unpublished).

TABLE 5. ORIENTATION IN THE HALOGENATION OF TOLUENE BY MOLECULAR HALOGENS

Halogen	% *o-*	% *m-*	% *p-*	$\frac{1}{2}o:p-$ ratio	$\frac{1}{2}m:p-$ ratio	$+RT \ln f_p/f_o$ (kcal.mole^{-1})
Chlorine	60	0·2	40	0·75	0·0025	0·12
Bromine	37	0·2	63	0·29	0·0016	0·52

With the positively charged halogenating agents (TABLE 3), *ortho*-substitution predominates. With molecular chlorine, on the other hand (TABLE 5), the $\frac{1}{2}o:p$-ratio has become much smaller, being now less than one; and with molecular bromine, the orientation has become completely reversed, so that now the main reaction product is that resulting from *para*-bromination. That there is a real difference between the orientation observed with molecular bromine and molecular chlorine seems to be a fairly general phenomenon; it has been illustrated many times before, as for example by Holleman (1924; *cf* TABLE 1). It seems reasonable to believe that it results, at least in part, from the greater size of bromine than of chlorine. If the relative rates are regarded as appropriate measures of the differences in energies of activation for the processes concerned, then the data given in TABLE 2 indicate a rather small difference between the energies of activation for chlorination and bromination by positive entities (about 0·13 kcal.mole^{-1}); and the data given in TABLE 5 show, for the corresponding molecular entities, a rather larger difference (about 0·35 kcal.mole^{-1}).

In these cases, however, polar influences might affect the $\frac{1}{2}o : p$-ratio in two ways. First, the direct inductive effect of the substituent could influence the attack by a positively charged entity more than it influenced the attack by a formally neutral molecule. This type of behaviour, first postulated by de la Mare and Robertson (1948) to explain differences between relative rates of nitration and molecular halogenation of the halogenobenzenes, would result in a greater proportion of *ortho*-substitution when Br^+ or $BrOH_2{}^+$ was the electrophilic reagent, just as is in fact observed.

Secondly, the electromeric effect of the substituent may be relatively more important in molecular halogenation (de la Mare, 1949, 1954; Berliner and Berliner, 1954; Brown and Nelson, 1953). This behaviour is revealed, in a general way, by the very large effect that conjugative electron-releasing substituents have on the rate of halogenation (*cf* Robertson, de la Mare and Swedlund, 1953). The writer considers that it results from the formation, as an intermediate in molecular halogenation, of a relatively stable complex of type II. In this structure, the halogen which attacks the aromatic nucleus has

II

an expanded octet, and is therefore analogous with the linear tri-bromide ion. Covalent bond formation between the reagent and the aromatic substrate is therefore particularly well developed in this reaction, and conjugative effects of substituents are likely to be dominant. The consequence, as far as the present argument is concerned, is that *para*-substitution will be favoured with this type of reagent, since *para*-quinonoid structures appear to be more favourable energetically than the corresponding *ortho*-quinonoid structures (*cf* Waters, 1948; Bradfield and Jones, 1941). To what extent these two polar influences combine with steric effects in producing differences in orientation in these aromatic substitutions cannot yet be considered certain.

Displacements in Polynuclear Systems: Steric Acceleration

Although there is very little definite experimental evidence relating to displacements in polynuclear aromatic systems, recent theoretical interest in this field makes it desirable to consider in what cases one might expect to find steric effects which would disturb the orientation defined otherwise by conjugative influences. In such compounds, certain positions may be subject to steric effects resulting from the proximity of hydrogen atoms attached to another ring. Consider, for example, a planar model of phenanthrene (III). The hydrogen atom in the 5-position is only 1·69 Å distant from that in the 4-position, well within the van der Waals touching distance of 2·40 Å. This implies that there will be steric strain in the initial state of the molecule, resulting from a hydrogen–hydrogen compression of 0·71 Å. If we consider a model of the transition-state as in IV, in which a Br^+ ion has been attached to the 4-position, the angle between the entering bromine and leaving hydrogen being assumed to be 109°, and the bonds being assumed to be of ordinary single-bond character, simple geometrical considerations show that the hydrogen–hydrogen com·pression is now small (0·20 Å), and there is a hydrogen–bromine compression of 0·83 Å. The actual initial and transition states will not

III   IV

take up these precise forms, since strain can be relieved by stretching and bending of the bonds and by distortion of the aromatic ring. Such distortions are, however, likely to be rather more helpful to the transition state than to the initial state, since the former has an extra bond to share in the distortions. It seems fair to say, therefore, that very little steric hindrance to bromination in such a position would be expected, since both the initial and the transition state are likely to be destabilized, roughly to equal extents, by steric strain. The final state would be more strained than the initial state ; but this is irrelevant as far as the rate of substitution is concerned, though in suitably hindered cases, the aromatic substitution might thereby be rendered more measurably reversible than it is ordinarily.

The above considerations lead us to think that, in certain cases, steric acceleration might be observed in electrophilic aromatic displacements. It seems unlikely that there would often be steric acceleration of bromination or nitration, when hydrogen was being replaced ; but it is clear, for example, that deuteration of phenanthrene in the 4-position might well be accelerated sterically by the release, in the transition state, of internal steric strain.

Steric Acceleration in Electrophilic Displacements by Hydrogen

A variety of electrophilic displacement reactions are known in which groups other than hydrogen are replaced. Benkeser and Krysiak (1954) have recently argued that steric acceleration contributes to the reactions of certain of the trimethylsilyl xylenes with toluene-*p*-

sulphonic acid in acetic acid. The reaction was shown to involve electrophilic displacement of the $SiMe_3$ group by H; and from the kinetic form, the nature of the products, and the effects observed when substituents were introduced, the reaction was considered to take the form :

$$Ar \cdot SiMe_3 + H^+ \rightleftharpoons \left[Ar \begin{matrix} H \\ \diagup \\ \diagdown \\ SiMe_3 \end{matrix} \right]^+ \xrightarrow{H_2O} ArH + Me_3SiOH_2^+ \qquad . \quad (1)$$

The relative rates of replacement of the $SiMe_3$ group in this reaction are given in TABLE 6, and are compared with the isomeric proportions found in nitration, as far as these are known, corrected where necessary for the statistical factor when equivalent positions are available for substitution. The significant facts are these. There is a general correlation between the electron-availability at the various nuclear positions and the ease of displacement of the $SiMe_3$ group from the corresponding positions. The data relating to isomeric proportions formed in nitration of the various compounds support this statement, which can further be illustrated by calculations, given in the last column, of partial rate-factors for bromination by Br^+, by using the partial rate-factors for the bromination of toluene by Br^+ (TABLE 2), assuming that the effects of two methyl groups will be independent and additive. There is one large discrepancy, namely the unexpected ease of replacement of the $SiMe_3$ group when this is situated between two methyl groups in 2-trimethylsilyl-m-xylene. This compound is too reactive, as compared with 4-trimethylsilyl-m-xylene, by a rate-factor of about 10, and this additional reactivity can reasonably be attributed to steric acceleration ; the orientation suggests that there is correspondingly some steric retardation of the entry of the nitro-group between two methyl groups. It should be noted that Benkeser and Krysiak were misled in their discussion of the case of 3-trimethylsilyl-o-xylene. This, they thought, also provided an example of steric acceleration, but it in fact shows little sign of this effect, when comparison is made with its 4-isomer through the values calculated for bromination by Br^+. These, or alternatively the corresponding values for nitration, provide a much better standard of reference than those chosen by Benkeser and Krysiak, namely the data for molecular halogenation, which is known to determine a pattern of orientation considerably different from that observed in reactions of positively charged reagents.

Decarboxylations

Decarboxylations of aromatic compounds involve the replacement of the CO_2H group by H; and hence, whether they are unimolecular or bimolecular (Brown, B. R., 1951), they might be sterically accelerated

TABLE 6. RATES OF REACTION OF TRIMETHYLSILYL XYLENES WITH HYDROGEN ION IN ACETIC ACID COMPARED WITH THE RELATIVE REACTIVITIES OF THE NUCLEAR POSITIONS IN ELECTROPHILIC REPLACEMENT OF HYDROGEN

Compound (Ar·X)	Observed k for reaction $ArSiMe_3 + H^+$ in HOAc	Observed isomeric proportions* in reaction $ArH + NO_2^+$ (Kobe et al., 1952, 1954)	Calculated partial rate factors for $ArH + Br^+$ from data given in TABLE 2
	3·1	—	190
	280	$(15 \times 1) = 15\%$	5776
	24·5	$(42·5 \times 2) = 85\%$	4484
	0·30	$(0 \times 1) = 0\%$	6·25
	4·2	$(29 \times 2) = 58\%$	190
	3·0	$(21 \times 2) = 42\%$	148

* i.e., % substitution at position marked ● in column 1.

75

by the presence of bulky *ortho*-substituents. There is some evidence that this factor may be important in this reaction (*cf* Schubert, 1949), as also in analogous decompositions of aromatic aldehydes and ketones (*cf* Arnold and Rondesvedt, 1946). Kinetic measurements of the rates of these reactions (Schubert, 1949; Schubert, Donohue and Gardner, 1954) show that more than one kinetic path may in some cases be available, and this complicates the interpretation. The latter authors observed that, whereas the activating effects of the methyl, ethyl and *iso*propyl groups were about the same for aromatic decarboxylations, yet 2 : 4 : 6-tri-*iso*propylbenzoic acid underwent decarboxylation much more rapidly than 2 : 4 : 6-triethylbenzoic acid, which itself is decarboxylated more readily than 2 : 4 : 6-trimethyl-benzoic acid. It is difficult to escape the conclusion that steric acceleration plays a part in determining this rate-sequence.

Other Electrophilic Displacements

Bromine is known to replace the SO_3H group in sulphanilic acid, the $B(OH)_2$ group in aromatic boronic acids (Kuivila and Hendrickson, 1952), the $SiMe_3$ group in phenylsilanes (*cf* Benkeser and Torkelson, 1954), and the *tert.*-butyl group in 1 : 3 : 5-tri-*tert.*-butyl benzene (Bartlett *et al.*, 1954), according to the following equations:

$$H_2N \cdot C_6H_4 \cdot SO_3H + 3Br_2 + H_2O \longrightarrow H_2N \cdot C_6H_2Br_3 + H_2SO_4 + 3HBr \quad . \quad . \quad (2)$$

$$Ph \cdot B(OH)_2 + Br_2 + H_2O \longrightarrow PhBr + HBr + H_3BO_3 \quad . \quad . \quad . \quad . \quad (3)$$

$$Ph \cdot SiMe_3 + Br_2 \longrightarrow PhBr + Me_3SiBr \quad . \quad . \quad . \quad . \quad (4)$$

$$C_6H_3Bu^t_3 + Br_2 \longrightarrow C_6H_3Bu^t_2Br + Bu^tBr \quad . \quad . \quad . \quad (5)$$

Displacements of groups other than hydrogen under conditions usually conducive to nitration are also well known, particularly in poly-substituted benzenes, and reactions of this type have been surveyed by Nightingale (1947).

Although none of these reactions appear to have been investigated from the point of view of steric acceleration, the above discussion would suggest that there might be cases in which the introduction of a bulky *ortho*-substituent would produce an internal steric strain, which might be released partially when the molecule was attacked by an electrophilic reagent of sufficiently small effective radius.

Intermediate Stages in Electrophilic Displacements

In the above discussion, it has been assumed that the relative rates of the reactions under discussion could properly be discussed as if the reaction were a one-stage process involving, in the rate-determining transition state, only the aromatic compound and the effective electrophilic reagent. For nitration, the studies, using tritium derivatives of toluene and of other aromatic compounds, made by Melander (1950) show that tritium and hydrogen are displaced at equal rates by the nitronium ion, and hence that the stage of the reaction which involves removal of the proton from covalent binding with the aromatic nucleus is not important in the rate-determining transition state. This is probably true also for halogenation, at least under some conditions (*cf* Melander, 1950; de la Mare, Dunn and Harvey, 1957).

Zollinger (1955, 1956) has recently investigated kinetically the reaction between diazonium ions and certain naphtholsulphonic acids. In some of the reactions, as when the 4-chlorobenzenediazonium cation reacts with 2-naphthol-6 : 7-disulphonic acid, displacement of deuterium proceeds 6 times more slowly than displacement of hydrogen. The reaction was shown to be catalysed by added bases; when the concentration of base was increased, the rate fell increasingly below that required for a first-order dependence of rate upon base-concentration.

The above results were interpreted as implying a reaction path of the following type:

$$\text{ArH} + \text{X}^+ \underset{k_{-1}}{\overset{k_1}{\rightleftarrows} } \text{ArHX}^+ ; \quad \text{ArHX}^+ + \text{B} \overset{k_2}{\longrightarrow} \text{ArX} + \text{HB}^+$$

Both the pre-equilibrium (k_1, k_{-1}) and the removal of the proton (k_2), are concerned in determining the rate, and for a complete description of such a reaction-process, two transition states need to be considered; in the second, the steric requirements of the base must be involved. Zollinger (1955, 1956) has argued that, in cases in which the bulky entering electrophilic diazonium group, X^+, is obstructed considerably by adjacent substituents, the relative rate of the back reaction, k_{-1}, will be high, and consequently a particularly large isotope-effect will be observed, as found experimentally for 2-naphthol-6 : 8-disulphonic acid which couples in the 1-position.

It was also shown that the catalytic power of substituted pyridine bases followed their basic strength, except for 2- and 2 : 6-substituted bases which were relatively ineffective. From this it was argued that bases containing bulky groups adjacent to the centre of reaction were sterically impeded in their access to the departing hydrogen atom.

NUCLEOPHILIC AROMATIC DISPLACEMENTS

Polar Effects

Nucleophilic displacements in aromatic systems are somewhat difficult when no electron-withdrawing substituents are present in the molecule; but the presence of a single nitro-group is sufficient to activate the nucleus considerably. In these reactions, a wide variety of groups (*e.g.* halide, azide, nitro-, sulphonate, and aryloxyl, sulphydryl, alkyl and aryl sulphide, amine and hydroxyl groups) can be displaced from the aromatic nucleus, and the corresponding anions can usually be employed as the nucleophilic reagent. In kinetic studies, investigators have been most concerned with the displacement of halide ions from aromatic halides, using alkoxides and related ions, or alternatively amines, as the nucleophilic reagent. The values given in TABLE 7, selected from Bunnett and Zahler's comprehensive review (1951), illustrate the way in which electron-withdrawing groups activate, and electron-donating groups deactivate the nucleus. The list can be

TABLE 7. EFFECTS OF NUCLEAR SUBSTITUENTS IN DETERMINING THE RATE OF NUCLEOPHILIC DISPLACEMENT OF HALIDE FROM DERIVATIVES OF THE HALOGENO-NITROBENZENES

Substituent (R)	NO_2	Me_3N^+	MeCO	Cl	I	H	F	Bu^t	Me	OMe	NMe_2
k_R/k_H for (a) R—⟨⟩—Cl with NO₂ +NaOMe at 25°:	2×10^5	6×10^3	2×10^3	12	—	1	—	—	—	—	—
(b) R—⟨⟩—Br with NO₂ +C_5H_{11}N at 25°:	—	—	—	5·6	5·4	1	0·26	0·17	0·14	0·018	0·0012

extended (cf Bunnett, Draper, Ryason, Noble, Tonkyn and Zahler, 1953; Berliner and Monack, 1952; Downing, Heppolette and Miller, 1953); it is sufficient to illustrate that polar effects are of such dominating importance that steric influences are likely to appear only as minor disturbances.

Mechanism and Possible Intermediates

Little is known concerning the detailed mechanisms of these reactions, though there has been much speculation on this matter. The reactions are consistently of the second kinetic order, and it seems quite certain that the establishment of the new bond with the reagent is relatively more important in aromatic than in aliphatic nucleophilic displacement. This is shown strikingly by the fact that aromatic fluorides often undergo displacement reactions considerably more readily than do the corresponding chlorides, bromides, or iodides. TABLE 8 illustrates this point, using data given by Hughes (1938), Chapman and Parker (1951), Bevan (1951), Chapman and Levy (1952), and Beckwith, Miller and Leahy (1952). The different behaviour, expected and found when bond-breaking is more important than bond-formation, as with simple aliphatic halides, is also illustrated in this table.

Extreme examples of the type of behaviour, in which the formation of the new bond dominates in the reaction, occur in the chemistry of polynitro-compounds, which react with simple anions to form coloured adducts. Meisenheimer (1902) showed that the same adduct was

TABLE 8. RELATIVE REACTIVITIES (RCl = 1) OF AROMATIC AND ALIPHATIC
HALIDES IN NUCLEOPHILIC DISPLACEMENTS

Reaction	X =	F	Cl	Br	I
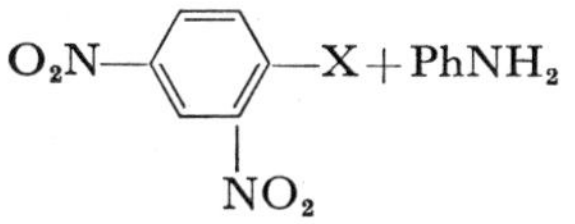 O_2N—⟨ ⟩—X + $PhNH_2$ (with NO_2) in ethanol at 50° :		60	1·00	1·50	0·45
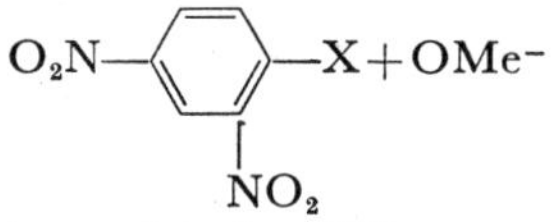 O_2N—⟨ ⟩—X + OMe^- (with NO_2) in methanol at 25° :		1800	1·00	0·66	0·20
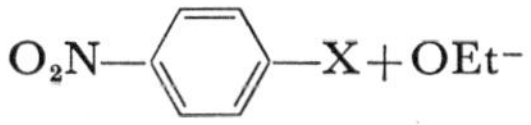 O_2N—⟨ ⟩—X + OEt^- in ethanol at 91° :		228	1·00	0·87	0·073
n-C_4H_9·X + OEt^- in ethanol at 50° :		0·004	—	29	—
C_2H_5·X + OEt^- in ethanol at 55° :		—	1·00	29	58

formed from 2 : 4 : 6-trinitro-anisole and ethanolic potassium hydroxide
as was obtained from 2 : 4 : 6-trinitrophenetole and methanolic
potassium hydroxide. In each case, the adduct was decomposed by
acids to give the same mixture of trinitro-anisole and trinitrophenetole.

SCHEME 1

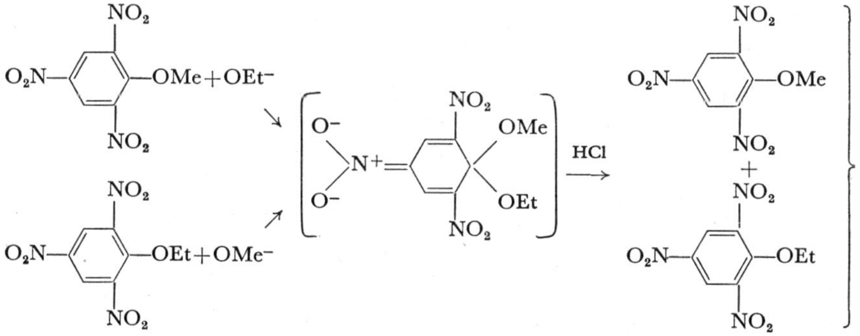

This and similar evidence has led many workers (*cf* Bunnett and
Zahler, 1951; Berliner, Quinn and Edgerton, 1950) to presume that
the analogous displacement reactions in aromatic halides were best to
be represented as passing through transient intermediates:

79

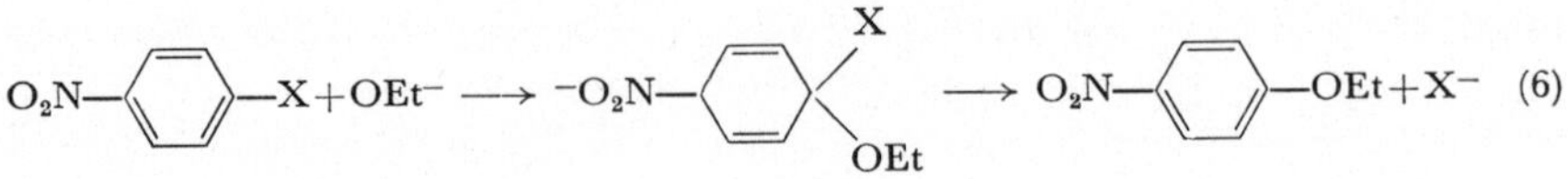

$$O_2N\!\!-\!\!\langle\!\!\!\rangle\!\!-\!\!X + OEt^- \longrightarrow \ ^-O_2N\!\!-\!\!\langle\!\!\!\rangle\!\!\underset{OEt}{\overset{X}{\diagdown}} \longrightarrow O_2N\!\!-\!\!\langle\!\!\!\rangle\!\!-\!\!OEt + X^- \quad (6)$$

V

The consequences of variations in the degree of stability of such an intermediate relative to the reactants and products have been discussed by Bunnett and Zahler (1951), as also by Hammond (1955; cf also Hammond and Parks, 1955).

None of this evidence conclusively proves the formation of an intermediate of the above structure as a transient molecular entity, and the alternative view, that the reactions may often be direct one-stage bimolecular displacements, is sometimes held (cf Chapman and Parker, 1951). It seems to the writer, however, that the balance of evidence favours the hypothesis that intermediates are formed, though it is possible that cases exist which approximate in character to the one-stage type.

Geometry of the Transition Complex

In any case, it is almost certain that the rate-determining process requires a considerable degree of bonding of a new group to an activated aromatic centre, which has approached tetrahedral hybridization at the attacked carbon atom. The geometry of the system (VI)

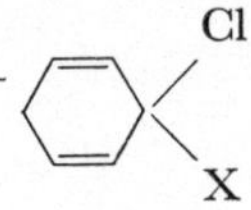

$$^-\langle\!\!\!\rangle\!\!\underset{X}{\overset{Cl}{\diagdown}}$$

VI

is likely, therefore, to resemble closely that taken up in electrophilic displacement, and as far as primary steric effects are concerned, some of the conclusions which have been reached on experimental grounds in the latter type of system can in theory be applied, with some modifications, to nucleophilic aromatic displacement.

Primary Steric Effects

Substituents ortho- to the centre of displacement would be expected, in principle, to introduce steric effects in these reactions, and these could in principle be effects either of steric hindrance or of steric acceleration. It is convenient first to consider substituents which are spherically symmetrical, or nearly so (e.g. I, Me, Bu^t). In these cases, if the leaving group is small and the entering group is large, steric effects may be negligible in the initial state but significant in the transition state, and steric hindrance to the displacement may be observed. An example of steric hindrance by an o-iodine substituent

80

was studied qualitatively by Sandin and Liskear (1935), as Bunnett and Zahler (1951) observed. More recently, Fierens and Halleux (1955) have studied the reactions of the 1-alkyl-2-bromo-3 : 5-dinitro-benzenes with potassium iodide in acetone. Their results are as follows :

1-substituent :	H	Me	Et	Pr^i	Bu^t
E (kcal.mole^{-1}) :	23·6	22·3	21·8	22·1	22·8
$\log_{10}pz$ (l.mole^{-1} sec.$^{-1}$) :	12·0	10·6	10·1	10·2	8·8
10^4k_2 (80° ; l.mole^{-1} sec.$^{-1}$) :	28	6·2	3·6	4·3	0·05

Here, the decrease in rate, and the increase in energy of activation, from the methyl- to the *tert.*-butyl-substituted compound, can reasonably be interpreted as the result of steric hindrance. The initial decrease in energy of activation between the unsubstituted and the methyl-substituted compound was attributed by the authors to steric acceleration of the reaction in the case of the latter compound.

Bevan, Fayiga and Hirst (1956) have made similar studies of the effects of *o*-, *m*-, and *p*-methyl and *tert.*-butyl groups on the rate of displacement of fluoride from *m*-fluoronitrobenzene by methoxide ions in methanol, and have concluded that their results give evidence for the steric hindrance by the *o-tert.*-butyl group in this reaction.

Capon and Chapman (1957) have investigated the effect of increasing the size of the nucleophilic reagent. The presence of a methyl group introduced in the 6-position (*o*- to the chlorine) in 2 : 4-dinitrochloro-benzene caused a reduction in the rate of displacement of chloride by a factor of 13·5 for methoxide ions, 22 for aniline, and 276 for piperidine which had considerably greater steric requirements. Although such examples are somewhat complicated by the inductive effects of the substituents, careful analysis of the data led all these groups of workers to the conclusion that steric hindrance was at least partly responsible for the deactivating influence of *o*-alkyl groups in these reactions. It is to be noted, however, that there might exist structural situations, involving a very large displaced group and a small nucleophilic reagent, in which the displacement reaction might be subjected to steric acceleration.

Secondary Steric Effects

Many nucleophilic displacements involve an activating nitro-group, and in these cases steric effects may take on a very complicated pattern. The mesomeric and electromeric effects of such substituents are greatest when the group is coplanar with the aromatic ring. The introduction of bulky flanking substituents may then powerfully depress the rate of reaction, largely by forcing the nitro-group to maintain its position out of the plane of the ring. Effects which were attributed to this cause, in the naphthalene series, have been reported by Berliner, Quinn and Edgerton (1950, *cf* Brower and Amstutz, 1953).

A number of examples of this type of phenomenon have recently been given. Capon and Chapman (1957) have studied the effects of *m*-alkyl substituents introduced into 2 : 4-dinitrochlorobenzene. The relative rates for the reactions with piperidine in ethanol are given below ; in the absence of interference between the alkyl and the nitro-group, the effects of alkyl substituents *m*- to the centre of displacement would be very small, and the very large reduction in rate when a methyl group is introduced between two nitro-groups is very striking.

163	44·9	2·8	0·168

When the activating nitro-group is adjacent to the centre of substitution, the problem arises as to whether steric effects will be largest when the nitro-group is coplanar with, or at right angles to, the plane of the aromatic ring. In the molecule of picryl iodide (VII), for example, the *ortho*-nitro-groups are inclined at 80° to the plane of the aromatic ring (Huse and Powell, 1940). Hence steric strain in the initial state has been relieved, at some cost of conjugation energy, by rotation of the nitro-group about the C—N bond. It seems possible that for some shapes of entering reagents Y, some such conformation as VIII might be sterically more favourable than IX, and hence in these cases, but possibly not in some others, the activating power of the *ortho*-nitro-groups might be regained in the transition state. Considerations of a similar nature have been discussed by Hammond (1956).

VII	VIII	IX

Correlation of Nucleophilic Power with Basic Strength

Several attempts have been made to deduce the existence of steric effects by correlating the rates of reactions of amines with their basic strengths, and observing discrepancies which can be attributed to steric hindrance. Brady and Cropper (1950) examined the rates of reaction of a number of aliphatic amines with chloro-2 : 4-dinitrobenzene in ethanol. In certain cases, as in the first series given in TABLE 9, the relative rate of reaction followed the basicity. In other cases, as in the second series, the rate-coefficients were obviously not directly related to the basic strengths. It was suggested that, in conformations such as X and XI, amines such as diethylamine and *iso*propylamine

X   XI

would suffer steric retardation in approach to the aromatic nucleus. Such retardation would be smaller in the methylamines, which have no branching methyl group; or in piperidine, in which the alkyl

TABLE 9. CORRELATION, FOR AMINES, OF BASICITY WITH RATE OF REACTION
WITH CHLORO-2 : 4-DINITROBENZENE

(i) Amine :	NH_3	NH_2Me	$NHMe_2$			
$10^4 k_2$ (25°) :	0·04	31·6	355			
$10^4 K_b$:	3·4	4·0	5·0			
(ii) Amine :	NH_2Me	NH_2Pr^i	NH_2Et	$NHPr_2$	$NHEt_2$	Piperidine
$10^4 k_2$ (25°) :	31·6	1·0	9·1	1·6	1·9	153
$10^4 K_b$:	4·0	4·3	4·6	8·2	10·0	12·5

groups are held by the ring away from the aromatic nucleus. Hence, *iso*propylamine, diethylamine, and their higher homologues show reactivities which are abnormally low as judged by their relative basicities.

Bishop, Cavell and Chapman (1952) have argued similarly in discussing the reactions of chloro-nitro-benzenes and chloro-nitro-pyridines with aromatic amines. Some of their data are given in TABLE 10. Pyridine, though more strongly basic than aniline, is

TABLE 10. RELATIVE REACTIVITIES OF BASES WITH AROMATIC CHLORIDES

Amine (B) :	*p*-Anisidine	*p*-Toluidine	Aniline	Pyridine
Relative rate B+chloro-2 : 4-dinitro-benzene :	8·4	2·7	1·0	0·045
B+2-chloro-3-nitro-pyridine :	—	2·9	1·0	0·059
B+2-chloro-5-nitro-pyridine :	8·4	2·8	1·0	0·16
Basic strength of B(pK_H ; Hall and Sprinkle, 1932) :	5·3	5·1	4·6	5·2

considerably less reactive; and consideration of plausible models of the transition state led these authors to consider that there is more steric hindrance to the approach of pyridine than of aniline, and that this contributes to the relative unreactivity with the former reagent. It was pointed out, however, that this can only be a part of the whole picture, since a similar trend, though one of somewhat smaller magnitude, is noted with 2-chloro-5-nitro-pyridine, in which case steric effects would be much smaller.

Hydrogen-bonding

In nucleophilic displacements involving primary and secondary amines as the attacking species, a further complication arises in the possibility of hydrogen-bonding between the NH-bond of the attacking amine and an o-nitro or other substituent. Bishop, Cavell and Chapman (1952) made this proposal, which has recently been examined by Bunnett *et al.* (1955). These authors have approached the problem experimentally by examining the influence of change in solvent on the change in ratio of reactivities of halogen *ortho-* and *para-* to the nitro- and carboxylate-ion group. Some of their values are given in TABLE 11.

TABLE 11. RATES AND ARRHENIUS PARAMETERS FOR THE REACTIONS OF THE CHLORONITROBENZENES WITH PIPERIDINE AT 102°

Solvent	$10^3 k_2$ (l.mole^{-1} min^{-1})		E (kcal.mole^{-1})		k_o/k_p
	o	p	o	p	
1% Dioxan	44	32·5	17·6	17·9	1·4
75% Methanol	5·2	3·0	17·8	17·2	1·7
93% Ethanol	4·0	1·7	17·7	15·2	2·3
99·8% Ethanol	4·0	1·4	18·1	17·1	29
Benzene	5·1	0·1	13·4	13·7	46
Xylene	—	—	—	—	80

As the solvent is made more polar, the ease of replacement of the p-chlorine atom increases. The reactivity of the o-chlorine atom increases also, but very much less markedly, so that the ratio of rates in these positions changes by a factor of more than 50 as the solvent changes from xylene towards water. These changes are a reflection of changes more particularly in the entropy (*cf* also Chapman, Parker and Soanes, 1954), than in the energy of activation, which is rather irregular in its variation with solvent.

Bunnett and Morath (1955) proposed that the transition state for replacement of the p-chlorine atom (XII) is stabilized by solvation, to an extent which increases with the solvating power of the solvent. The transition state for replacement of the o-chlorine atom is, however, not subject to such large changes in free energy of solvation, since the charges in the transition state are partly neutralized by internal solvation, in which the nitro-group hydrogen-bonds with the secondary NH group of piperidine (XIII).

XII   XIII

It may be noted that this conclusion is in disagreement with that reached by Hawthorne (1954). He examined the relative rates of the reaction of *o*- and *p*-chloronitrobenzene with piperidine and with deuteropiperidine, and found no isotope effect in either reaction. He concluded from this that there is no significant hydrogen-bonding in the transition state for the reaction of the *o*-compound. This conclusion is not tenable, however. Substitution of deuterium for hydrogen does not in general have a large effect on the energetics of hydrogen bonding. Even the strongest hydrogen bond, the F·····H—F bond, is only changed in heat of formation by 0·05 kcal.mole^{-1} by the replacement of deuterium for hydrogen (*cf* Long, Hildebrand and Morrell, 1943). An even smaller change would be expected in such a situation as that involving the relatively weak O·····H—N bond in the transition state envisaged by Bishop, Cavell and Chapman (1952) and by Bunnett and Morath (1955).

Both the latter groups of authors, therefore, regarded the reaction of aromatic halides with primary and secondary amines as a rather special case, in which internal solvation of the transition state plays a large part in determining the relative ease of displacement of *o*- and *p*-halogen atoms. With other, and particularly with anionic reagents, the *o*-halogenonitrobenzenes are less reactive than the *p*-compounds (*cf* Bunnett and Snipes, 1955), and this could be the combined result of steric inhibition of resonance and steric strain in the transition state. The fact that, in the 2 : 4-dihalogenonitrobenzenes, the 2-halogen atom is preferentially replaced, even by anions (Bunnett and Morath, 1955) is of considerable interest in this connection. Here, the nitro-group has a better opportunity to become coplanar with the aromatic ring in the transition state for *o*- than for *p*-displacement since, in the former case, the displaced halogen is moved downwards away from the flanking nitro-group. For more detailed discussion of the problem of steric effects on mesomerism, Chapter 4 should be consulted.

Intrinsic Relative Reactivities of ortho- *and* para-*Activated Positions*

It does not seem to the writer that any of these experiments give conclusive evidence concerning the intrinsic relative reactivities of *ortho-* and *para-*activated substituents, since in all of them there are involved several steric factors, the relative contributions of which cannot be assessed quantitatively. The reactivities of heterocyclic compounds (*e.g.* the azabenzenes and azanaphthalenes) might be thought to be more suitable for this purpose, since many theoretical predictions of their relative reactivities have been made. Thus Longuet-Higgins and Coulson (1949) have calculated the π-electron density distribution in pyridine as shown in XIV. On this basis, it

0·100
XIV ⬡ 0·023
N 0·106
−0·359

0·126
XV ⬡ 0·020
N 0·054
−0·274

would be predicted that 2-chloropyridine would be attacked by nucleophilic reagents more rapidly than 4-chloropyridine. On the other hand, a similar calculation by Brown and Dewar (1953) using different values for the arbitrary numerical parameters used in the calculations, gave the electron-densities shown in XV; from which the opposite prediction could be drawn. Green (1954), using valence-bond theory, has made calculations of the relative stabilities of the possible transition states in nucleophilic displacement in these compounds, and has reached the conclusion that 2-displacement would be favoured relative to 4-displacement. That the simplified molecular orbital method, due to Longuet-Higgins (1950), applied to calculations of the relative energies of formation of the transition state, gives the result that 2-chloropyridine and 4-chloropyridine should have similar energies of activation for nucleophilic displacement, has been shown by Chapman and Russell-Hill (1956). The latter authors have determined the rate-coefficients and Arrhenius parameters for the reactions of these compounds with ethoxide ions in ethanol. 4-Chloropyridine is at 25° slightly less reactive than 2-chloropyridine, but the activation energies (20·2 and 26·2 kcal.mole^{-1} respectively) are so different that at a not much lower temperature the 4-chloro-compound must be the more reactive. The relative reactivities, and corresponding Arrhenius parameters, in the reactions of the chloronitrobenzenes with piperidine have already been given in TABLE 11. It can be seen that, though there is some scatter in the results, the differences in activation energy on the whole favour the *p*-isomer, and *p*-activation would therefore be considered to be intrinsically preferred, perhaps because *p*-quinonoid structures are energetically preferable to *o*-quinonoid structures (*cf* Waters, 1948; Bradfield and Jones, 1941; de la Mare, 1949; Ingold, 1953, p. 267).

' Cine-substitution '

A number of nucleophilic displacement reactions are known in which the entering group appears in the aromatic ring at a position different from that relinquished by the leaving group. This has been called ' cine-substitution ' (Bunnett and Zahler, 1951).

Reactions involving ' benzyne ' intermediates

One recent example was studied by Roberts and his co-workers (1953). They examined the reaction in liquid ammonia between sodamide and chlorobenzene labelled with ^{14}C on the 1-carbon atom. The aniline which they prepared in this way was shown to be labelled equally on the 1- and on the adjacent carbon atoms. They proposed the mechanism shown in SCHEME 2, involving a ' benzyne ' intermediate (XVI).

SCHEME 2

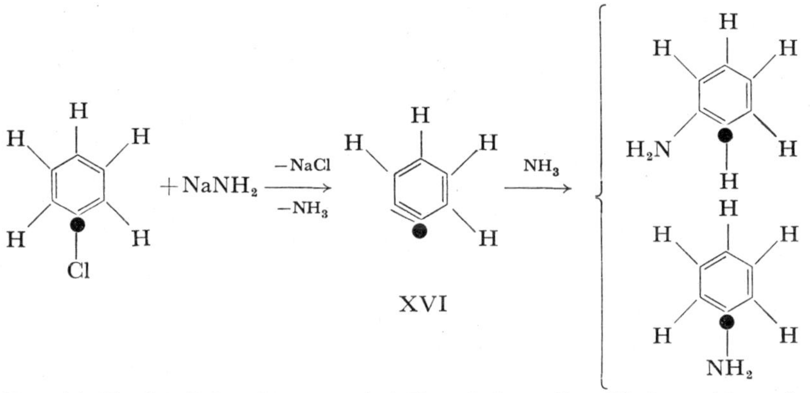

XVI

Note—(a) The labelled carbon atom is indicated thus: ●; (b) the positions of all substituent H-atoms are indicated; (c) each structure is only one of several canonical forms.

It seems probable that a number of ' cine-substitutions ' involving amination of substituted halogenobenzenes in liquid ammonia also proceed in this way. Bunnett and Zahler (1951) summarized some of the earlier experimental observations; and Roberts and his co-workers (1956) have recently extended the experimental data to include demonstration that, since compounds like bromomesitylene and 2-bromo-3-methylanisole do not react readily with potassamide, the presence of an o-hydrogen atom is essential to a facile rearrangement of the above type. Furthermore, these authors showed that o-deuterochloro- (or bromo-) benzene reacts with potassamide in liquid ammonia more rapidly than does the corresponding undeuterated compound. From this it can be deduced that the removal of a proton occurs during or before the rate-determining stage of the reaction. The orientation of such aminations was also studied, with results some of which are shown in TABLE 12.

TABLE 12. ORIENTATION IN THE AMINATION, BY POTASSAMIDE IN LIQUID AMMONIA, OF SUBSTITUTED HALOGENOBENZENES, $R \cdot C_6H_4 \cdot X$;

$$R \cdot C_6H_4 \cdot X + NH_2^- \longrightarrow R \cdot C_6H_4 \cdot NH_2 + X^-$$

| Starting material | | Product orientation | | |
R	X	o	m	p
o-OMe	Br	—	100	—
m-OMe	Br	—	100	—
p-OMe	Br	—	49	51
o-CF₃	Cl	—	100	—
m-CF₃	Cl	—	100	—
p-CF₃	Cl	—	50	50
o-Me	Br	49	51	—
m-Me	Br	22	56	22
p-Me	Cl	—	62	38
p-F	Br	—	20	80

The results are clearly consistent with the intervention of benzyne intermediates, $R \cdot C_6H_3$, in some, or all, of the reactions. Two problems are involved in interpretation of the observed orientation, namely (a), the relative acidities of the hydrogen atoms, which will partly determine the proportions of isomeric intermediates formed; and (b), the direction and rate of addition to these intermediates. The first seems largely to be determined by the inductive effects of the substituents, and the second is influenced both by this and by the conjugative electronic influences. For further details of the interpretation, the original papers should be consulted. Another example, which may be similar, in the thianaphthene series, has been studied by Brower and Amstutz (1954).

The von Richter reaction

This reaction, which Bunnett and his co-workers have also considered (1950, 1951, 1954), and have themselves studied extensively, is probably of a different type. A typical example is given below:

$$(c. \ 37\% \ \text{yield}) \qquad . \quad (7)$$

Under the same conditions, m-bromonitrobenzene gives a mixture of o- and p-bromobenzoic acids; and o-bromonitrobenzene gives in very small yield m-bromobenzoic acid. The carboxyl group appears always to enter *ortho-* to the position vacated by the nitro-group, since dibromonitrobenzenes having bromine *ortho*- to the nitro-group react poorly, whereas those with unflanked nitro-groups give fair yields of product. Hydrogen atoms from the solvent were shown, by tracer experiments, to become attached to the aromatic nucleus during the reaction. For this reason, mechanisms involving an internal hydrogen shift are untenable. The nitriles, which might be presumed to be intermediates in these displacements, have been shown in very recent work (Bunnett and Rauhut, 1956) not to be concerned in these processes.

The von Richter reaction of *p*-bromonitrobenzene (Equation 7) could be considered to follow a sequence involving a ' benzyne ' intermediate, XVII, if it were considered that the latter would add

XVII (hypothetical)

HCN specifically to give the established product, the position *para*-to the bromine being activated for attack by hydrogen. Orientation observed in other cases is, however, inconsistent with such a view of the reaction. Thus 1 : 3-dichloro-5-nitrobenzene on this view would give a benzyne intermediate, XVIII, which with HCN must give 1 : 3-dichloro-5-cyanobenzene, according to Equation 8 :

$$\text{(8)}$$

XVIII
(hypothetical)   (not formed)

In fact, the main product of this reaction has been shown by Bunnett, Rauhut, Knutson and Burrell (1954) to be 1 : 3-dichlorobenzene-4-carboxylic acid, with no trace of the 5-isomer. SCHEME 3 has been suggested by Bunnett and Rauhut (1956), and represents a revision of ideas proposed earlier by these authors. It involves nucleophilic attack by a cyanide ion on a carbon atom activated by an *o*-nitro group ; this is followed by interaction between the nitro-group and the *o*-cyano-substituent to form an ' imino-anhydride ', which on hydrolysis gives the acid.

SCHEME 3

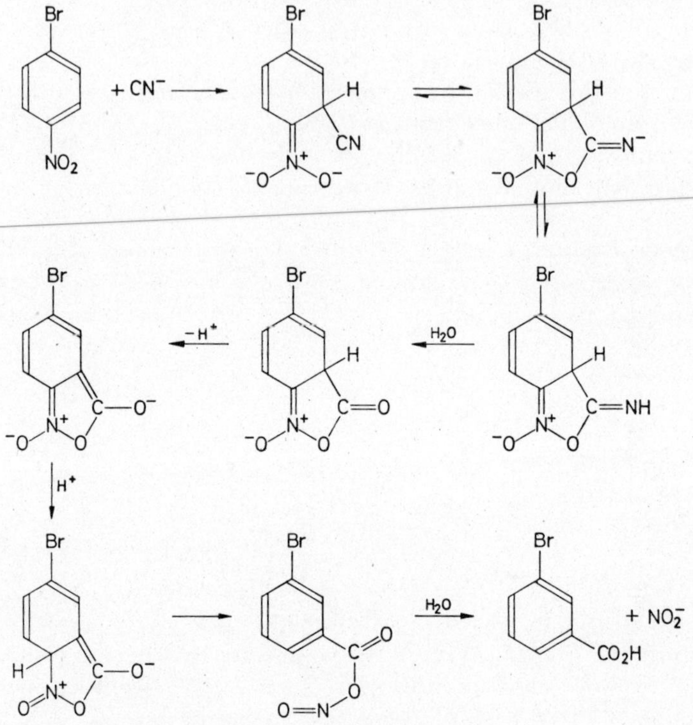

NUCLEOPHILIC DISPLACEMENTS AT VINYLIC CENTRES

Nucleophilic displacements at vinylic centres in general proceed only with some difficulty. Simple vinyl halides react with ethoxide ions and similar reagents at relatively high temperatures, and the corresponding acetylenic compound is usually the main product. With reagents such as sodium thioethoxide, however, in which the power of the reagent to substitute has been increased much more than its power to take part in elimination, Loevenich, Losen and Dierichs (1927) showed that vinylic halides give the corresponding thio-ethers:

$$RCH:CHBr + SEt^- \longrightarrow R \cdot CH:CH \cdot SEt + Br^- \qquad . \qquad . \quad (9)$$

The conditions needed for the reaction are considerably more drastic than those needed for reaction of analogous saturated halides.

As in aromatic substitution, it is possible, by attachment of electron-withdrawing groups to the vinylic carbon atom, to activate a suitably placed halogen substituent. Autenreith (1887, 1889, 1890, 1896) studied the reactions of β-chlorocrotonic acid and its derivatives with nucleophilic reagents, and showed that very rapid displacements occurred, which he formulated as follows:

90

$$\underset{\substack{\| \\ \text{H·C·CO}_2\text{H}}}{\text{Me·C·Cl}} \; + \; RS^- \; \longrightarrow \; \underset{\substack{\| \\ \text{H·C·CO}_2\text{H}}}{\text{Me·C·SR}} \; + \; Br^- \quad . \quad . \quad (10)$$

Stereochemical and mechanistic evidence concerning reactions of this type is not extensive. At least two investigations have, however, been carried out which throw a light on the nature of the processes involved. Gidvani, Kon and Wright (1932) have studied the reactions of ethyl chlorocrotonate (XIX) and of ethyl chloro-*iso*-crotonate (XX) with ethyl sodiomalonate. Their reaction sequences, embodying their structural conclusions, are shown in SCHEME 4. Theoretical interpre-

SCHEME 4

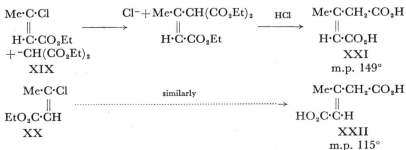

tation of these results depends on certainty in the assignment of structures of starting materials and products. With regard to the former, it has been shown by Paal, Schiedewitz and Rauscher (1931) that β-chloro-crotonic and -*iso*crotonic acids are reduced by hydrogen over a palladium catalyst to give respectively *trans*- and *cis*-crotonic acids. These hydrogenations are usually considered to involve replacement without change of configuration. It has also been shown by Michael (1888) that base-induced elimination of hydrogen chloride is considerably more rapid for β-chlorocrotonic acid than for its geometric isomer. This establishes with little doubt that, in the former isomer, the hydrogen and chlorine atoms are *trans*- to each other, and the structures shown in the scheme are a consequence.

With regard to the products, which are finally the geometric isomers (XXI and XXII) of β-methylglutaconic acid, the evidence concerning their structures has been summarized by Feist (1922). The crucial piece of evidence is the fact that hydrolysis under mild conditions of β-methylglutaconic anhydride (XXIII) gives the isomer (XXI), m.p. 149°.

$$\underset{\substack{\| \\ \text{H·C·CO} \\ \text{XXIII}}}{\overset{\text{Me·C·CH}_2\text{·CO}}{\Big\rangle}\text{O}} \; \underset{\text{H}_2\text{O}}{\longrightarrow} \; \underset{\substack{\| \\ \text{H·C·CO}_2\text{H} \\ \text{XXI} \\ \text{m.p. 149°}}}{\text{Me·C·CH}_2\text{·CO}_2\text{H}} \quad . \quad . \quad (11)$$

This is very strong evidence that in this isomer the carboxyl groups are *cis*- to each other*.

There seems little doubt, therefore, that this reaction is a bimolecular nucleophilic displacement at a vinyl centre, proceeding with retention of stereochemical configuration†, though the kinetics of the process have yet to be studied. Jones and Vernon (1955) have recently provided an example of the same phenomenon, in which both kinetic and stereochemical evidence is available. They studied the reactions of the same two halides with sodium ethoxide and sodium thio-phenoxide in ethanol. The reactions were shown to be kinetically of the second order, and the experimental findings are summarized in TABLE 13. The products indicated were identified in two ways: examination of the infra-red spectra of the isomers and of the starting

TABLE 13. REACTIONS OF ETHYL β-CHLOROCROTONATES WITH NUCLEOPHILIC REAGENTS

Compound	Nucleo-philic reagent	k_2 (0°) (l.mole^{-1} min^{-1})	E (kcal.mole^{-1})	$\log_{10}B$ (l.mole^{-1} min^{-1})	Products of reaction at 0°
Ethyl β-chloro-*trans*-crotonate	OEt$^-$	0·055	19·2	14·2	Ethyl β-ethoxy-*trans*(?)-crotonate.
	SPh$^-$	0·336	14·5	11·2	92% Ethyl β-thio-phenoxy-*trans*-crotonate‡.
Ethyl β-chloro-*cis*-crotonate	OEt$^-$	0·26	17·0	13·0	Ethyl β-ethoxy-*trans*(?)-crotonate.
	SPh$^-$	0·148	14·1	10·5	81% Ethyl β-thio-phenoxy-*cis*-crotonate¶.

‡ Together with 8% of the *cis*-isomer.

¶ Together with 19% of the *trans*-isomer. Reaction under reflux in ethanol gave similar stereospecificity.

materials were best interpreted as shown; and desulphurization of the *trans*- and *cis*-thioethoxy-esters gave, after hydrolysis, *trans*- and *cis*-crotonic acids respectively.

SCHEME 5

$$Me \cdot CCl : CH \cdot CO_2Et \xrightarrow[-HCl]{NaB} Me \cdot C : C \cdot CO_2Et$$

$$Me \cdot C : C \cdot CO_2Et + HB \longrightarrow Me \cdot CB : CH \cdot CO_2Et$$

In discussing possible mechanisms for these reactions, the sequence of SCHEME 5, involving elimination followed by addition, requires careful consideration, since reactions following this path would be expected to occur with greater readiness in olefinic than in benzenoid systems. If both isomers were to react in this way, they would give the

* It should be noted that this isomer can be regarded as a derivative of *trans*-crotonic acid; this fact has led to some confusion in the nomenclature of these compounds.

† The writer is indebted to Mr. C. A. Vernon for suggesting this interpretation.

same product. This mechanism is a possible one for the reactions with ethoxide ions. On the other hand, one or other, and most probably both, of the reactions in which thioethoxide is concerned must, by this criterion, be a true displacement reaction at a vinyl centre. It may be noted in passing also that this argument makes it certain that the substitution reactions of α-chlorocrotonic acid and its derivatives, which are known (Autenreith, 1889) to yield α-substituted products, must also be true vinylic displacements:

$$Me \cdot CH : CCl \cdot CO_2Et + SPh^- \longrightarrow Me \cdot CH : C(SPh)CO_2Et + Cl^-$$

Addition of PhSH to the acetylenic ester ($Me \cdot C : C \cdot CO_2Et$) would of necessity give β- rather than α-substituted products (*cf* Feist, 1906).

In theoretical discussions (*cf* Gold, 1951; Bunnett and Zahler, 1951) of possible transition states for vinyl displacements, it has usually been considered that a transition state of the type illustrated for ethyl β-chlorocrotonate, in formula XXIV, would be preferred energetically, and therefore that inversion of configuration would be predicted in stereospecific vinyl substitutions.

XXIV   XXV

The experimental results (TABLE 13) invalidate these conclusions, as far as the examples studied are concerned; and it has been proposed by Jones and Vernon (1955) that the reactions involve the adoption of an approximately tetrahedral distribution of valencies about the attacked carbon atom, with development of a carbanionic centre on the ethylenic carbon atom not involved in the reaction (see XXV); this anionic charge can, of course, in these β-substituted esters, be partly distributed on to the ethoxycarbonyl group. If this intermediate had any lifetime in solution, substitution would be accompanied by considerable geometrical isomerisation, and the same mixture of products would, in the limiting case, be obtained from each isomer. The consideration which permits the reaction to be stereospecific is that the reaction approximates to a synchronous displacement. The geometrical situation intermediate between reactants and products (XXV) represents an energy maximum, and is therefore to be regarded as a true transition state, at least to the extent to which the reaction is stereospecific. Retention of configuration occurs essentially because it is energetically easier, in the course of the formation of the new bond, to disturb the position of the more easily displaced chlorine substituent than to move the fully bound methyl group.

Stereospecific *cis*-replacements of chloride in compounds of the type $Ar \cdot SO_2 \cdot CH : CHCl$ by arylthio-ions have recently been described by Montanari (1956).

ELECTROPHILIC DISPLACEMENT AT VINYLIC CENTRES

Electrophilic displacements at vinylic centres are theoretically possible, and can sometimes be realized. Considerations which govern such reactions are, however, often very different from those which govern similar reactions in aromatic systems. Attack by an electrophilic reagent X^+ on an aromatic molecule ArH gives, or may give, a carbonium ion ($ArHX^+$), but such is the reluctance of the system to form finally a product which does not maintain aromatic resonance energy, that there is little tendency, except in special structural situations, to form addition products by further reaction of $ArHX^+$ with nucleophilic reagents. Instead, the proton is directly expelled from the attacked carbon atom.

In vinylic systems, $R_2C=CH_2$, there is considerable evidence that carbonium ions, $R_2C^+ \cdot CH_2X$, are the initial products of attack by electrophilic reagents. This matter was reviewed in Volume 1 (de la Mare, 1954b), and the stereochemistry of the over-all addition reactions was discussed in relation to the structure of these carbonium intermediates. This account can now be reinforced and supplemented by new experimental data on addition to allylic olefins, provided by de la Mare and Pritchard (1954) and by Winstein and Goodman (1954).

SCHEME 6. CHLORINATION OF *iso*BUTYLENE IN A LIQUID FILM OF THE REACTANTS (Burgin *et al.*, 1939)

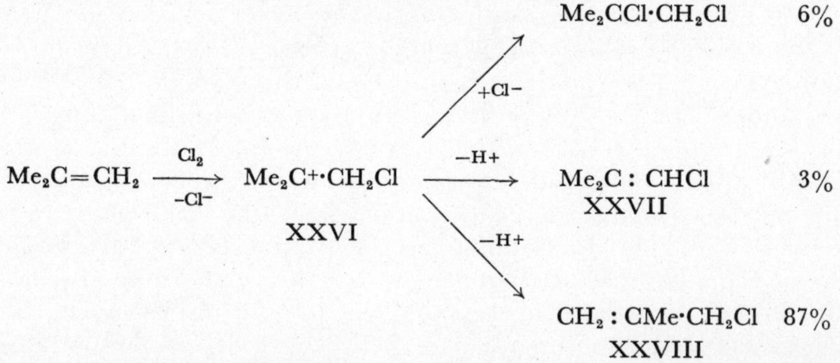

$$Me_2CCl \cdot CH_2Cl \qquad 6\%$$

$$+Cl^-$$

$$Me_2C=CH_2 \xrightarrow[-Cl^-]{Cl_2} Me_2C^+ \cdot CH_2Cl \xrightarrow{-H+} \quad Me_2C : CHCl \qquad 3\%$$
$$XXVII$$

$$XXVI$$

$$-H+$$

$$CH_2 : CMe \cdot CH_2Cl \quad 87\%$$
$$XXVIII$$

Little is known concerning the stereochemistry of the elimination processes which can in principle accompany such reactions, as indicated, for the specific case of the chlorination of *iso*butylene, in SCHEME 6. It has been presumed (*cf* Taft, 1948) that the carbonium ionic intermediate XXVI is formed under these conditions. De la Mare and

Salama (1956) have recently examined the reaction of acidified hypochlorous acid with *iso*butylene in aqueous solution. Under these conditions, one can be more certain that a carbonium intermediate is concerned, and use of methods of isotopic dilution confirmed that, in the product, allylic olefin (XXVIII) predominates over vinylic olefin (XXVII) in a proportion of at least 30 : 1 (SCHEME 7).

SCHEME 7. REACTION OF *iso*BUTYLENE WITH AQUEOUS HYPOCHLOROUS ACID

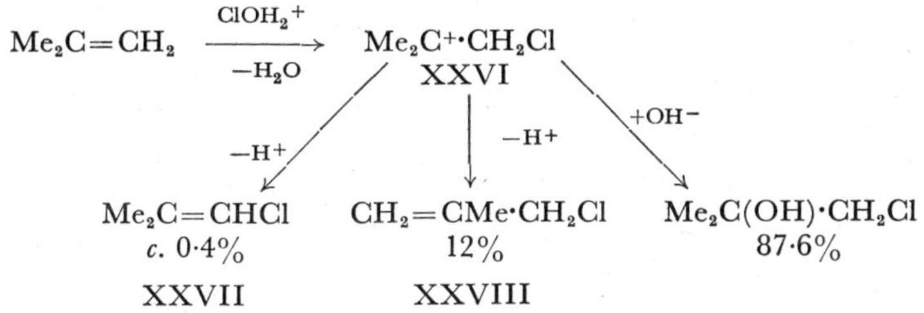

$$Me_2C{=}CH_2 \xrightarrow[-H_2O]{ClOH_2^+} Me_2C^+{\cdot}CH_2Cl$$

XXVI

−H+ ↙   ↓ −H+   +OH− ↘

$Me_2C{=}CHCl$ $CH_2{=}CMe{\cdot}CH_2Cl$ $Me_2C(OH){\cdot}CH_2Cl$
c. 0·4% 12% 87·6%

XXVII XXVIII

In eliminations from alkyl carbonium ions, the electromeric effects of the attached substituents seem to control the proportions of isomeric olefins produced (*cf* Dhar, Hughes, Ingold *et al.*, 1948). In the case of reactions involving the intermediate XXVI (SCHEMES 6 and 7), however, the olefinic product-ratio must be controlled by other factors, since the combined electromeric effects of the two methyl groups and the chlorine substituent in *iso*-crotyl chloride (XXVII) must be considerably greater than that of the methyl and chloromethyl groups in the major olefinic product, β-methylallyl chloride (XXVIII). De la Mare and Salama have proposed that this difficulty may be resolved by considering the detailed geometry of the two transition

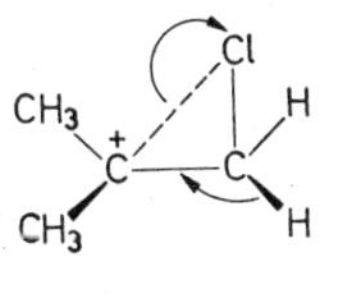

XXIX 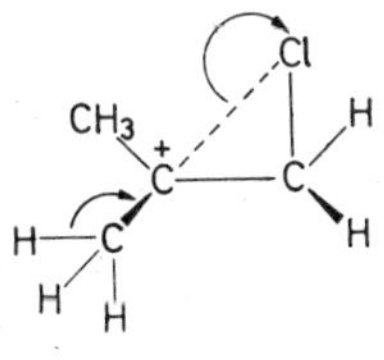   XXX

states (XXIX and XXX). In the former, the distortion resulting from neighbouring-group interaction between the chlorine substituent and the carbonium ionic centre tends to maintain the chlorine atom in a position which is particularly strained relative to the final positions of these atoms in the product. The similar distortion in XXX does not adversely affect the geometrical requirements of the developing double bond, since the chlorine atom is not located as precisely, relative to the rest of the molecule, in β-methylallyl chloride (XXVIII) as it is in *iso*-crotyl chloride (XXVII). So the allylic olefin is the preferred product in these systems.

Little is known concerning the ratio of *cis-* to *trans-*isomers occurring in the vinylic products of such reactions. Groll and Hearne (1939) have studied the high temperature chlorination of allyl chloride, which gives *cis-* and *trans-* 1 : 3-dichloropropenes in the ratio 42 : 47, but this reaction could well be of homolytic character. Substitutions in the styrenes (Ar·CH : CH$_2$) and stilbenes (Ar·CH : CHAr) are well known, but again the problem of *cis-trans-*isomerism in the products does not seem to have been investigated under conditions of established mechanisms.

A very interesting reaction which falls within the present category was examined by Van der Lee (1926, 1928). Compounds of the type O$_2$N·C$_6$H$_4$CH : CHR, where R = CO$_2$H, or COAr, can undergo nitration :

$$O_2N \cdot C_6H_4 \cdot CH : CH \cdot R \xrightarrow{\text{HNO}_3} O_2N \cdot C_6H_4 \cdot CH : CR \cdot NO_2$$

This reaction is formally an electrophilic displacement. Evidence was adduced, for the case R = CO$_2$H, by isolation of intermediates, that the reaction then went through stages involving successive addition of nitric acid, loss of water, and decarboxylation. Stereochemical data on the products of one of these reactions have been recorded by Pfeiffer (1914). Both the geometrical isomers of PhCH : CCl·CO$_2$H give, on nitration, as a by-product, the same *p* : ω-dinitrostyrene, O$_2$N·C$_6$H$_4$·CH : CCl(NO$_2$), m.p. 150–153°.

Nesmayanov and Borisov (1957) have surveyed the stereochemistry of electrophilic displacements from organometallic compounds. These proceed in general with retention of configuration. Thus chlorination of *trans-*chlorovinyl mercuric chloride gives pure *trans-*dichloroethylene :

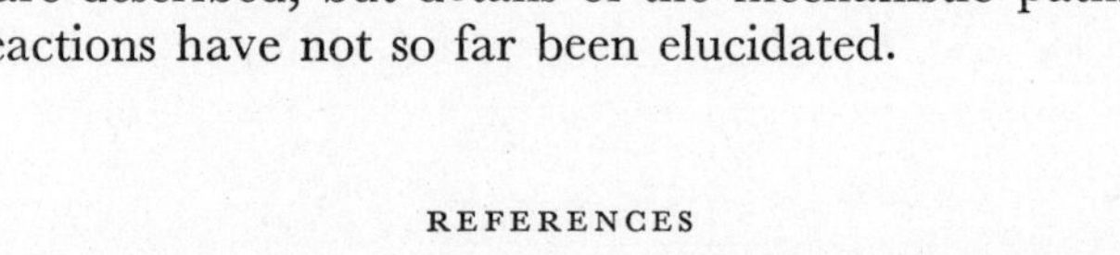

The *cis-*isomer behaves with equal stereospecificity. Many other related examples are described, but details of the mechanistic paths involved in these reactions have not so far been elucidated.

REFERENCES

Arnold, R. T. and Rondesvedt, E. (1946) *J. Amer. chem. Soc.* **68**, 2176
Autenreith, W. (1887) *Ber. dtsch. chem. Ges.* **20**, 1531; (1889) *Liebigs Ann.* **254**, 222, 246; (1890) *ibid* **259**, 332; (1896) *Ber. dtsch. chem. Ges.* **29**, 1639
Bartlett, P. D., Roha, M. and Stiles, R. M. (1954) *J. Amer. chem. Soc.* **76**, 2349
Beckwith, A. L., Miller, J. and Leahy, G. D. (1952) *J. chem. Soc.* 3552
Benkeser, R. A. and Krysiak, A. R. (1954) *J. Amer. chem. Soc.* **76**, 6353
— and Torkelson, A. (1954) *ibid* **76**, 1252

Berliner, E. and Berliner, F. J. (1954) *ibid* **76,** 6179
— and Bondhus, F. J. (1946) *ibid* **68,** 2355
— and Monack, L. C. (1952) *ibid* **74,** 1574
— Quinn, M. J. and Edgerton, P. J. (1950) *ibid* **72,** 5305
Bevan, C. W. L. (1951) *J. chem. Soc.* 2340
— Fayiga, T. O. and Hirst, J. (1956) *J. chem. Soc.* 4284
Bishop, R. R., Cavell, E. A. S. and Chapman, N. B. (1952) *ibid* 437
Bonner, T. G., Bowyer, F. and Williams, Gwyn (1953) *ibid* 2650
Bradfield, A. E. and Jones, B. (1941) *Trans. Faraday Soc.* **37,** 726
Brady, O. L. and Cropper, F. R. (1950) *J. chem. Soc.* 507
Brower, K. R. and Amstutz, E. D. (1953) *J. org. Chem.* **18,** 1075 ; (1954) *ibid* **19,** 411
Brown, B. R. (1951) *Quart. Rev. chem. Soc., Lond.* **5,** 131
Brown, D. A. and Dewar, M. J. S. (1953) *J. chem. Soc.* 2406
Brown, H. C. and Bonner, W. H. (1954) *J. Amer. chem. Soc.* **76,** 605
— and McGary, C. W. jun. (1955) *ibid* **77,** 2306, 2310
— and Nelson, K. L. (1953) *ibid* **75,** 6292
— and Smoot, C. R. (1956) *ibid* **78,** 6255
Bunnett, J. F. (1954) : quoted in *Chem. Engng. News* **32,** 4019 ; *J. chem. Soc.* 4717
— Cormack, J. F. and McKay, F. C. (1950) *J. org. Chem.* **15,** 481
— Draper, F., Ryason, P. R., Noble, P., Tonkyn, R. G. and Zahler, R. E. (1953) *J. Amer. chem. Soc.* **75,** 642
— and Morath, R. J. (1955) *ibid* **77,** 5051
— — and Okamoto, T. (1955) *ibid* **77,** 5055
— and Rauhut, M. M. (1956) *J. org. Chem.* **21,** 934, 939, 944
— — Knutson, D. and Bussell, G. E. (1954) *J. Amer. chem. Soc.* **76,** 5755
— and Snipes, R. F. (1955) *ibid* **77,** 5422
— and Zahler, R. E. (1951) *Chem. Rev.* **49,** 273
Burgin, J., Engs, W., Groll, H. R. A. and Hearne, G. (1939) *Industr. Engng Chem.* **31,** 1413
Capon, B. and Chapman, N. B. (1957) *J. chem. Soc.* 600
Chapman, N. B. and Levy, J. L. (1952) *ibid* 1673, 1679
— and Parker, R. E. (1951) *ibid* 3301
— — and Soanes, P. W. (1954) *ibid* 2109
— and Russell-Hill, D. Q. (1956) *ibid* 1563
Cohn, H., Hughes, E. D., Jones, M. H. and Peeling, M. (1952) *Nature, Lond.* **169,** 291
Cowdrey, W. A., Hughes, E. D., Ingold, C. K., Masterman, S. and Scott, A. D. (1937) *J. chem. Soc.* 1257
de la Mare, P. B. D. (1949) *ibid* 2871 ; (1954a) *ibid* 4450 ; (1954b) *Progress in Stereochemistry*, Vol. 1, Ed. W. Klyne, Chap. 3, London, Butterworths
— Dunn, T. M. and Harvey, J. T. (1957) *J. chem. Soc.* 923
— and Harvey, J. T. (1956) *ibid* 36 ; (1957) 131
— Hughes, E. D. and Vernon, C. A. (1950) *Research, Lond.* **3,** 192
— and Pritchard, J. G. (1954) *J. chem. Soc.* 3910, 3990
— and Robertson, P. W. (1943) *ibid* 279 ; (1948) *ibid* 100
— and Salama, A. (1956) *ibid* 3337
Derbyshire, A. E. and Waters, W. A. (1951) *ibid* 73
Dhar, M. L., Hughes, E. D., Ingold, C. K., Mandour, A. M. M., Maw, G. and Woolf, L. T. (1948) *ibid* 2093
Downing, D. T., Heppolette, R. L. and Miller, J. (1953) *Chem. & Ind.* 1260
Feist, F. (1906) *Liebigs Ann.* **345,** 104 ; (1922) *ibid* **428,** 25
Ferguson, L. N. (1955) *J. chem. Educ.* **32,** 421
Fierens, P. J. C. and Halleux, A. (1955) *Bull. Soc. chim. Belg.* **64,** 696, 717
Gidvani, B. S., Kon, G. A. R. and Wright, C. R. (1932) *J. chem. Soc.* 1027

97

Gindraux, L. (1929) *Helv. chim. Acta* **12,** 921
Gold, V. (1951) *J. chem. Soc.* 1430
Green, A. L. (1954) *ibid* 3538
Groll, H. P. A. and Hearne, G. (1939) *Industr. Engng Chem.* **31,** 1530
Hall, N. F. and Sprinkle, M. R. (1932) *J. Amer. chem. Soc.* **54,** 3469
Hammond, G. S. (1955) *ibid* **77,** 334 ; (1956) *Steric Effects in Organic Chemistry*, Ed.
   M. S. Newman, New York, Wiley
— and Parks, L. R. (1955) *ibid* **77,** 340
Hawthorne, M. F. (1954) *ibid* **76,** 6358
Holleman, A. F. (1914) *Rec. Trav. chim. Pays-Bas* **33,** 1 (1924) *Chem. Rev.* **1,** 187
Hughes, E. D. (1938) *Trans. Faraday Soc.* **34,** 185
Huse, G. and Powell, H. M. (1940) *J. chem. Soc.* 1398
Ingold, C. K. (1953) *Structure and Mechanism in Organic Chemistry*, London, Bell
— and Shaw, F. R. (1949) *J. chem. Soc.* 575
Jones, E. and Vernon, C. A. (1955) *Nature, Lond.* **176,** 791
Kobe, K. A. and Brennecke, H. M. (1954) *Industr. Engng Chem.* **46,** 728
— and Pritchett, P. W. (1952) *ibid* **44,** 1398
Kuivila, H. G. and Hendrickson, A. R. (1952) *J. Amer. chem. Soc.* **74,** 5068
LeFevre, R. J. W. (1933) *J. chem. Soc.* 980 ; (1934) *ibid* 1501
Loevenich, J., Losen, J. and Dierichs, A. (1923) *Ber. dtsch. chem. Ges.* **10,** 950
Long, R. W., Hildebrand, J. H. and Morrell, W. E. (1943) *J. Amer. chem. Soc.*
   65, 182
Longuet-Higgins, H. C. (1950) *J. chem. Phys.* **18,** 265
— and Coulson, C. A. (1949) *J. chem. Soc.* 971
McGary, C. W. jun., Okamoto, Y. and Brown, H. C. (1955) *J. Amer. chem. Soc.*
   77, 3037
Meisenheimer, J. (1902) *Liebigs Ann.* **323,** 205
Melander, L. (1950) *Ark. Kemi* **2,** 213
Michael, A. (1888) *J. prakt. Chem.* (2) **38,** 9
Miller, J. and Williams, V. A. (1953) *J. chem. Soc.* 1475
Montanari, F. (1956) *Gazz. chim. Ital.* **86,** 747
Nesmayanov, A. N. and Borisov, A. E. (1957) *Tetrahedron*, **1,** 158
Nightingale, D. V. (1947) *Chem. Rev.* **40,** 117
Paal, C., Schiedewitz, H. and Rauscher, K. (1931) *Ber. dtsch. chem. Ges.* **64,** 1521
Pfeiffer, P. (1914) *ibid* **47,** 1755
Remick, A. E. (1949) *Electronic Interpretations of Organic Chemistry*, 2nd ed., New
   York, Wiley
Roberts, J. D., Semenow, D. A., Simmons, H. E. and Carlsmith, L. A. (1956)
   J. Amer. chem. Soc. **78,** 601
— Simmons, H. E., Carlsmith, L. A. and Vaughan, C. W. (1953) *ibid* **75,** 3290
— Vaughan, C. W., Carlsmith, L. A. and Semenow, D. A. (1956) *ibid* **78,** 611
Robertson, P. W. (1954) *J. chem. Soc.* 1267
— Allan, J. E., Haldane, K. N. and Simmers, M. G. (1949) *ibid* 933
— de la Mare, P. B. D. and Swedlund, B. E. (1953) *ibid* 782
Sandin, R. B. and Liskear, M. (1935) *J. Amer. chem. Soc.* **57,** 1304
Schubert, W. M. (1949) *ibid* **71,** 2639
— Donohue, J. and Gardner, J. D. (1954) *ibid* **76,** 9
Shilov, E. A. and Kaniev, N. P. (1939) *C.R. Acad. Sci., U.S.S.R.* **24,** 890
Taft, R. W (1948) *J. Amer. chem. Soc.* **70,** 3364
Waters W. A. (1948) *J. chem. Soc.* 727
Wheland, G. W. (1942) *J. Amer. chem. Soc.* **64,** 900
Winstein, S. and Goodman, L. (1954) *ibid* **76,** 4368, 4373
Van der Lee, J. (1926) *Rec. trav. Chim., Pays-Bas* **45,** 674 ; (1928) *ibid* **47,** 920
Zollinger, H. (1955) *Helv. chim. Acta* **38,** 1597, 1617, 1624 ; (1956) *Experientia* **12,** 165

STERIC EFFECTS ON MESOMERISM

B. M. Wepster

THE thesis, stating that a conjugated system tends to planarity because of its maximal mesomeric interaction and its minimal electronic potential energy in that configuration, is nowadays accepted as one of the basic rules of stereochemistry. Its importance can easily be appreciated when it is considered that it applies not only to the classical conjugated systems (*e.g.* I, II) but also to those systems (*e.g.* III, IV) which since the advent of the electronic theory have been recognized as having the same type of mesomeric interaction.

| I | II | III | IV | V |

Hampson initiated the first experimental test of this thesis in 1935. The argument was that a potentially conjugated compound, in which for steric reasons coplanarity is not obtained, should possess properties different from those to be expected if the mesomeric interaction were fully operative. This situation was, for example, encountered with the dipole moment of nitrodurene (V). In this molecule, the planar conformation shows considerable overlapping of the van der Waals radii of the oxygen atoms and the nearby methyl groups. The consequent strain can be relieved by rotation of the nitro group about the carbon–nitrogen bond, and therefore a non-planar conformation is likely to be more stable (*cf* p. 104). Hence, the dipole moment of nitrodurene should differ from that of nitrobenzene—and this is what is actually found. By this and other examples Birtles and Hampson (1937) demonstrated that mesomerism could be influenced by steric factors, and provided an experimental basis for the phenomenon in question.

Although similar ideas were in the minds of several other investigators (*e.g.* Kistiakowski, 1936) the general importance of this new branch of stereochemistry was not immediately grasped, not even after the thought-provoking note by Baddeley (1939) showing its applicability to a wide variety of physical and chemical properties and to various types of conjugation. Today, however, the examples are so numerous as to make a complete survey within the scope of this chapter impossible. In fact, completeness would be very difficult to achieve, since many cases are to be found in old literature, and others are hidden in, for instance, papers on the constitution of natural products or on the properties of dyestuffs. In what follows, examples illustrating principles are chosen mainly from the restricted field of benzene derivatives.

GENERAL CONSIDERATIONS

As the origin of the phenomenon of steric effects on mesomerism is to be found in the tendency of conjugated systems to be and to remain planar, it is useful to discuss first how this emerges both from the valence-bond and from the molecular-orbital point of view.

(i) The limiting structures to be used to describe a molecule like nitrobenzene can be divided into non-polar structures (*e.g.* VI) and

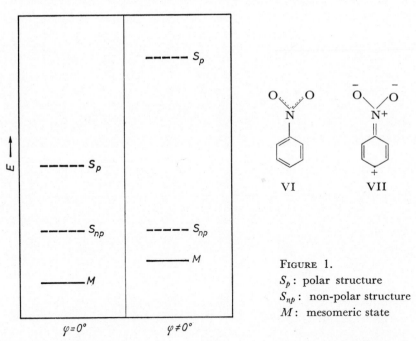

FIGURE 1.

S_p: polar structure
S_{np}: non-polar structure
M: mesomeric state

polar, quinonoid structures (*e.g.* VII). In VI there is formally free rotation around the C—N bond, in VII there is a strong preference for the coplanar conformation. Defining the angle of rotation, φ, as the angle between the planes of benzene ring and nitro group*, the difference in energy between these two structural types increases when φ increases from 0° to 90°. As a corollary, the mesomeric energy decreases with increasing φ, and so also does the stability of the

---

* For another, more general, definition of the angle of rotation, see p. 116.

100

molecule ; this is illustrated by the energy-level diagram of FIGURE 1. Thus, during a rotation the mesomeric stabilization will be at a maximum for the coplanar conformation.

It will be noted that the preference for coplanarity can also be derived from the simple, but less complete, argument that the contribution of the quinonoid structures confers some double-bond character on the carbon–nitrogen bond.

(ii) In the molecular-orbital description, the mesomeric interaction between the benzene ring and the nitro group is a consequence of the overlapping of the p-orbital of carbon atom 1 and that of the nitrogen atom—see VIII. It is obvious that this overlap is at a maximum when

VIII

the symmetry axes of these orbitals are parallel, *i.e.* in the coplanar conformation, with $\varphi = 0°$. Applying the principle that maximum overlap provides maximum stability, the coplanar conformation is again expected to be preferred.

It may be concluded that if, for some reason, coplanarity is not obtained, the mesomeric interaction will not be fully developed. If this situation arises as the result of steric effects, then it can be said that there is steric inhibition of mesomerism.

In many examples, non-planarity can be regarded as the result of overcrowding of the coplanar conformation, as with nitrodurene (V). Another important type can be exemplified by 2 : 3-benzo*cyclo*octanone (IX), in which non-planarity of benzene ring and carbonyl group is

IX   X

imposed by the size of the alicyclic ring. As a counterpart may be mentioned indan-1-one (X) in which deviations from planarity are never likely to be serious.

With these few examples in mind, a more detailed picture will be developed with the help of potential-energy curves. In a simple compound like nitrobenzene, in which there are no important van der Waals interactions between the oxygen atoms and the *ortho*-hydrogen atoms, the potential energy E as a function of the angle of twist φ can be approximated by a cosine-square curve:

$$E_\varphi = E_{90} - (E_{90} - E_0) \cos^2\varphi$$

since the extra mesomeric energy M can be approximated by a cosine-square curve (Coulson, 1951; Pauling and Corey, 1952; Dewar, 1952a):

$$M_\varphi = M_0 \cos^2\varphi.$$

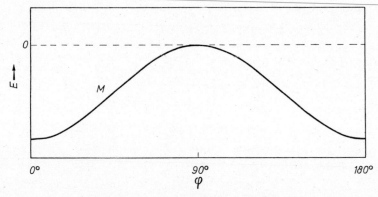

FIGURE 2.   Mesomerism curve M

This is illustrated in FIGURE 2, in which the potential energy of the perpendicular conformation ($\varphi = 90°$) has been taken arbitrarily as zero since here the mesomeric interaction is zero (*cf* Wepster, 1952a). It should be noted that this relationship is by no means strictly quantitative, and that, for instance, calculations by Guy (1949) provided a sigmoid mesomeric-energy curve which can be approximated as a $\cos^5\varphi$ function for φ between 0° and 90° (R. D. Brown, 1952b). However, the $\cos^2\varphi$ function also has a theoretical justification, is used by most authors, and is probably no worse than other approximations. Moreover, some data available for compounds in which φ is fixed and known, do not support Guy's function (p. 122).

If, now, a hydrogen atom in the *ortho*-position is replaced by a larger group, important van der Waals interactions between the oxygen atoms and the substituent may arise. The energies involved are also dependent upon φ, and may correspond to any section of the well-known van der Waals potential energy–distance curve shown in FIGURE 3. The letters indicate the limits between which sections may be taken; these limits are determined by the distances between the interacting groups when $\varphi = 0°$ and when $\varphi = 90°$. The resulting curve representing the relationship between φ and the van der Waals energy may on this basis have one of a variety of forms, some of which are shown in FIGURES 4–8.

It will be clear that, by algebraic addition of the appropriate mesomerism curve M and the appropriate van der Waals curve W, a total-energy curve T may be obtained, the minima of which correspond

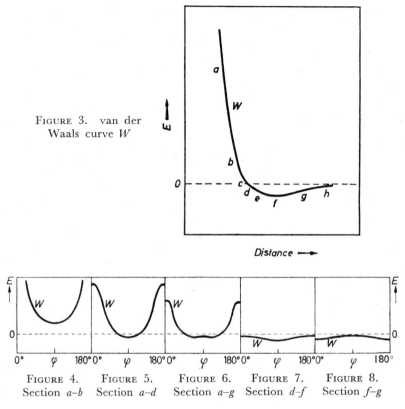

FIGURE 3. van der Waals curve W

Distance →

FIGURE 4.   FIGURE 5.   FIGURE 6.   FIGURE 7.   FIGURE 8.
Section a–b Section a–d Section a–g Section d–f Section f–g

with the preferred conformations. In FIGURE 9 this is illustrated for a symmetrical molecule such as nitrodurene in which the mesomerism is partly inhibited.

It will be observed that ring-compounds like the benzocyclanones (IX and X) can be treated in a similar way by combining the mesomerism curve with a curve representing ring-strains.

Unfortunately, the application of this treatment to specific examples is very difficult, since the component curves are known at best approximately. However, the picture evolved offers a background to a better understanding of the complex character of the phenomenon under discussion, and as such may serve as the basis of the following.

It should be realized that the molecule does not possess exactly the conformation of the minimum of the potential-energy curve. Of the vibrations occurring, the one of greatest interest for us is the torsional vibration affecting the angle of twist φ. The fact that, as a rule, at ordinary temperatures, not only the ground vibrational level but also one or more excited levels will be populated, means that from an experimental point of view there is no such thing as the *unique* angle of twist. Thus at best we can hope to find an approximate value of an average angle φ_a (*cf* Klemm *et al.*, 1955; Heilbronner and Gerdil, 1956).

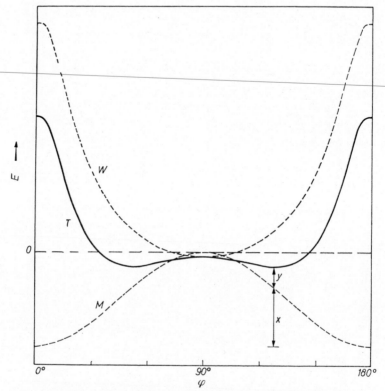

FIGURE 9.   Total potential-energy curve T, as obtained from mesomerism curve M and van der Waals curve W. The 'electronic strain' at the minima is given by x, the 'steric strain' by y (*cf* p. 105)

This argument gains in weight when the shapes of van der Waals curves such as those of FIGURES 4–6 are considered. Although, of course, these curves are certainly not the mirror-image of the mesomerism curve, the possibility that the total-energy curve may be very flat in parts is strongly suggested. Consequently steric inhibition of mesomerism may frequently provide the bond in question with a remarkable degree of rotational freedom. This warns us to accept many of the calculations of angles of rotation—for instance from spectral data—and their comparison with those from molecular models, with much reserve (*cf* also Chapter 5).

FIGURE 8 illustrates another possibility, namely the stabilization of the planar form by van der Waals attraction. This can be termed *steric promotion of mesomerism.* Such promotions will never be very strong; indeed, the van der Waals attraction involved will hardly ever exceed a few tenths of a kilocalorie per mole. Nevertheless they may be of some importance, especially in determining small differences in reaction rates.

More important steric promotions of mesomerism can be encountered in cross-conjugated systems (*cf* Baddeley, 1942; Leonard and Blout, 1950; Huisgen *et al.*, 1954c; and p. 130). For example, in derivatives of acetanilide (XI), two paths *a* and *b* are available for the migration

XI

of the lone electron pair of the nitrogen atom. If one of these is made less accessible, the other will gain in importance. Thus, two methyl groups in the *ortho*-positions will effectively block path *a* and, therefore, will increase the negative charge on the oxygen atom. Other cases of steric promotion of mesomerism are to be found in, for example, *cyclo*pentane derivatives, if a decrease of (repulsive) bond-opposition forces is accompanied by an increase of mesomeric interaction (p. 141).

A further question of considerable interest can be illustrated by considering the aromatic base $N N$-dimethyl-*o*-toluidine (XII). As will appear later, there is no doubt that in this molecule there is a

considerable steric inhibition of the mesomerism. At the equilibrium angle a balance is reached between the forces trying to decrease φ and the van der Waals repulsions trying to increase φ. This means that the resulting strain is twofold; first, electronic strain, which can be equated to the loss of mesomeric energy as compared with dimethyl-aniline, and secondly, steric strain resulting from interpenetration of van der Waals spheres. These two strains are indicated in FIGURE 9 as x and y, respectively (*cf* especially Baddeley *et al.*, 1954, 1956c).

The important and quite general point to be stressed here is that these strains may reveal themselves both separately and combined, according to the compound and the property studied. Thus, with

NN-dimethyl-o-toluidine, the ultra-violet spectrum will, to a first approximation, reflect only electronic strain, since excitation is so rapid that, by the Franck–Condon principle, no reorganization can occur during the electronic transition. The basic strength of the same compound, however, will reflect the sum of both strains, since in the ion (XIII) free rotation is possible about the single C_{ar}—N bond, so that the van der Waals repulsion will be relieved and, in fact, might even change to van der Waals attraction.

An extreme case is that of an aromatic amine in which $\varphi = 0°$ or very nearly so notwithstanding the steric strain involved. Then the spectrum will not show an inhibition of the mesomerism, but when, in the ion, reorganization is allowed and is effective, the steric strain in the molecule will be revealed by the basic strength. Probably the relatively high basic strength of NN-diethylaniline is to be explained on these lines (p. 128).

Finally, if the angle of twist is approaching $90°$, spectrum and basic strength should reflect electronic strain only; NN-dimethyl-o-tert.-butylaniline and benzoquinuclidine (pp. 121 and 150) may serve as examples of this kind.

It will be obvious from the above that steric effects on mesomerism as revealed by different criteria should be compared judiciously. As a rule, changes which occur so rapidly that only electronic reorganizations can be involved respond to electronic strains only, whereas equilibria and chemical reactivity are sensitive both to electronic and to steric strains. It is also clear that, in a sense, in the examples discussed above, the ultra-violet spectrum provides the purest picture of the steric effect on the mesomerism. The case mentioned above in which there is no spectral effect but a high basic strength (NN-diethylaniline) is particularly intriguing from this point of view. Indeed it is hard to maintain that the mesomerism is sterically affected, and it seems more logical to say that the basic strength is changed as the result of steric hindrance in the amine (cf Baddeley et al., 1956c). On the other hand, when considering the fact that the steric strain is caused by the tendency to planarity, the relationship with the mesomeric interaction cannot be denied; the term steric effect due to the mesomerism seems most appropriate here.

The above treatment, concentrating on rotation about a partial double bond, neglects several other factors. The system strives for maximum stability, and to this end will make any other possible steric adjustments. Of these, changes in bond lengths are, as a rule, not very effective in reducing strain, although they may be of some consequence from an energetic point of view (cf Westheimer, 1947). Valency deflections, and the buttressing effects that often accompany them, are doubtless very common, and will be mentioned occasionally in the following discussion.

Rotations about single bonds not directly involved in the mesomerism may also be important. Thus, the *tert.*-butyl group would, in certain molecules, produce considerably larger strains when in the all-staggered conformation than when in the all-eclipsed conformation (*cf* p. 119). In such a case a balance is reached in which the bonds are partly staggered, partly opposed. It should be noted that these rotational orientations are by no means of secondary importance, since the differences in energy may amount to several kcal.mole^{-1}, *i.e.* they are of the same order of magnitude as the energies of mesomerism usually encountered. Accordingly, it is often hardly possible to assess the steric effectiveness of a *tert.*-butyl group in a satisfactory way from molecular models.

Finally, attention should be called to interactions which, up till now, have received very little attention, *viz.* interactions such as those in nitrobenzene between the NO bonds and the C_1C_2 and C_1C_6 bonds, which in the planar conformation may be regarded as opposed. Since, however, as far as the writer is aware, nothing is known about the forces in question, they will not be considered further.

Terminology

The reasons for the use of 'steric effects on mesomerism' as a general, non-committal description of the phenomenon in question will be clear from the foregoing. Terms such as 'steric inhibition of mesomerism' and 'steric promotion of mesomerism' indicate sub-divisions, and will be used freely in appropriate cases. Fortunately the word 'hindrance' is hardly ever used in this connection; it should be reserved for discussions of steric hindrance in the more classical sense only.

STERIC EFFECTS ON MESOMERISM AS REVEALED BY PHYSICAL AND CHEMICAL DATA

PHYSICAL PROPERTIES

Electronic Spectra

Electronic spectra, *i.e.* ultra-violet and visible absorption spectra, will be considered first, because the mass of experimental data permits the illustration of a multitude of types of steric effects. Examples, different from those discussed below, can be found in reviews by Brooker *et al.* (1947); Braude and Waight (1954); and Ingraham (1956).

The most general consequence of non-planarity on electronic spectra is a decrease in the absorption intensity of the so-called *K* bands, *i.e.* absorption bands which owe their existence to the presence of fully extended conjugation (Konjugation). This holds equally well for the intensity expressed as the molecular extinction coefficient at the absorption maximum, ε_{max}, and for the intensity expressed as the oscillator strength f, a measure of the surface area under the band envelope when ε is plotted against wave number; in fact, in a series of compounds, ε_{max} and f are often approximately linearly related.

This decrease in absorption intensity may be accompanied by a shift of the absorption maximum, λ_{max}, either to shorter or to longer wavelengths; very frequently, however, no significant change in wavelength is observed.

The interpretation of these phenomena is by no means simple. Extending earlier arguments by Remington (1945), Braude and co-workers (Braude *et al.*, 1954; Braude and Waight, 1954; Braude and Sondheimer, 1955; Braude, 1955) have given an explanation of the decrease in ε on the basis of the difference in preferred angle of rotation in the ground state and the excited state, resulting from the difference in the relative contributions of polar and non-polar structures. However, even in rigid molecules, in which φ is constrained to be practically equal in both states, a strong decrease in ε may be found (see p. 121). This casts some doubt on the value of their argument. More quantitative discussions have been given recently by Murrell (1956) and by Heilbronner and Gerdil (1956).

As to the changes in λ_{max}, those to shorter wavelengths can be expected for molecules in which excitation is attended by an increase of the double-bond character of the bond around which the rotation occurs. For then a rotation out of the coplanar conformation lifts the energy level of the excited state more than that of the ground state, so that the transition energy is increased. On similar arguments, shifts to longer wavelengths may be expected if excitation is attended by a decrease of double-bond character. Examples of this type have been discussed by Ingraham (1956; *cf* also Braude and Waight, 1954).

From the same point of view, the absence of any significant change in wavelength may be regarded as the result of only a relatively small difference in double-bond character between the ground state and the excited state. This interpretation is at variance with the commonly accepted idea that excited states always have a very strong ionic character, and, therefore, also with the views of Braude and co-workers on the point at issue. It is supported, however, by calculations (Coulson and Jacobs, 1949) which give the bond orders of the C—N bond in aniline in the ground and in the first excited state as 1·30 and 1·39, respectively. Again, the fact that a rigid aromatic amine like 1 : 5-methano-2 : 3 : 4 : 5-tetrahydro-benzo(b)azepin (LI; p. 122), in which $\varphi \sim 60°$, absorbs at practically the same wavelength as NN-dimethylaniline, can be understood only on this basis.

(i) *Benzene ring conjugated with symmetrical planar groups*—Examples of parent compounds XIV and XV. TABLE 1 contains a choice of data on the decrease in absorption intensity of the 250 mμ band of nitro-

XIV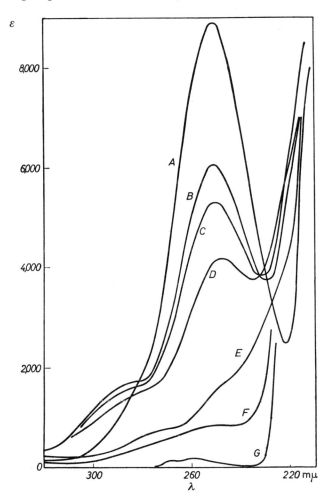

XV

benzene in *iso*octane (*cf* FIGURE 10) and the 380 mμ band of 4-amino-nitrobenzene in 96% ethanol when the mesomeric interaction between the nitro group and the rest of the system is inhibited by substituents in

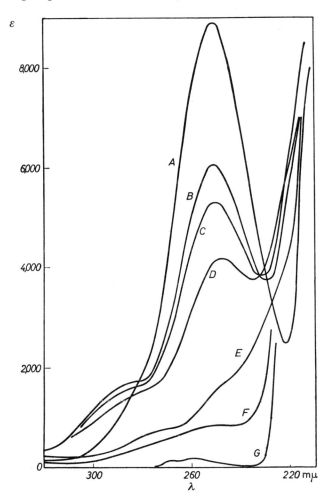

FIGURE 10. Ultra-violet spectra in *iso*octane of: *A*. nitrobenzene; *B. o*-nitro-toluene; *C. o*-nitro-ethylbenzene; *D. o*-nitro-*iso*propylbenzene; *E. o*-nitro-*tert.*-butylbenzene; *F.* 2 : 4 : 6-tri-*tert.*-butyl-nitrobenzene; *G.* 1 : 3 : 5-tri-*tert.*-butyl-benzene

the benzene ring. The changes in λ_{max} are insignificant for the compounds in question. The table also records average angles of twist φ_a, calculated from $\varepsilon/\varepsilon_0 = \cos^2\varphi_a$. This equation, in which ε_0 refers to nitrobenzene or 4-aminonitrobenzene, will be justified later (p. 146).

TABLE 1. ULTRA-VIOLET ABSORPTION OF NITROBENZENES AND 4-AMINONITROBENZENES

Nitrobenzenes (NO$_2$-1) $\lambda \sim 250$ mμ, in isooctane		ε_{max}	$\varphi_a{}^\circ$	4-Aminonitrobenzenes (NO$_2$-1-NH$_2$-4) $\lambda \sim 380$ mμ, in 96% ethanol	ε_{max}	$\varphi_a{}^\circ$
Unsubstituted[a]	(A)	8,900	(0)	Unsubstituted[a]	15,500	(0)
2-Me[a]	(B)	6,070	34	2-Me[a]	13,200	23
2-Et[a]	(C)	5,300	40	2 : 5-di-Me[b]	13,600	21
2-i-Pr[a]	(D)	4,150	47	2 : 3-di-Me[b]	9,750	38
2-t-Bu[a]	(E)	1,540*	65	2 : 6-di-Me[a]	4,840	56
2 : 5-di-Me[b]		5,640	37	2 : 3 : 5 : 6-tetra-Me[a]	1,560	72
2 : 3-di-Me[b]		4,210	47	2 : 6-di-t-Bu[c]	540	79
2 : 6-di-Me[a]		1,500*	66	2 : 3-trimethylene[d]	13,900	19
2 : 4 : 6-tri-Me[a]		2,170	60	2 : 3-tetramethylene[b]	11,200	32
2 : 3 : 5 : 6-tetra-Me[a]		990	71	Amino-nitro-hydrin-		
2 : 4-di-Me-6-t-Bu[c]		1,050	70	dacene[e] (XVII)	12,800	25
2 : 4 : 6-tri-t-Bu[c]	(F)	830	71	Amino-nitro-octa-		
2 : 6-di-t-Bu[c]		640*	74	hydroanthracene[e]	2,240	68

* No maximum; ε at 250 mμ and 380 mμ, respectively, have been given.
References: (a) Wepster, 1957a; cf W. G. Brown and Reagan, 1947; (b) van Helden et al., 1954; (c) Burgers et al., 1957; (d) Arnold and Richter, 1948; (e) Arnold and Craig, 1950.
See also FIGURE 10. Letters A–F refer to curves in this figure.

The data in TABLE 1 and FIGURE 10 illustrate the following points:

(a) In the series of increasing effect 2-Me < 2-Et < 2-iso-Pr < 2-tert.-Bu, the largest decrease in absorption intensity occurs between the last two members. This behaviour has been found in other similar series, and may be ascribed to the fact that all the groups except the last have at least one α-hydrogen atom which allows a favourable orientation (XVI). The tert.-butyl group has no such possibilities, and thus its effective size should be by far the largest.

XVI

(b) In both nitrobenzenes and 4-aminonitrobenzenes the 2 : 3-dimethyl grouping appears to be more effective than the 2-methyl group. This 'ortho-xylene effect' can be regarded as a form of 'buttressing' (cf Rieger and Westheimer, 1950), and is probably connected with valency deflections in the o-nitrotoluene grouping which are energetically more difficult when the methyl group is backed by another methyl group (cf van Helden et al., 1954; van Berk et al., 1956).

(c) In molecular models of the rigid Stuart type, the presence of two identical ortho-substituents does not require the angle of twist to be greater than when only one of them causes non-planarity. This should not be expected to hold in reality, for while the mesomerism curve is the same in both cases, the van der Waals energies are twice as large with di-ortho-substitution as with mono-ortho-substitution. Therefore, the angle of twist should be expected to be greatest in the former case. Moreover, the effective size of each group will be larger with di-substitution, since bending away of the nitro group is no longer of help.

The magnitude of the resulting differences between mono- and di-ortho-substituted compounds may be quite considerable, especially when the steeper part of the mesomerism curve is involved; this situation probably holds—with nitrobenzenes—for the 2-methyl and the 2 : 6-dimethyl substituents. Only a small difference should, however, be observed, when one substituent is already very effective in damping the mesomerism, and the same should apply when even two substituents produce very little inhibition. The first case can be exemplified from the comparison of the effect of the 2-tert.-butyl and

XVII

the 2 : 6-di-tert.-butyl substituents. The second case is exemplified by amino-nitrohydrindacene (XVII; in ethanol $\varepsilon_{\max}$, 12,800) as compared with 4-amino-7-nitroindane ($\varepsilon_{\max}$, 13,900) and 4-aminonitrobenzene ($\varepsilon_{\max}$, 15,500).

(d) Similarly-substituted nitrobenzenes and 4-aminonitrobenzenes qualitatively show the same regular decrease of ε with increasing size and number of the substituents. It should be realized, however, that the mean angle of twist φ_a should be smaller for the 4-aminonitrobenzenes. Indeed, the introduction of the amino group in the para-position increases the height of the mesomerism curve in question by 2·3 kcal.mole^{-1} as a consequence of the extra para-interaction (see p. 145), and this increase will cause a shift in the total energy curve with the result indicated. This is also borne out by the experimental data;

111

the values of φ_a calculated for 4-aminonitrobenzenes are smaller than those for the corresponding nitrobenzenes (see TABLE 1).

(e) Complete elimination of the mesomeric interaction between the nitro- group and the rest of the system is very difficult to achieve; even two *tert.*-butyl groups in *ortho*-position leave some residual mesomerism. It should be noted that this conclusion is most reliable for the 4-aminonitrobenzenes. At 380 mμ, ε for alkyl-nitrobenzenes hardly exceeds 100, while alkyl-anilines do not absorb at all; therefore, the absorption found for 2 : 6-di-*tert.*-butyl-4-amino-nitrobenzene, $\varepsilon = 480$ at 380 mμ, leaves little doubt as to the presence of some *para*-interaction, though it is not more than a few per cent of that in 4-aminonitrobenzene.

(f) Considering the fact that when the mesomerism is increasingly inhibited, the intensity of the 250 mμ band of nitrobenzene decreases strongly without marked change in wavelength, the suggestion that this band corresponds with the 250 mμ band system of benzene appears highly plausible. This band assignment, which is similar to that given for dimethylaniline by Klevens and Platt (1949) is not in harmony with those based on other considerations (*cf* Doub and Vandenbelt, 1947; Platt, 1951; Wenzel, 1954).

The case in which there are two *ortho*-substituents, equal in size but not symmetrically placed with respect to the plane of the benzene ring, has not yet been realized experimentally but could be with a

XVIII   XIX   XX

compound such as XVIII. The parent hydrocarbon should exist in a *meso*-form in which both methyl groups project on one side of the benzene ring (*cf* the projection formula XIX in which the dotted line is the plane of the benzene ring), and a racemic form in which the methyl groups are on either side (*cf* XX). These two forms could be differentiated by the ultra-violet spectra of the nitro derivatives; that of the *meso*-form should show a much stronger inhibition than that of the racemic form. Recently, Hawthorne and Cram (1952) have tried a similar analysis for a pair of diastereomeric compounds with results in agreement with an absolute configurational proof. The smallness of the difference in intensity of absorption observed, as well as the conformational analysis involved, are such, however, as to make their reasoning seem highly uncertain to the present author.

Several important examples from the diphenyl series might be classified here. Notwithstanding a large number of data, no agreement has been reached as to the interpretation of these spectra. Since recent discussions are available, these systems will not be considered here (*cf* Beaven *et al.*, 1952; Braude and Waight, 1954; Braude and Forbes, 1955; Wenzel, 1953; Wheland, 1955; Murrell and Longuet-Higgins, 1955; Truce and Emrick, 1956; Beaven and Johnson, 1957).

(ii) *Benzene ring conjugated with asymmetrical planar groups*—Examples of parent compounds XXI–XXIII. In these systems, the asymmetry

| XXI | XXII | XXIII |

of the group in question implies that, with one voluminous *ortho*-substituent, the van der Waals energy curve is asymmetrical with respect to $\varphi = 90°$. Thus there is a preferred conformation in which the bulkier side of the group is directed away from the *ortho*-substituent.

With two identical *ortho*-substituents, symmetry is restored, and the bulkier side of the group can no longer escape the proximity of an *ortho*-position with large steric requirements. Therefore, in these systems there is a factor which, over and above those given in the previous section, tends to make the consequences of di-*ortho*-substitution much greater than those of mono-*ortho*-substitution. Frequently the first substituent has little, if any, effect, whereas introduction of the second has a large effect.

A very extensive literature is available with respect to nuclear-substituted compounds of the present types, including, for instance, styrenes (*cf* Braude and Sondheimer, 1955b), benzaldehydes (*cf* Braude and Sondheimer, 1955a), acetophenones (*cf* Forbes and Mueller, 1955), phenols and phenyl ethers (Coggeshall and Lang, 1948; Burawoy and Chamberlain, 1952; Baddeley *et al.*, 1956c), phenyl thioethers (*cf* Fehnel and Carmack, 1949), benzoic acids (*cf* Dippy *et al.*, 1954; Forbes and Sheratte, 1955; Betts and Barclay, 1955), acetanilides (Ungnade, 1954; see also p. 150). Since many examples have been discussed in recent reviews (Braude and Waight, 1954; Braude, 1955) further discussion is omitted.

Some series of compounds exemplified by XXIV–XXVII, in which steric inhibition of mesomerism is brought about by increasing the

| XXIV | XXV | XXVI | XXVII |

TABLE 2. EXTINCTION COEFFICIENTS OF COMPOUNDS OF TYPES XXIV–XXVII

Formula	Substituent R =	Me	Et	iso-Pr	tert.-Bu
XXIV	Phenyl ethers[a]	1,579	1,938	1,920	454
XXV	Phenyl thioethers[b]	9,550	7,950	5,600	1,550
XXVI	Acetophenones[c]	13,040	11,450	11,500	8,100
XXVII	Styrenes[d]	11,400	10,100	7,800	small

References: (a) Baddeley et al., 1956c (at about 270 mμ, in hexane); (b) Fehnel and Carmack, 1949 (at about 260 mμ, in ethanol); (c) Hedden and Brown, 1953 (at about 240 mμ, in heptane); cf also Cram and Knight, 1952; (d) Overberger and Tanner, 1955 (at about 240 mμ, in ethanol); Ramart-Lucas, 1954 (R = t.-Bu).

steric requirements of the group R, deserve special attention. The spectral data for R = Me, Et, iso-Pr and tert.-Bu have been summarized in TABLE 2. It is seen that in these series, the tert.-butyl derivatives provide clear cases of steric inhibition of mesomerism. The reason for this becomes obvious when molecular models are examined. In each case coplanarity can only be achieved with considerable interpenetration of the van der Waals spheres of the tert.-butyl group and an ortho-hydrogen atom, so that this conformation is energetically unfavourable. Thus, these compounds provide examples in which steric inhibition of mesomerism occurs in the absence of ortho-substituents proper.

Considering next α-isopropylstyrene, a probably significant lowering of the absorption intensity is observed, although it might be argued that the conformation XXVIII rather suggests a spectral behaviour

XXVIII

practically equal to that of α-methylstyrene (cf o-nitro-isopropyl-benzene discussed on p. 110). Such a reasoning, however, neglects the fact that in XXVIII a conformation similar to that in skew butane occurs twice. The corresponding strain (cf e.g. Barton and Cookson, 1956; Dauben and Pitzer, 1956) can be relieved by twisting the methyl groups downwards, but then the isopropyl group will simulate the steric requirements of the tert.-butyl group with respect to the ortho-hydrogen atom. On this basis it is not surprising that some loss of mesomeric interaction occurs.

Following up this line of thought, the absence of steric inhibition of mesomerism in the isopropyl ketone and the isopropyl ether can be understood as the result of the smaller effective size of the oxygen atom in the former compound, the absence of a group other than R

114

in the latter; indeed, in both cases the conformations corresponding to XXVIII appear more likely. Some evidence supporting this explanation will be discussed below (p. 119), but it should be realized that differences in bond lengths, bond angles and mesomeric energies tend to make comparisons of this kind of dubious value, especially when relatively small variations in spectra are involved. In fact, the low absorption intensity of the *iso*propyl thioether can hardly be explained on the same basis, and shows that the finer details of the data of TABLE 2 should be interpreted with caution.

Another aspect of the consequences of steric inhibition of meso-merism may be illustrated by consideration of the spectra of 2 : 6-dimethyl-4-nitrophenol XXIX and 2 : 6-dimethyl-4-nitroanisole XXX (Burawoy and Chamberlain, 1952). The main absorption bands

XXIX   XXX

of these compounds, in ethanol, differ little in intensity (ε_{max}, 11,000 and 9,500 respectively), but considerably in wavelength (λ_{max}, 323 mμ and 289 mμ, respectively). If these bands corresponded with each other, the data would present a highly unusual effect of the steric inhibition of mesomerism occurring in XXX. To the writer, however, it appears much more probable that the shoulder observed for the latter compound at about 330 mμ, with ε about 3,000, corresponds with the 323 mμ band of the former; and that the 289 mμ band should be identified as a modified nitrobenzene ' partial ' which is not or hardly present when the *para*-interaction is fully operative. The spectrum of 3 : 5-dimethylnitrobenzene (in ethanol $\varepsilon_{max} = 7,500$ at 271 mμ; Wepster, unpublished) is entirely consistent with this interpretation. Such a reappearance of a partial band, accompanying the disappearance of a band originating from the fully extended con-jugation, may be observed quite often. In favourable cases the bands in question may even be well separated (*cf e.g.* 2 : 6-dimethyl-4-nitro-NN-dimethylaniline; Wepster, 1957b).

(iii) *Benzene ring conjugated with symmetrical, non-planar substituents*— Examples of parent compounds XXXI and XXXII. In the most

XXXI   XXXII

important examples of this type, *i.e.* aromatic amines, the nitrogen atom is pyramidal (*cf* Wepster, 1953); assuming the valency angles (α) to be equal, these are less than 120° (XXXIII). Consequently the angle of twist should be re-defined as the angle between the plane through the $C_{ar}N$ bond perpendicular to the benzene ring and the plane through the $C_{ar}N$ bond and the axis of symmetry of the lone pair of the nitrogen atom. In fact, such a definition appears as entirely natural from the molecular-orbital point of view, and is more generally applicable than that used before. The definition has been illustrated in the projection formula XXXIV. Here the plane of the benzene ring, perpendicular to the paper, is indicated by the broken line; the symmetry axis of the lone pair of electrons appears as a full line; α has been taken as 109·5°; the angle of twist $\varphi = 60°$.

XXXIII   XXXIV

The spectra of a series of *ortho*-substituted primary amines have been investigated as far as 2 : 6-di-*tert.*-butylaniline and 2 : 4 : 6-tri-*tert.*-butylaniline (Wepster, 1957b; Burgers *et al.*, 1957). No systematic differences are apparent which would point to a steric inhibition of mesomerism of any importance. In the compounds mentioned, $\varphi = 0°$ in spite of considerable strain in this conformation. It is worthwhile pointing out that these results leave no doubt that, in less heavily substituted amines like 2 : 6-dimethylaniline, there is no steric inhibition at all, a conclusion which is of some weight with respect to the interpretation of other data pertaining to this grouping.

Derivatives of NN-dimethylaniline behave qualitatively like those of nitrobenzene; the most useful band, at about 250 mμ, changes little in wavelength, but there is a decrease in absorption intensity with increasing inhibition of the mesomerism. The same holds for the 380 mμ band, in ethanol, of derivatives of *p*-nitro-NN-dimethylaniline substituted *ortho*- to the dimethylamino group. However, with the correspondingly substituted $p(NN$-dimethylamino)azobenzenes (*trans*-forms) a clear shift in λ_{max} is found, along with a decrease of ε_{max}. Thus, in ethanol, the first absorption maximum of 4-(dimethylamino)-azobenzene occurs at 408 mμ, $\varepsilon = 27,000$, as compared with 375 mμ, $\varepsilon = 18,000$ for 3-methyl-4-(dimethylamino)azobenzene (*cf* Miller *et al.*, 1948; Kiprianov and Zhmurova, 1953; van Loon, unpublished). TABLE 3 contains some data for the first two types of compounds.

116

TABLE 3. ULTRA-VIOLET ABSORPTION OF NN-DIMETHYLANILINES AND 4-NITRO-NN-DIMETHYLANILINES

Dimethylanilines (NMe$_2$-1) $\lambda \sim 250$ mμ, in isooctane	ε_{max}	$\varphi_a{}^\circ$	4-Nitrodimethylanilines and related compounds $\lambda \sim 380$ mμ, in 96% ethanol	ε_{max}	$\varphi_a{}^\circ$
Unsubstituted[a]	15,500	(0)	Unsubstituted[a]	20,000	(0)
2-Me[b]	6,360	50	2-Me[a]	10,200	44
2-Et[a]	4,950	56	2-t-Bu[a]	570*	80
2-i-Pr[a]	4,300	58	2 : 6-di-Me[a]	5,450	59
2-t-Bu[c]	630*	78	1 : 2-dimethyl-4-nitro-		
2 : 6-di-Me[a]	2,240	68	benzene[e]	133*	—
2 : 4-di-Me-6-t-Bu[d]	800*	77	6-Nitrobenzoquinu-		
			clidine[e]	76*	(90)
			Nitrodimethylamino-		
			durene[f]	650	—

* No maximum; ε at 250 mμ and 380 mμ, respectively, have been given.

References: (a) Wepster, 1957b; (b) van Helden et al., 1954; (c) Wepster, 1952a; (d) Burgers et al., 1957; (e) Wepster, unpublished; (f) idem, in 50% ethanol.

The stereochemistry of these amines is very complicated, not only because the pyramidal nature of the nitrogen valencies produces a more intricate van der Waals curve, but also since the angle (α) between these valencies changes during a rotation, being larger for $\varphi = 0°$ than for $\varphi = 90°$ (cf Wepster, 1953). This complication arises because the molecule compromises between the intrinsic tendency of the tervalent nitrogen to be pyramidal, and its tendency in conjugated systems to become planar in order to ensure maximum mesomeric interaction. Since the second factor is more important for small values of φ, the compromise obtained will be dependent upon φ in the sense indicated.

Apart from this, there is the inversion of configuration of the nitrogen atom, which causes an equilibrium to exist between, for example, two configurations like XXXV ($\varphi = 20°$) and XXXVI ($\varphi = 80°$), even when conversion by rotation would be impossible.

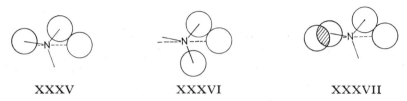

XXXV   XXXVI   XXXVII

In this particular case it is not difficult to decide which form will be most stable, since XXXV has more mesomeric energy than XXXVI whereas the steric strains are comparable. In other cases, however, the choice is hardly possible, and both forms may be important.

XXXV may also serve to illustrate a peculiarity of the present type of compound with respect to the relative influences of mono- versus di-*ortho*-substitution. If, as in XXXV, one *ortho*-substituent causes a rotation of 20°, the introduction of the second *ortho*-substituent will make this conformation highly strained (XXXVII), and hence the conformation corresponding to XXXVI may now be more favourable energetically. The second *ortho*-substituent, therefore, may once again be much more effective than the first, though for other reasons than in the cases discussed before.

The data in TABLE 3 enable us to make reasonable estimates of the average conformations of the amines in question, as indicated by φ_a calculated as before for the nitrobenzene derivatives. For most details reference can be made to the discussion of the nitrobenzene derivatives. Special attention is to be given to the low intensity of absorption prevailing for 2-*tert.*-butyl-NN-dimethylaniline, which is so near to that of benzene or *ortho*-xylene that it may be concluded that the residual mesomerism can be neglected for most practical purposes (p. 151). However, even with this bulky group in the *ortho*-position there is some remnant of mesomeric interaction, as is shown by the fact that the absorption intensity in ethanol decreases when acid is added (Wepster, 1952a).

(iv) *Benzene ring conjugated with asymmetrical, non-planar substituents*— Examples of parent compounds XXXVIII and XXXIX. The most

XXXVIII   XXXIX

interesting peculiarity of this type of compound occurs with nuclear-substituted secondary amines. Here, 2 : 6-di-substitution may cause a considerable steric inhibition of mesomerism, but even with two *tert.*-butyl groups the inhibition is by no means complete (Burgers *et al.*, 1957). This is readily understood by considering the projection formula XL in which the N—C_{al} bond appears as perpendicular to

XL

the benzene ring since the methyl group is constrained between the *tert.*-butyl groups. Thus, the angle of twist φ will be about 60°. In fact, from these considerations it follows that larger values of φ will be very hard, if not impossible, to produce (*cf* also pp. 148–9).

It has been found that both *N-tert.*-butylaniline and *N*-methyl-*N*-*tert.*-butylaniline exhibit a decreased intensity of absorption when compared with the corresponding *n*-butyl isomers, but that the effect is much larger in the second case (XLI–XLIV; van Hoek, 1954; Girault-Vexlearschi, 1956).

H nBu	H tBu	Me nBu	Me tBu
N	N	N	N
(benzene ring)	(benzene ring)	(benzene ring)	(benzene ring)
XLI	XLII	XLIII	XLIV
14,300	12,600	17,500	3,410

ε_{max} at about 250 mμ, in *iso*octane

Inspection of a molecular model of *N-tert.*-butylaniline with $\varphi = 0°$ and with bond-staggering in the non-aromatic moiety, shows that an *ortho*-hydrogen atom and one of the hydrogen atoms of the *tert.*-butyl group are almost coincident. The molecule will escape the corresponding enormous strain by a combination of changes involving rotation about the $C_{ar}N$ bond, rotational re-orientation of, and in, the *tert.*-butyl group (producing partially opposed conformations), and valency deflections. It is quite impossible to predict the most stable conformation, but it seems very likely that the *ortho*-hydrogen atom will finally be situated in the ' pocket ' between two methyl groups of the *tert.*-butyl group (XLV). Judging from the spectra, the value of φ is not high.

XLV

In the last-mentioned conformation of *N-tert.*-butylaniline the CC bond of the third methyl group and the NH bond are nearly opposed. Therefore, introduction of a methyl group on the nitrogen atom will introduce a strain comparable with that of the *cis*-butane conformation (about 3 kcal.mole^{-1}). The molecule can largely relieve this strain by a rotation of 60° about the *N—tert.*-butyl bond, but as the *tert.*-butyl group will then collide with the *ortho*-hydrogen atom, considerable rotation about $C_{ar}N$ may be expected to occur. Although once more the incompleteness of this analysis should be stressed, it gives at least a reasonable explanation of the strong influence of the methyl group. Further, the fact that a group, the size of which is insufficient to cause steric inhibition directly, may have a considerable indirect influence, provides some support for the tentative interpretation offered for the difference in behaviour between α-*iso*propyl-styrene and *iso*propyl phenyl ether (p. 114).

(v) *Ring compounds*—Compounds in which the presence of rings causes special stereochemical conditions have been studied extensively and provide interesting examples of steric effects on mesomerism. In a sense, *cyclo*octatetraene forms the simplest example, for in the most probable conformation, the tub form, the four planar ethylenic systems are sterically well isolated with regard to conjugation, the angles of twist being about 70°. The low energy of mesomerism, calculated for this hydrocarbon from thermochemical data (about 5 kcal.mole^{-1}; Wheland, 1955), is in harmony with this point of view. It has to be doubted, however, whether a loss of true aromatic character is involved here, since quantum mechanical calculations do not agree as to whether in a flat model of *cyclo*octatetraene a benzenoid stabilization would occur or not (Craig, 1951; Dewar, 1952b; *cf* Wheland, 1955).

That steric effects in ring-compounds can lead to a loss of aromatic character has been shown by Prelog and his co-workers (1948) for *meta*-bridged benzene derivatives of the type XLVI. Here, with $n = 8$

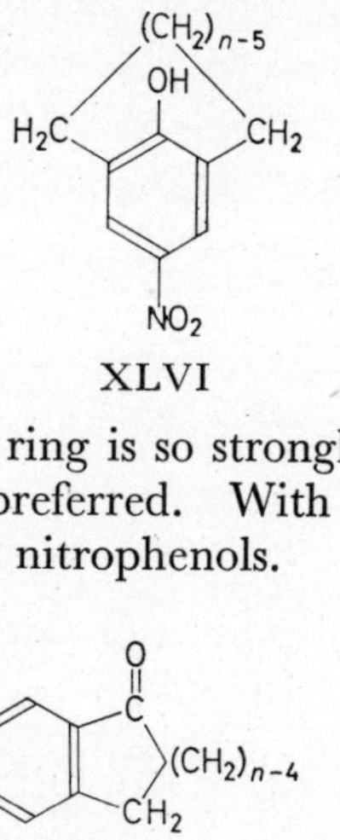

XLVI 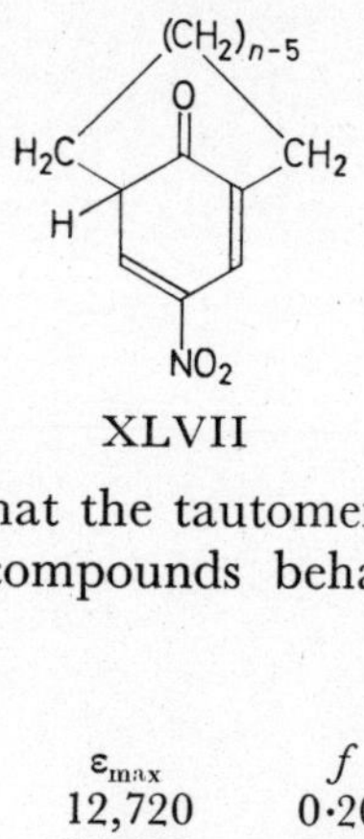   XLVII

the benzene ring is so strongly distorted that the tautomeric structure XLVII is preferred. With $n > 8$ the compounds behave spectroscopically as nitrophenols.

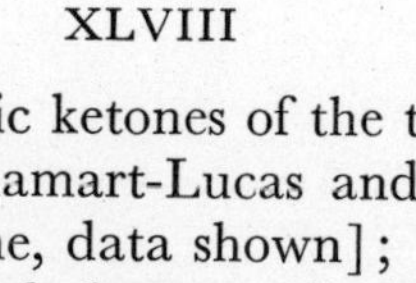

XLVIII

	ε_{max}	f
$n = 5$	12,720	0·208
6	11,450	0·196
7	9,000	0·153
8	6,500	0·115

Aromatic ketones of the type XLVIII have been studied by several groups (Ramart-Lucas and Hoch, 1935; Hedden and Brown, 1953 [in heptane, data shown]; Huisgen and Rapp, 1952; Huisgen *et al.*, 1954b; Schubert *et al.*, 1954). Deviations from coplanarity in the Ph—CO grouping are indicated by the spectra of the seven- and eight-membered ring compounds. It should be noted that the forces keeping the oxygen atom out of the plane of the benzene ring are of the same nature as those causing strain in medium-sized rings, *viz.* bond-opposition forces and *cis*-butane interactions (*cf* Prelog, 1950). In fact, when these forces are not taken into account, as in molecular models of the ball and spoke type, coplanarity can be achieved without any distortion of valency angles. Similar results, to which similar considerations apply, have been obtained for aromatic amines and ethers derived from XLVIII by replacing the carbonyl group by NMe and oxygen, respectively (Remington, 1945; Baddeley *et al.*, 1956c).

Huisgen *et al.* (1954b) also studied related systems, of which may be mentioned the oximes of the ketones XLVIII. Since by oximation the mesomeric interaction with the benzene ring is made less important, it may be expected that in the oximes there will be greater deviations from planarity than in the corresponding ketones. This expectation is borne out by the spectral data. Thus, with $n = 8$ the oxime shows a much closer approximation to the benzene spectrum than does the ketone (*cf* p. 111, d).

From the same laboratory (Huisgen *et al.*, 1954a) has come an investigation of the *para*-bridged ketones (XLIX). With $n = 18$ to 14,

XLIX

the absorption intensity decreases slowly and regularly (ε_{max}, 14,500–11,800) and remains similar to that of *p*-methylacetophenone (ε_{max}, 14,700); with $n = 13$, a sharp and considerable decrease is observed (ε_{max}, 6,600). The reason for this becomes apparent on studying molecular models; with $n = 13$ the methylene chain is so short that the ring cannot be closed if the $CO \cdot C_{al}$ grouping is allowed to be coplanar with the benzene ring.

Aromatic amines offer special possibilities in that there are two valencies available for ring closure. Advantage has been taken of this in preparing compounds in which the angle of twist is fixed and can be estimated with reasonable accuracy. Examples are benzoquinuclidine (L) (Wepster, 1952a) and 1 : 5-methano-2 : 3 : 4 : 5-tetrahydro-benzo[b]azepin (LI) (ten Bruggen Cate and Wepster, unpublished); Troeger's base (LII) also belongs to this class (Wepster, 1953).

Benzoquinuclidine is the simplest compound of this series; the molecule is very rigid, with $\varphi = 90°$, *i.e.* the symmetry axis of the lone pair orbital of the nitrogen atom lies in the plane of the benzene ring.

Therefore, the observation that its spectrum in ethanol is virtually the same as that of tetralin and changes very little when acid is added, may be taken as experimental evidence that for $\varphi = 90°$ the mesomeric

	L	LI	LII	LIII

interaction is completely eliminated. The spectral behaviour of 6-nitrobenzoquinuclidine confirms this conclusion (see TABLE 3).

	L	LI	LII	LIII
in isooctane	$\varphi = 90°$	$\varphi \simeq 60°$	$\varphi \simeq 45°$	$\varphi = 0°$
ε_{max}	482	2,750	4,250 (0·5ε)	15,500
λ_{max}	261·0	247	247·5	251
f (C band)	0·006	0·052	0·075 (0·5f)	0·291

The spectra of the other two compounds mentioned, LI with $\varphi \simeq 60°$, and LII with $\varphi \simeq 45°$ are of interest for several reasons. In the first place they show that mesomerism is present to a remarkable degree even when the nitrogen is pyramidal and φ substantial. It follows that $\pi\text{-}sp^3$ conjugation—as approximated in LI and LII— and $\pi\text{-}\pi$-conjugation are of comparable importance, a conclusion which is of considerable consequence with respect to the stereochemistry of aromatic amines (cf Wepster, 1953). Again, on the basis of a linear relationship between ε_{max} or f and the mesomeric energy— this not unreasonable assumption will be justified later (p. 146)— Guy's relationship between φ and the mesomeric energy (p. 102) would predict much lower values for the absorption intensities, especially of LI. Indeed, the fact that a cosine-square function (p. 102) gives much better agreement with experiment is one of the reasons why this function has been adopted in the general discussion.

Finally, it will be observed that, even with LI and LII, in which φ cannot possibly be zero in the electronically excited states, there are no significant changes in λ_{max} as compared with dimethylaniline (LIII). This is in definite disagreement with Braude's speculations on this subject (cf p. 108), as also is the constancy of λ_{max} in other types of compounds mentioned above, though these are less convincing examples in this connection.

Molecular Refractions

The well-known exaltation in the molecular refraction MR_D that, as a rule, accompanies conjugation, should decrease with increasing steric inhibition of the mesomerism. This was first investigated systematically for derivatives of nitrobenzene and NN-dimethylaniline by Thomson (1944), with results in agreement with theory. TABLE 4,

TABLE 4. MOLECULAR REFRACTION DATA (ΔMR_D) OF NITROBENZENES AND
NN-DIMETHYLANILINES

Substituent:	H	2-Me	2-Et	2-i-Pr	2-t-Bu	2 : 6-di-Me
Nitrobenzenes	6·52	6·25	6·26	6·17	5·68	5·66
NN-Dimethylanilines	14·65	13·60	13·49	13·48	13·02	13·26

References: van Helden *et al.*, 1954; Wepster, 1957a, b.

based on more recent data, gives some values for ΔMR_D, derived from
MR_D (*e.g.* of *o*-nitrotoluene) by subtracting MR_D of the parent hydrocarbon (*e.g.* toluene); this ΔMR_D value contains the exaltation in
question in addition to some constant terms. For both nitrobenzenes
and NN-dimethylanilines, a decrease of ΔMR_D is observed with
increasing size or number of the *ortho*-substituents.

More spectacular changes in the exaltation are, of course, to be
found in systems in which the exaltation for the planar conformation
is higher. Curran and Palermiti (1951) discussed several examples of
para-disubstituted benzenes for which this obtains. Thus, the molecular
refraction of NN-dimethylaminonitrodurene is only 7·5 cm³ greater than
that for *p*-nitro-NN-dimethylaniline, whereas the introduction of the
four methyl groups would be expected to produce an increase of about
19·8 cm³. The difference, 12·3 cm³, is to be ascribed to the very strong
steric inhibition of the mesomerism in the former compound (*cf*
TABLE 3). When comparing this difference with the exaltations in
nitrobenzene and in NN-dimethylaniline—about 0·9 cm³ and 1·7 cm³,
respectively (*cf* Wepster, 1957a, b)—it may be concluded that the loss
of *para*-interaction in the durene derivative results in a decrease of the
exaltation of no less than about 10 cm³.

Dipole Moments
As already noted, the first evidence that steric effects may influence
mesomerism came from dipole moment measurements (Birtles and
Hampson, 1937). This criterion has the definite advantage over those
discussed above that no electronically excited levels are involved, but
often difficulties in the interpretation arise from the smallness of
mesomeric moments and the uncertainty of the magnitude and direction
of bond and lone-pair moments.

TABLE 5 provides a review of the more important data and shows
many of the features discussed above. For example, with the nitrobenzene derivatives it is found that: (a) two methyl groups in *ortho*-
position are much more effective than one *ortho*-methyl group;
(b) two methyl groups are about as effective as one *tert.*-butyl group;
(c) the 'ortho*-xylene effect' exhibits itself, as appears, first from a
comparison of nitromesitylene and nitrodurene, and secondly, and

123

TABLE 5. DIPOLE MOMENTS OF BENZENE DERIVATIVES

All values in Debye units; solvent benzene; temperature 25°, except ref. b, 30°

Substituents		A ⬡ B	A Me⬡Me Me	A Me⬡Me Me⬡Me B
A	B			
F	H	1·41 ; 1·47[a]	1·36[b]	
Br	H	1·52[c]	1·52[b]	1·55[c]
NH₂	H	1·53[c]	1·40[d]	1·39[c]
		1·53[e]	1·45[e]	1·45[e]
OH	H	1·61[d]	1·36[b]	1·68[d]
HCO	H	2·92[f]	2·96[f]	
MeCO	H	2·88[f]	2·71[f]	2·68[f]
		2·96[g]	2·81[g]	
ClCO	H	3·32[f]	2·95[f]	
NO₂	H	3·95[h]	3·70[h]	3·62[i]
NMe₂	H	1·58[d]	1·03[d]	
NH₂	Me	1·36[c]		1·10[c]
NH₂	Br	2·93[c]		2·75[c]
NO₂	Br	2·65[c]		2·36[c]
NO₂	NH₂	6·10[c]		4·98[c]
NO₂	OH	5·04[d]		4·08[d]
NO₂	NMe₂	6·87[d]		4·11[d]
NO₂	OEt	4·76[d] (OMe)		3·69[d]

Acetyl-p-xylene (2 : 5-dimethylacetophenone) 2·85[g]; nitro-p-xylene 3·91[h]; nitro-p-di-tert.-butylbenzene 3·70[h]; 3 : 5-dimethyl-4-nitroaniline 5·04[d].

References: (a) Wesson, 1948; (b) F. Brown et al., 1934; (c) Birtles and Hampson, 1937; (d) Ingham and Hampson, 1939; (e) Smith, 1953; (f) Kadesch and Weller, 1941; (g) Bentley et al., 1949; (h) Kofod et al., 1957; (i) Kofod et al., 1952.

more convincingly, from a comparison of aminonitrodurene and 4-amino-2 : 6-dimethyl-1-nitrobenzene (moment, corrected for the contribution of the methyl groups, about 5·4 D). It should be emphasized that in general not much reliance can be placed on differences of up to about 0·1 D. Thus, the difference of 0·04 D between 2 : 5-dimethylacetophenone and 2 : 4 : 6-trimethylacetophenone does not allow any reliable conclusion with respect to the relative steric inhibitions of mesomerism in these compounds. From the same point of view, the calculations of angles of twist from such data by Braude and co-workers (1954, 1955a) would seem almost meaningless.

The most convincing evidence comes from the moments of the di-substituted durene derivatives, where decreases of 1–2 D have been found. Here, the fact that the moment of nitrodimethylaminodurene is 0·54 D lower than the algebraic sum of the moments of nitrodurene and NN-dimethylaminomesitylene at first sight seems to be in disagreement with theory, but can easily be understood when the pyramidal geometry of the amino-nitrogen atom is taken into account.

Attention should be called to the possibility of deriving mesomeric moments from these data. In fact, by taking the difference between the moments of nitrobenzene and nitrodurene (0·33 D), and correcting for the small residual mesomerism in the latter molecule, a value of 0·35–0·40 D is obtained for the mesomeric moment of nitrobenzene. This value may even be regarded as the most reliable estimate available. For less symmetrical molecules the analysis on such lines is less easy and correspondingly imprecise, but can be carried through (Everard and Sutton, 1951 ; cf Rogers, 1955).

Bond Lengths and Valency Angles

Rotation about a bond connecting two parts of a conjugated system brings about variation in the proportion of double-bond character in that bond. The bond length should be minimal when coplanarity is obtained, and should approach the sum of the covalent single-bond radii in perpendicular configuration. An interesting illustration of this is found in 1-iodo-2 : 4 : 6-trinitrobenzene studied by Huse and Powell (1940). The planes of the nitro groups *ortho*- to the iodine atom are almost perpendicular to the plane of the benzene ring, the nitro group in the *para*-position is in that plane ; the C_2N and C_6N bonds are given as 1·45 Å—*i.e.* close to the single bond length 1·47 Å— and the C_4N bond as only 1·35 Å—*i.e.* intermediate between the single and the double CN bond length, 1·265 Å. Quite recently, the structure of 3 : 5-dichloro-4-nitroaniline has been investigated by Zhdanov and Gol'der (1955). The $C—NO_2$ bond is $1·44 \pm 0·02$ Å, with an angle of twist of 64°. It should be noted that this angle of twist is in pleasing harmony with the value (56°) calculated for 3 : 5-dimethyl-4-nitro-aniline from ultra-violet spectra (TABLE 1), bearing in mind that chlorine and methyl substituents are almost equally effective in causing steric inhibition of mesomerism (p. 138). Another example is found in the structures of *cis*- and *trans*-azobenzene (de Lange *et al.*, 1939) ; here the CN bonds are $1·46 \pm 0·03$ Å in the non-planar *cis*-form, and $1·40 \pm 0·03$ Å in the planar *trans*-form (*cf* also Hampson and Robertson, 1941).

LIV

The positions indicated for the hydrogen atoms are diagrammatic and were not determined experimentally.

The reality of valency deflections in sterically strained systems has been abundantly demonstrated in recent years. In the present context the crystal structure of 1 : 5-dinitronaphthalene (LIV) is of special

125

importance. The molecule is flat but can acquire this conformation only by bending the nitro groups away from the nearby methine hydrogen atoms at C-8 and C-4 respectively; the angles C_9C_1N and $C_{10}C_5N$ are 125° (Sevast'yanov *et al.*, 1948). Thus, coplanarity is obtained notwithstanding the strains involved (*cf* p. 106).

CHEMICAL PROPERTIES

Equilibria

Considering the basic properties of aromatic amines, the situation is quite simple in principle since mesomeric interaction can occur only in the free base and not in the conjugate acid. Therefore, steric inhibition of mesomerism, by lowering the relative stability of the amine, should result in an increase of the basic strength, and a decrease of the strength of the conjugate acid. The experimental results (TABLE 6) do not, however, show a satisfactory correlation between the basic strength and the angle of twist in the amine as judged from molecular models, ultra-violet spectra (TABLE 3) or molecular refractions (TABLE 4). Thus, in the series of aniline derivatives, the basic strengths decrease strongly with increasing bulk of the *ortho*-alkyl substituents, although the spectra do not exhibit a significant change in mesomeric interaction, and the polar effects of the alkyl groups would be expected to increase the basic strengths. Again, with the *ortho*-substituted *NN*-dimethylanilines the basic strength would be expected to increase in the order:

$$H < 2\text{-Me} < 2:6\text{-di-Me} \sim 2\text{-}tert.\text{-Bu},$$

whereas the observed order is:

$$2\text{-}tert.\text{-Bu} < H < 2:6\text{-di-Me} < 2\text{-Me}.$$

Two explanations, both depending on the relative instability of the ion, have been advanced for these apparent anomalies (H. C. Brown and Cahn, 1950). The first is based on the assumption that, with bulky *ortho*-substituents present, ionization results in an increase of steric strain. The second explanation concentrates on the steric hindrance to solvation—especially important in the charged ion—occurring when *ortho*-hydrogen is replaced by larger groups. For reasons which cannot be discussed here, the present author is convinced that steric hindrance to solvation is the most important single factor (Wepster, 1957b).

The series of secondary and tertiary *N*-alkylated anilines without *ortho*-substituents exemplify another complication. The high basic strength of *N-tert.*-butyl-*N*-methylaniline as compared with *N-n*-butyl-*N*-methylaniline can be largely ascribed to steric inhibition of mesomerism, since: (a) the ultra-violet spectrum indicates a large angle of twist (p. 119); (b) steric hindrance to solvation should play only a

TABLE 6. BASIC STRENGTHS OF AROMATIC AND ALIPHATIC AMINES

Anilines (NH$_2$-1)	pK$_a$^{25} (50% ethanol)*	PhNR$_1$R$_2$		pK$_a$^{25} (50% ethanol)*	(water)
		R$_1$	R$_2$		
Unsubstituted[a]	4·26	H	Me[a]	4·29	4·86
2-Me[a]	4·09	H	Et[d]	4·71	5·25
2-Et[a]	4·04	H	i-Pr[d]	5·14	5·69
2-i-Pr[a]	4·06	H	t-Bu[c]	6·51	6·95
4-Me[a]	4·74	Me	Et[d]	5·02	5·87
2 : 6-di-Me[a]	3·49	Me	n-Bu[c]	4·75	5·68
2-t-Bu[a]	3·38	Me	t-Bu[c]	6·74	7·52
2 : 4-di-Me-6-t-Bu[b]	3·40	Et	t-Bu[d]	7·47	8·40
2 : 6-di-t-Bu[b]	1·80	Et	Et[d]	5·86	6·86
2 : 4 : 6-tri-t-Bu[b]	2·20	i-Pr	i-Pr[d]	7·33	8·25

Dimethylanilines (NMe$_2$-1)	pK$_a$^{25} (50% ethanol)*	HNR$_1$R$_2$		pK$_a$^{25} (water)
		R$_1$	R$_2$	
Unsubstituted[a]	4·39	H	H[e]	9·27
2-Me[a]	5·15	H	Me[e]	10·64
2-Et[a]	5·20	H	Et[e]	10·67
2-i-Pr[a]	5·05	H	i-Pr[e]	10·63
2 : 6-di-Me[a]	4·81	H	t-Bu	10·68
2-t-Bu[a]	4·28	Me	Me[e]	10·71
2 : 4-di-Me-6-t-Bu[b]	2·93	Et	Et[e]	10·98
2-Me-4 : 6-di-t-Bu[b]	2·77	i-Pr	i-Pr[e]	11·05

References: (a) Wepster, 1957b; (b) Burgers et al., 1957; (c) van Hoek, 1954; (d) Wepster, unpublished; (e) Hall and Sprinkle, 1932; (f) Girault-Vexlearschi, 1956.

* Here, and elsewhere in this chapter, ' 50% ethanol ' means 50% ethanol by volume.

minor part in the absence of *ortho*-substituents; (c) the basic strengths of aliphatic amines are fairly constant (TABLE 6). Then, however, the fact that *N-tert.*-butylaniline is almost as strong a base as *N-tert.*-butyl-*N*-methylaniline would seem anomalous in view of the small angle of twist indicated by the ultra-violet spectrum of the former compound (p. 119). There can be little doubt that this is an example of the discrepancy which, as discussed earlier (p. 106), is often to be expected when comparing electronic spectra with basic strengths. As reflected by its spectrum, *N-tert.*-butylaniline approaches coplanarity, but it can do so only at the cost of some steric strain (p. 119). This strain is relieved, at least partially, in the ion since here free rotation about the C$_{ar}$N bond occurs. This means that the ion is stabilized with respect to the free base, and that the basic strength is higher than would be anticipated from the ultra-violet spectrum.

Similar arguments may be applied to other compounds of the present types, with *N*-ethyl-*N*-methylaniline as the simplest case. If in this compound the non-aromatic moiety would possess its most stable all-staggered conformation (*cf trans*-butane), a deviation from coplanarity might be expected; indeed, in that conformation the ethyl group simulates the steric requirements of a *tert.*-butyl group with respect to the *ortho*-hydrogen atom (LV). In reality, judging from spectral data, coplanarity is obtained, so that it must be assumed that rotation around the C—C and the N—C$_{al}$ bonds in the MeNEt

LV

grouping has occurred in such a way as to minimize the total of the steric strains resulting from ethyl-*ortho*-hydrogen repulsions and bond-opposition forces in the MeNEt grouping. Since, once more, these strains will be relieved in the ion, the basic strength may be expected to be higher than that of NN-dimethylaniline, notwithstanding the absence of steric inhibition of mesomerism. The further increase in basic strength observed for NN-diethylaniline and NN-di-*iso*propyl-aniline—the spectrum of which compound indicates some inhibition of mesomerism (ε_{max}, 10,200 in *iso*octane; Wepster, unpublished measurements)—appears natural from the present line of thought, although the magnitude of the differences cannot be predicted, and possibly entropy factors are of importance as well.

The picture is, for obvious reasons, less complicated with those *p*-nitroanilines in which only the mesomeric interaction between the nitro group and the rest of the system is involved. A good measure of the consequence of steric inhibition of mesomerism can be obtained by subtracting the value of pK_a from that of the correspondingly substituted aniline. The value thus calculated, ΔpK_a, reflects the sum of the (varying) mesomeric effect and the (constant) inductive effect of the nitro group; some of these ΔpK_a values are given below (Wepster, 1957a).

	Δp$K_a{}^{25}$ (water)
4-Nitroaniline	3·49
4-Nitro-3-methylaniline	3·19
4-Nitro-2 : 3-dimethylaniline	2·76
4-Nitro-3 : 5-dimethylaniline	2·32
4-Nitro-2 : 3 : 5 : 6-tetramethylaniline	1·94

These data are qualitatively in agreement with theory and will be further evaluated later (pp. 144–5).

Considering the acid strengths of phenols, the situation is somewhat different from that encountered with the aromatic amines. Here, both phenol and phenoxide ion, *i.e.* both acid and conjugate base, are stabilized by mesomerism, whereas with the amines this holds only for the (conjugate) base. Since the stronger stabilization occurs with the phenoxide ion—a consequence of the greater mesomeric effect of the negatively charged oxygen atom—the results are to be expected to be qualitatively similar to those found for the amines, in that the acid strength should decrease when the mesomerism is inhibited. The ΔpK_a values for the p-nitrophenols shown below, and derived as above for the p-nitroanilines, bear out this contention (Wheland *et al.*, 1948; *cf* Wheland, 1955).

	ΔpK_a^{25} (water)
4-Nitrophenol	2·83
4-Nitro-3 : 5-dimethylphenol	1·93
4-Cyanophenol	2·04
4-Cyano-3 : 5-dimethylphenol	1·97

The cyanophenols were included in this investigation in order to show that, in the case of the nitrophenols, the major part of the difference is really due to steric inhibition of the mesomerism. The argument was, that, since the cyano group is linear, it cannot be subject to serious impediment of the mesomeric interaction. The smallness of the difference observed yields strong evidence in favour of the accepted interpretation.

Benzoic acid and its derivatives form another class of compounds the dissociation constants of which are partly governed by the differences in mesomeric energy between acid and conjugate base. Here, however, in contradistinction from the phenols, the mesomeric interaction will be stronger in the acid than in the anion, and thus steric inhibition of mesomerism should lead to an increase of acid strength. This was pointed out by Baddeley (1939) with respect to 2-methyl- and 2-*tert.*-butyl-benzoic acid, and has recently been confirmed by Dippy and his co-workers (1954; but *cf* Betts and Barclay, 1955) for these and other examples.

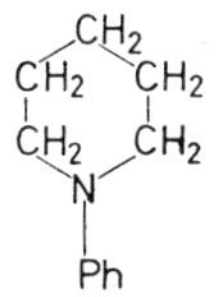

LVI   LVII
5·22   3·52

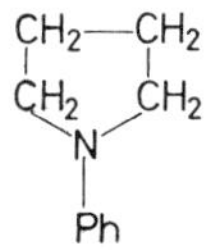

pK_a in 50% ethanol

The basic strengths of pyrrolidine and piperidine derivatives provide some interesting features. Whereas pyrrolidine and piperidine have very much the same basic properties, as also have their correspondingly substituted alkyl derivatives (Craig and Hixon, 1931; Hall and Sprinkle, 1932; Craig, 1933; Baddeley *et al.*, 1956b), N-phenylpiperidine (LVI) and N-phenylpyrrolidine (LVII) differ strongly (Wepster, unpublished; *cf* Baddeley *et al.*, 1956b). It seems likely that the low basic strength of N-phenylpyrrolidine is at least partly

129

due to steric promotion of mesomerism. With pyramidal configuration of the nitrogen atom the N—Ph bond is in bond-opposition with respect to two C—H bonds of the five-membered ring. The corresponding strain will be relieved by some flattening of the nitrogen pyramid, and this means an increase of the mesomeric interaction. Since, further, bond opposition is fully operative in the conjugate acid, the basic strength should be low. As to N-phenylpiperidine, the bond opposition which is set up when the nitrogen atom is flattened is a factor opposing the mesomeric interaction, and should increase the basic strength (*cf* Bent *et al.*, 1951 ; Baddeley *et al.*, 1956b ; H. C. Brown, 1956).

A further illustration of steric promotion of mesomerism is given by the basic strengths of the benzlactams (LVIII) in which the oxygen atom is known to be the basic centre (Huisgen *et al.*, 1954c). The

$$
\begin{array}{c}
\text{H} \\
\text{N} \\
\end{array}
\quad
\text{C}=\text{O}
$$

$$(\text{CH}_2)_{n-4}$$

LVIII

expectation that increasing n from 5 to 9 would progressively inhibit the mesomeric interaction between the lone pair of the nitrogen atom and the benzene ring is confirmed by the ultra-violet spectra. As a consequence, the mesomeric interaction between nitrogen atom and carbonyl group gains in importance, so that the negative charge on the oxygen atom is increased. In agreement with this reasoning, the basic strength in glacial acetic acid is found to increase by about 1.5 pK_a units. It should be added that the decrease in frequency of the infra-red carbonyl band at about 1,680 cm^{-1}, indicating a decrease in double-bond character, almost exactly parallels the increase in basic strength.

Reaction Rates

Steric effects on mesomerism may be of importance both in the initial state and in the transition state of a chemical reaction. Either the initial state or the transition state, or both, may be destabilized and stabilized by steric inhibition and steric promotion of mesomerism, respectively. On this basis, five different ways can be foreseen in which the energy differences between these two states might be increased, and five different ways in which this difference might be decreased by these factors. This classification is illustrated in FIGURE 11, which forms a convenient background for the discussion. If desired, the various classes can be labelled as shown, with + and — signs, separated by / to distinguish between initial state and transition state.

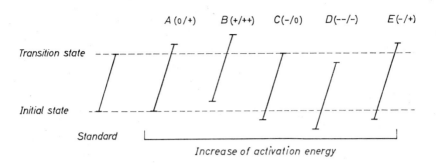

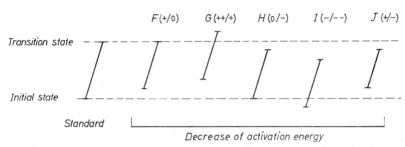

FIGURE 11.   Ten possible ways of changing relative energy levels

It will be noted that the same classification can also be derived by more descriptive reasoning; thus, class A $(0/+)$ concerns a reaction in which no mesomeric interaction is present initially, but is developing during the reaction. Clearly, steric inhibition of mesomerism must lead to a destabilization of the transition state, and a decrease in the rate of reaction. Further, the fact that, just as with equilibria, 'electronic strain' is usually accompanied and sometimes even dominated by 'steric strain', should be emphasized once more (cf p. 105).

In the following, examples will be taken from the classes A, B, G, H and I; examples of the other classes are either unknown or unconvincing, or even inconceivable to the present author.

(i) *Class A* $(0/+)$. The most extensively studied examples of this class relate to S_N1 reactions of benzyl chloride derivatives of various

types. For the present discussion, the most important common feature of these reactions is that the mesomeric interaction in the transition state between the benzene ring and the incipient carbonium-ion centre is best developed if the chlorine atom recedes as indicated by the projection formula LIX, *i.e.* in a direction approximately perpendicular to the benzene ring. With this in mind the behaviour of the systems in question can be explained on lines similar to those used in preceding cases.

The S_N1 reactions of *ortho*-methyl-substituted benzyl chlorides (LX) do not show any signs of steric inhibition of mesomerism. This is evidenced by the fact that the rate-increasing effect of one *ortho*-methyl

LX

LXI

group—no doubt a consequence of the polar effects—is repeated or even surpassed by a second *ortho*-methyl group (TABLE 7). This quite reasonable result is of importance with respect to the interpretation of the data obtained with *ortho*-methyl-substituted 1-phenylethyl chlorides (LXI) (TABLE 7). Here one *ortho*-methyl group has an

TABLE 7. SOLVOLYSIS OF SUBSTITUTED BENZYL CHLORIDES (LX) IN 50% ETHANOL, AND OF SUBSTITUTED 1-PHENYLETHYL CHLORIDES (LXI) IN ABSOLUTE ETHANOL

Substituents:	H	2-Me	4-Me	2 : 6-di-Me	2 : 4-di-Me	2 : 4 : 6-tri-Me
LX; $k_{rel.}$, 35°	1	5·2	9·6	$(5·2^2) \times 1·06$	$(5·2 \times 9·6) \times 1·70$	$(5·2^2 \times 9·6) \times 5·0$
LXI $\{ k_{rel.}$, 35°	1	16	40	$(16^2) \times 0·12$	$(16 \times 40) \times 0·88$	$(16^2 \times 40) \times 0·14$
$\{ E$ (kcal.mole⁻¹)	22·8	21·5	22·2	21·6	20·7	20·6

References: Charlton and Hughes, 1956; *cf* also Baddeley and Chadwick, 1951.

accelerating influence similar to that of the previous case, as might be expected since there is a favoured conformation in which it is the α-hydrogen atom that is close to the *ortho*-substituent. Introduction of a second methyl group, however, although further increasing the rate, produces only about one tenth of the effect to be expected when additivity would apply. This is paralleled by the several activation energies, and, of course, very strongly points to the presence of steric inhibition of mesomerism. As to the strains in the transition state, it seems most likely that not only steric strain plays a part (as tacitly assumed by Charlton and Hughes, 1956), but electronic strain as well; indeed, in view of the deviations from coplanarity found with, for instance, homomorphous aromatic amines, a planar carbonium ion and a transition state of the form LIX are highly improbable.

As pointed out by Baddeley and co-workers (1954, 1956a) the rates of the S_N1 reactions of compounds of the types PhCHRCl (LXII) and PhCR¹R²Cl (LXIII) should run parallel to the basic strengths of the amines obtained by replacing CCl by N, since the same factors which affect the ionization of these benzyl chloride derivatives will be at work in the dissociation of the anilinium ions. Therefore, low S_N1

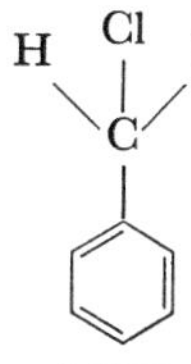

LXII 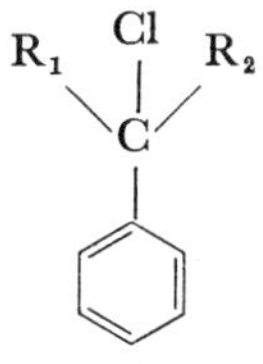   LXIII

reactivity should correspond with high basic strength. This prediction was confirmed by the experimental results, some of which are shown in TABLE 8. Thus, the *tert.*-butyl derivative of the first series, and the diethyl derivative of the second series, appear as outstandingly slow, in harmony with the relatively high basic strengths observed for N-*tert.*-butylaniline and NN-diethylaniline discussed above.

TABLE 8. SOLVOLYSIS OF BENZYL CHLORIDES OF THE TYPES PhCHRCl (LXII) IN 80% ETHANOL[a], AND PhCR^{1}R^{2}Cl (LXIII) IN ABSOLUTE ETHANOL[b]

R =	Me	Et	n-Pr	i-Pr	t.-Bu
LXII					
$10^7k_{45\cdot0^\circ}$ (sec^{-1})	1,180	273	327	58·7	2·18
E (kcal.mole^{-1})	20·4	20·7	20·3	22·9	25·4
LXIII					
$10^7k_{0\cdot0^\circ}$ (sec^{-1})	147	2·82	9·58		
E (kcal.mole^{-1})	21·4	25·3	24·5		

References: (a) Baddeley *et al.*, 1954; *cf* Wilputte-Steinert and Fierens, 1955; (b) Baddeley *et al.*, 1956a.

Very large differences in rates of solvolysis, in absolute ethanol, have been found with the chlorobenzocyclanes (LXIV) by Baddeley

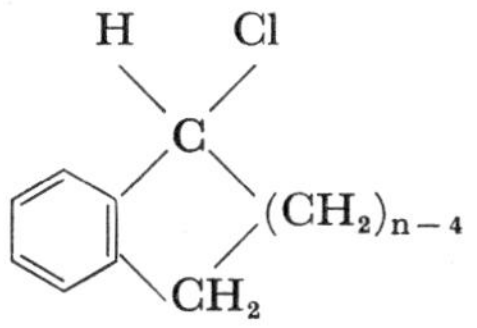

LXIV

	n =	5	6	7	8
For solvolysis $\int k_{rel.}$, 40°		781	210	6·07	0·768
with EtOH $\{ E$ (kcal.mole^{-1})		20·3	21·6	25·0	25·9

and Chadwick (1951) and by Huisgen and co-workers (1954b), whose data are shown. In the range $n = 5$–8, coplanarity of the ion is made increasingly difficult to obtain (*cf* the ultra-violet spectra of the corresponding ketones (XLVIII), p. 120), so that the rate of reaction should be expected to decrease and the activation energy to increase with increasing n. The results are in good agreement with this argument. Actually, only the last two members of this series belong to this class since the first two members may be better considered as examples of steric promotion of mesomerism (class H); this finer differentiation, which does not detract from the correctness of the above reasoning, will be discussed later (p. 141).

The most impressive example of steric inhibition of S_N1 reactivity is probably the inertness of triptycyl bromide (LXV) studied by

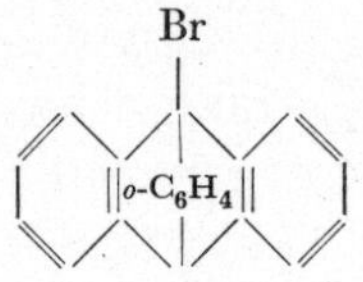

Br

$o\text{-}C_6H_4$

LXV

Bartlett and co-workers (Bartlett and Lewis, 1950; *cf* Bartlett and Greene, 1954; de la Mare, 1954). The difference in reactivity between this compound and trityl bromide is many powers of ten, and can be attributed mainly to steric elimination of the conjugation of all benzene rings with an incipient carbonium centre.

With respect to steric inhibition of mesomerism in homolytic reactions, attention should be called here to work by Kooyman and Strang (1953) on the abstraction of hydrogen by trichloromethyl radicals. It was found, for example, that the α-hydrogen atom of the *iso*-propyl group in *o*-cymene (LXVI), is much less reactive than that in *m*- and *p*-cymene (see below). An extreme case is the addition product of anthracene and maleic anhydride which reacts very slowly; this fact, of course, should be compared with the inertness of triptycyl bromide in S_N1 reactions, mentioned above (*cf* Bartlett and Greene, 1954).

Me—C(H)(Me)—Me   ·CCl₃ →   Me—C(·)(Me)—Me

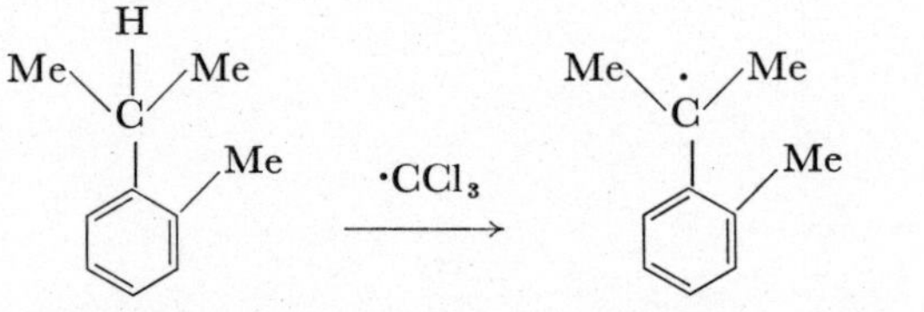

LXVI

R-*iso*propylbenzene; R=	H	4-*i*-Pr	4-Me	3-Me	2-Me
$k_{rel.}$	1·75	4·0	2·5	2·3	0·44

(ii) *Class B* $(+/++)$. It seems appropriate in the first place to mention here the extensive qualitative data regarding the long-known low reactivity of the *para*-position of *NN*-dimethyl-*o*-toluidine and similar compounds, with respect to electrophilic reagents such as diazonium salts or formaldehyde (see below). Initial state and

transition state are both destabilized by the inhibition of mesomerism, but the transition state more so because of the increase of the importance of polar structures during the rate-determining part of the reaction. It may be noted in passing that—as in many other cases—this remarkable behaviour could have been given a reasonable explanation in terms of quinonoid intermediates commonly used early in this century (cf e.g. W. G. Brown et al., 1939a), but survived this period as a mystery up till 1939 (Baddeley; W. G. Brown et al., a, b) when molecular dimensions were better known.

Semi-quantitative data were collected by W. G. Brown and co-workers on hydrogen–deuterium exchange in such aromatic amines and also aromatic ethers (see, e.g., W. G. Brown et al., 1939a, b; 1941; 1949), with results in agreement with theory (cf Baddeley et al., 1956b).

Huisgen and his co-workers (1954c), in their study of the benzlactams (LXVII), obtained quantitative data on the bromination of these compounds. These data show a very pronounced influence of steric

LXVII

$k_{\text{rel.}}$, 22°	$n = 6$	7	8	9	Acetanilide
(acetic acid)	3,700	580	78	0·79	2,400

inhibition of mesomerism on the rate of reaction. It is interesting to note that the bromine enters in the position para- to the nitrogen atom in all cases; thus, even with $n = 9$, the directing influence of the acylamido grouping prevails over that of the methylene grouping (cf Wepster, 1954). Decreases in rate of bromination, comparable as to their origin, but smaller in magnitude, have been observed by Baddeley and co-workers (1956c) with various types of aromatic ethers.

A classical example of the influences of steric inhibition of mesomerism on the rates of nucleophilic aromatic substitution is that given by Spitzer and Wheland (1940). The reactions studied were those between o- and p-bromonitrobenzenes and piperidine, which were found to be retarded by substituents in the position *ortho*- to the nitro group. This work has been for the greater part repeated and also extended by van Berk and co-workers (1956), some of whose results are quoted below.

| $k_{rel.}$ | 1590 | 1400 | 14 | 79 | 25 | 0·3 |

Recently, a thorough investigation of such substitution reactions, with derivatives of 1-chloro-2 : 4-dinitrobenzene, has been made by Capon and Chapman (1957; *cf* also Chapter 3). The observed decreases in rate were shown to be due almost entirely to increases in activation energy. Qualitative data of a similar character are scattered throughout the literature.

A bimolecular side-chain reaction which has been very extensively investigated is the deacylation, catalysed by sodium methoxide, of substituted (nitro)-acetanilides in boiling methanol (Verkade and Witjens, 1943; for a survey *cf* Verkade and Wepster, 1955). Initial state and transition state can be approximately represented as in LXVIII and LXIX, respectively, and clearly demonstrate the increase in mesomeric interaction between the nitrogen atom and the benzene ring with its eventual substituents during the reaction; indeed, the $+M$ effect of the nitrogen atom in the transition state will be

comparable to that of an amino group, and is, therefore, much larger than the $+M$ effect of the acetamido group. Thus, steric inhibition of mesomerism should be expected to decrease the rate of deacylation. TABLE 9 contains some of the relevant data, mostly pertaining to derivatives of o- and p-nitroacetanilide, and shows that the above reasoning is correct.

The simplest cases are provided by those compounds in which only the mesomeric interaction of the nitro group with the phenylamino grouping is inhibited, including the types 4-NO$_2$-3-R-acetanilide, 4-NO$_2$-3 : 5-di-R-acetanilide and 2-NO$_2$-3-R-acetanilide. With R = alkyl the powerfully activating influence of the nitro group is reduced

TABLE 9. RATES OF ALKALINE DEACYLATION CALCULATED FOR $0.1\ N$
SODIUM METHOXIDE IN BOILING METHANOL

Acetanilides (NHAc-1)	10^5k (min^{-1})	Acetanilides (contd.)	10^5k (min^{-1})
Unsubstituted[a]	3·7		
4-NO$_2$[b]	5,700	2-NO$_2$[b]	121,000
4-NO$_2$-2-Me[c]	11,500	2-NO$_2$-5-Me[c]	106,000
4-NO$_2$-2-t-Bu[b]	12,500	2-NO$_2$-5-t-Bu[b]	130,000
4-NO$_2$-2-F[c]	110,000	2-NO$_2$-5-Cl[c]	1,100,000
4-NO$_2$-2-Cl[c]	220,000	2 : 5-di-NO$_2$[c]	1,400,000
4-NO$_2$-2-Br[c]	140,000		
		2-NO$_2$-3-Me[f]	1,350
4-NO$_2$-3-Me[d]	1,600	2-NO$_2$-3 : 5-di-t-Bu[e]	41
4-NO$_2$-3-t-Bu[b]	75	2-NO$_2$-3-Cl[j]	5,000
4-NO$_2$-3 : 5-di-Me[b]	45	2 : 3-di-NO$_2$[j]	70,000
4-NO$_2$-3 : 5-di-t-Bu[e]	6·1		
4-NO$_2$-2 : 5-di-Me[f]	4,700	2-NO$_2$-6-Me[b]	122
4-NO$_2$-2 : 3-di-Me[f]	750	2-NO$_2$-6-t-Bu[b]	3·4
4-NO$_2$-3-Cl[d]	17,000	2-NO$_2$-6-F[j]	5,000
4-NO$_2$-3 : 5-di-Cl[d]	2,800	2-NO$_2$-6-Cl	1,800
		2-NO$_2$-6-Br	1,200
4-NO$_2$-2 : 6-di-Me[g]	26	2 : 6-di-NO$_2$[j]	11,000
4-NO$_2$-2:3:5:6-tetra-Me[h]	0·21	2-NO$_2$-3 : 6-di-Me[k]	8·9
4-CN[i]	140	3-NO$_2$[b]	20·7
4-CN-3-t-Bu[a]	83	3-NO$_2$-2 : 6-di-Me[k]	0·9
4-CN-3 : 5-di-Me[a]	70		
		N-Methylacetanilides (NMeAc-1)	
		4-NO$_2$[c]	30,000
		4-NO$_2$-2Me[l]	52

References: (a) Verkade and Wepster, 1955; (b) Biekart et al., 1952; (c) Wepster and Verkade, 1949a; (d) Wepster and Verkade, 1950; (e) Burgers et al., 1957; (f) van Helden et al., 1954; (g) Wepster, 1954; (h) Wepster, 1957a; (i) Kotch et al., 1952; (j) Wepster and Verkade, 1949b; (k) Wepster, unpublished; (l) Krol et al., 1952.

with increasing size or number of the substituents. These decreases in rate may be ascribed to steric inhibition of mesomerism, since (a) the reaction rates of 2-nitro-5-R-acetanilide and 2-nitro-acetanilide are practically equal with R = Me and R = tert.-Bu, and (b) the rates of reaction of 4-cyano-3 : 5-dimethylacetanilide and 4-cyano-3-tert.-butylacetanilide differ little from that of 4-cyano-acetanilide (cf p. 129). With R = Cl the polar effect of this substituent makes the assessment of the inhibition more difficult. Thus, 4-nitro-3-chloro-acetanilide is deacylated three times more rapidly than 4-nitro-acetanilide, and the presence of a small steric inhibition of mesomerism can only be inferred from the fact that 2-nitro-5-chloro-acetanilide reacts about ten times faster than 2-nitro-acetanilide. The same conclusion may be derived from the fact that 4-nitro-3 : 5-dichloroacetanilide is deacylated more slowly than 4-nitro-acetanilide, at the same time showing a similar disproportionality between mono-*ortho*- and di-*ortho*-substitution as found with the methyl group here and with other criteria. It will be observed that the steric inhibitions of mesomerism caused by chlorine are comparable to those caused by the methyl group (*cf* p. 125).

More complex situations are encountered with the types 4-nitro-2 : 6-di-R-acetanilide and 2-nitro-6-R-acetanilide. First, it is not only —as above—the mesomeric *ortho*- or *para*- interactions in initial state and transition state that are affected, but also the mesomeric inter-actions in the phenylamino grouping. As a result, and contrary to the previous cases, the reaction rate might even fall below that of acetanilide. Secondly, it should be noted that, although the mesomeric interactions mentioned may be fairly completely inhibited in the initial state, they will be not at all negligible in the transition state. Indeed, whereas the acetamido-nitrogen atom of the initial state is planar, the secondary amino-nitrogen atom of the transition state has a pyramidal configuration (*cf* p. 149). This means, that, for reasons discussed earlier in relation to 2 : 4 : 6-tri-*tert.*-butyl-N-methyl-aniline (p. 118), the angle of twist in the transition state will not exceed 60°. Consequently the nitro group preserves an appreciable part of its activating power by stabilizing the transition state through its conjugative effect. It is interesting to note that although the *percentage* decrease of mesomeric interaction is larger in the initial state than in the transition state, it is the energy level of the transition state that is lifted most. If, however, the mesomeric energies involved in the initial and transition state of the parent reacting system were closer together than appears to be so in the present case, the rate of reaction might have been increased (class G).

The decreases in rates of reaction can be understood on these lines. Special attention may be called to the fact that 4-nitro-2 : 6-dimethyl-acetanilide still reacts seven times as fast as acetanilide whereas 4-nitro-2 : 3 : 5 : 6-tetramethyl acetanilide—in which also the conjugative effect of the nitro group is largely put out of action—reacts about twenty times as slowly as acetanilide.

LXX

Finally, it is perhaps desirable to point out that, as a rule, steric hindrance in the classical sense plays no part of any importance in these compounds. This can be most easily derived from the steric

138

resemblance of the transition state of the present reaction with that of the alkaline hydrolysis of phenylacetic esters (*cf* LXIX and LXX). Since, in harmony with molecular models, the latter reaction is known to be free of classical steric hindrance, the deacylations of all acetanilides mentioned in TABLE 9, except perhaps of 2-nitro-6-*tert.*-butylacetanilide, are free from this factor (Wepster and Verkade, 1948). Only with two *tert.*-butyl groups in the *ortho*-positions steric hindrance should become a prominent factor, as is evidenced by the inertness of 4-nitro-2 : 6-di-*tert.*-butylacetanilide (Burgers *et al.*, 1957).

The reaction rates of the other types of compounds included in TABLE 9 need no discussion. In addition it may be noticed that the low rates of aqueous alkaline hydrolysis of 2 : 6-dimethylacetanilide, 2 : 4 : 6-trimethylacetanilide and 2 : 4 : 6-trichloro-acetanilide, found by Semerano (1931), fall into the same category.

Baddeley and co-workers (1956c) have investigated the S_N1 reactivity of *p*-alkoxybenzyl chlorides of various types. A relatively low rate of reaction, to be explained on similar lines as above, was found with 7-chloromethylhomochroman, 4-methoxy-3 : 5-dimethylbenzyl chloride and, though hardly convincing, with 4-*tert.*-butoxybenzyl chloride. The most remarkable aspect of this work was that in the first example the low rate appeared—as usual—mainly as a consequence of a high energy of activation, whereas in the second example it was mainly due to a low frequency factor of the Arrhenius equation. The reasons for this are not clear.

(iii) *Class G* $(++/+)$. It is well known that, when an amino or substituted amino group is introduced into the *para*-position in ethyl benzoate, there results a decrease of the rate of alkaline hydrolysis. This can be readily explained by considering the mesomeric interactions in the initial state and the transition state; in the former there is an extra stabilization resulting from the *para*-interaction between

LXXI   LXXII

amino and ester group (LXXI) which is partially or completely destroyed in the transition state (approximated by LXXII). If, now, ethyl 4-dimethylaminobenzoate is compared with ethyl 4-dimethyl-amino-3-methylbenzoate, both initial state and transition state of the latter compound will be relatively unstable; indeed, in either state mesomeric interactions are inhibited sterically. Since, further, in the transition state only the dimethylaniline mesomerism is inhibited, whereas in the initial state the *para*-interaction is involved as well, the destabilization should be strongest in the initial state. In agreement with this reasoning, inhibition of mesomerism is found to produce an increase in rate. This is demonstrated by the first column of TABLE 10; the $\Delta \log k$ values—obtained by subtracting $\log k$ found for the correspondingly (methyl-) substituted ethyl benzoate, from $\log k$ of the compound in question—indicate an increasingly smaller deactivating influence of the dimethylamino group, the stronger the inhibition of the mesomeric interactions (*cf* Wepster, 1957b; Taft, 1956).

TABLE 10. INFLUENCE OF *para*-SUBSTITUENTS ON THE RATES OF ALKALINE HYDROLYSIS OF SUBSTITUTED ETHYL BENZOATES

Ester	$\Delta \log k$		
	R = NMe$_2$	R = NH$_2$	R = NO$_2$
Ethyl 4-R-benzoate	$-1 \cdot 66$[a]	$-1 \cdot 63$[c]	$2 \cdot 02$[c]
Ethyl 4-R-3-Me-benzoate	$-0 \cdot 61$[b]	—	—
Ethyl 4-R-3 : 5-di-Me-benzoate	$-0 \cdot 26$[c]	$-1 \cdot 29$[c]	$1 \cdot 60$[c]

References: (a) Tommila and Hinshelwood, 1938; Tommila, 1941 (solvent 56% acetone, 25°); (b) Price and Lincoln, 1951 (56% acetone, 25°); (c) Westheimer and Metcalf, 1941 (70% ethanol, 55°).

The figures of the second column of TABLE 10 suggest a small steric inhibition of mesomerism in the 2 : 6-dimethylaniline grouping, and as such are in contradiction with spectral evidence (p. 116). The differences are too small, however, to be interpreted with certainty.

The behaviour of the nitrobenzoates is of considerable interest. It is known that two methyl groups *ortho*- to the nitro group strongly inhibit the mesomeric interaction (*cf e.g.* TABLE 1); notwithstanding this, the activating influence of the nitro group is only a little smaller in ethyl 3 : 5-dimethyl-4-nitrobenzoate than it is in ethyl 4-nitrobenzoate. As a corollary, it can be concluded that the influence of the nitro group is mainly due to its inductive effect. This conclusion will be evaluated further in the last section of this review (pp. 151–3).

Some other cases, more complicated because steric hindrance also plays a part, have been investigated by Fenton and co-workers (1955).

(iv) *Class H* $(0/-)$. A case of relatively high reactivity, which may be regarded as exemplifying this class, is the solvolysis of 1-chloro-1-phenyl*cyclo*pentane (LXXIII) which, in ethanol, at 0°, is about 70 times faster than that of its open-chain analogue 2-chloro-2-phenylpropane (LXXIV), with a difference in activation energy of about 4 kcal.mole^{-1} (Baddeley *et al.*, 1956b). The explanation of these results runs closely parallel to that given above for the low basic strength of N-phenylpyrrolidine (p. 129). In the transition state of the ionization of either compound the incipient carbonium ion centre strives for closest approach to planarity combined with coplanarity with the benzene ring, since in that configuration the mesomeric stabilization is maximal. The essential point is, that with LXXIII—in contradistinction to LXXIV—this approach to planarity is assisted and improved by the tendency of the system to avoid bond opposition between the C—Ph bond and two C—H bonds of the five-membered ring. This exists in the initial state but not in the carbonium ion.

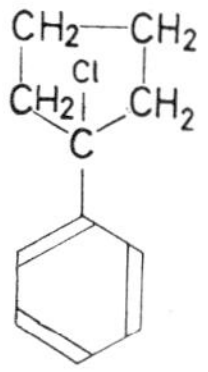

$$CH_2—CH_2$$

LXXIII 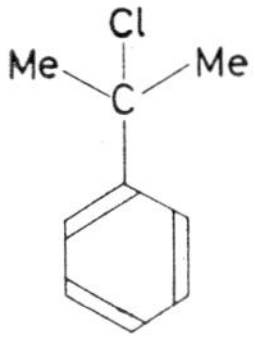   LXXIV

Thus, in the transition state in question, the mesomerism will be sterically promoted. It should be realized that from these arguments the high rate of reaction of LXXIII appears as the result of both the decrease of bond-opposition energy in forming the transition state— as already occurs with the aliphatic 1-chloro-1-methyl*cyclo*pentane (*cf* H. C. Brown and Borkowski, 1952)—and the promotion of meso- merism in the transition state. Which of these two factors is the more important cannot be decided at present.

The relative rates of solvolysis of the chlorobenzocyclanes (LXXV– LXXVII) have been correlated earlier (p. 133) with the amounts of mesomeric interaction to be expected in the several carbonium ions.

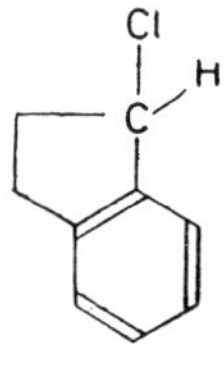

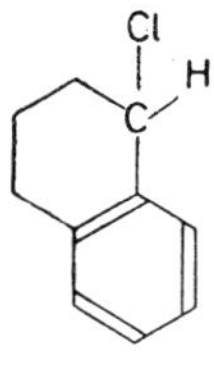

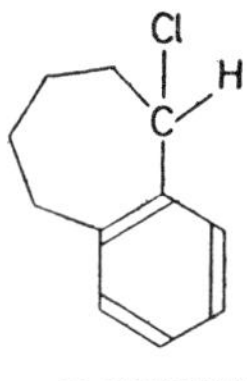

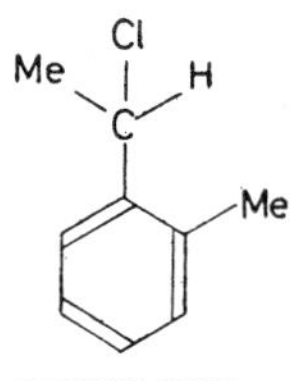

LXXV   LXXVI   LXXVII   LXXVIII

	LXXV	LXXVI	LXXVII	LXXVIII
$10^7 k$ (min^{-1})	4,000	1,070	23·5	66
E (kcal.mole^{-1})	20·0	20·2	23·9	22·8

This argument is too simple, however, as appears from the fact that the rate of reaction of 1-*o*-tolylethyl chloride (LXXVIII) is much lower than that of 1-chloro-indane (LXXV) and 1-chlorotetralin (LXXVI). The data shown above, due to Baddeley and Chadwick (1951), and relating to ethanolysis at 0°, illustrate this point.

The interpretation advanced by Baddeley and Chadwick is as follows. The most favourable conformation for LXXVIII is given by

141

the projection formula LXXIX (top view), or a similar one in which the methyl group in the side-chain is not in the plane of the benzene ring. In the transition state an approximation to LXXX will be

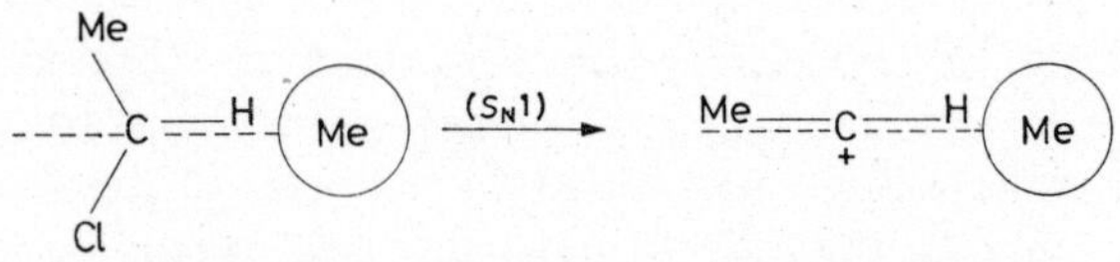

LXXIX   LXXX

favoured because of its maximal mesomeric interaction. This should be accompanied by the development of a steric strain resulting from the small distance between the side-chain methyl group and the *ortho*-hydrogen atom. By comparison with the situation in biphenyl and *cis*-butene, the energy required to obtain configuration LXXX is estimated to be about the energy difference between *cis*- and *trans*-butene, *i.e.* 1 kcal.mole^{-1}.

Turning to 1-chloro-indane (LXXV) and 1-chlorotetralin (LXXVI) it will be apparent that here the alkyl side-chain approaches coplanarity already in the initial state, so that now only the hydrogen atom has to be brought nearer to the plane, and this should be easier than the same process for a methyl group. From this point of view, and regarding LXXVIII as the standard, the mesomerism in the transition states of LXXV and LXXVI may be regarded as sterically promoted. The behaviour of these compounds, and also that of LXXVII, is in qualitative agreement with this reasoning.

In addition to the above, other factors will contribute to the observed differences. Thus, the changes in bond-opposition energies occurring during the reaction should be important for 1-chloro-indane (LXXV) in a similar way as with 1-chloro-1-phenyl*cyclo*pentane (LXXIII) discussed above. Again, it is interesting to note that with 1-chloro-indane (LXXV) the planarity of the five-membered ring not only causes the steric promotion of mesomerism mentioned above, but at the same time some steric inhibition of mesomerism. This becomes clear by considering the projection formula LXXXI for the transition

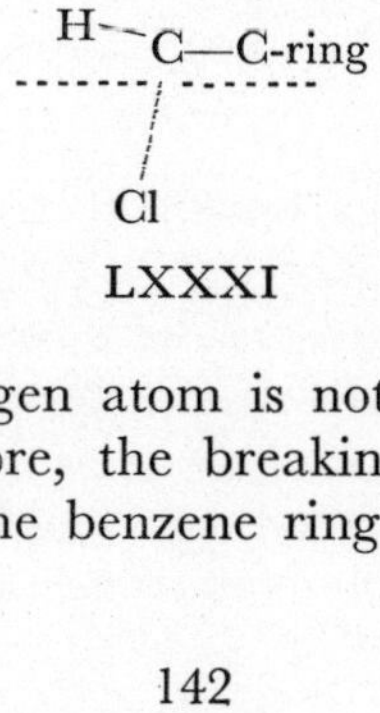

LXXXI

state; for here the hydrogen atom is not (yet) in the plane of the benzene ring, and, therefore, the breaking C········Cl bond does not appear perpendicular to the benzene ring as required for maximum mesomeric stabilization.

142

A further interpretation will not be attempted since the systems involved are so complex that they defy an entirely satisfactory analysis (*cf* Huisgen *et al.*, 1954b, c).

Certain reactions involving free radicals may also be classified here. As an example may be quoted the high rate of hydrogen abstraction at the α-carbon atom of phenyl*cyclo*pentane (Kooyman and Strang, 1953). The explanation is similar to that given above for the high S_N1 reactivity of 1-chloro-1-phenyl*cyclo*pentane.

(v) *Class I* $(-/--)$. Electrophilic substitution reactions of coumaran (LXXXII) as compared with those of 2-methylanisole (LXXXIII) form examples of this class. The enforced coplanarity in LXXXII entails a mesomeric stabilization which is greater in the

LXXXII   LXXXIII

transition state than in the initial state, and, therefore, increases the rate of reaction. This was shown to hold qualitatively by W. G. Brown and co-workers (1949) with respect to hydrogen–deuterium exchange, and quantitatively by Baddeley and co-workers (1951b; 1956c) with respect to bromination in the *para*-position to the oxygen atoms, for which, in acetic acid, at 20°, the rate ratio 12 : 1 was observed. A similar difference, similarly explained, has been found by Baddeley and his co-workers (1956c) for the S_N1 reactions of 5-chloromethyl-coumaran and 2-methyl-4-chloromethylanisole; in 90% ethanol, at 0°, the rate ratio is about 10 : 1, with activation energies of 17·3 and 19·6 kcal.mole^{-1}, respectively.

MISCELLANEOUS PROPERTIES

Steric effects on mesomerism have their impact on many other physical and chemical properties. Some of these may be mentioned here as further indications of the importance of the phenomenon in question (*cf* especially Ingraham, 1956):

a. melting-points (Arnold *et al.*, 1940);
b. boiling-points (see *e.g.* Friedlaender, 1898);
c. heats of combustion (Wolf and Trieschmann, 1934; Badoche, 1939; Magnus *et al.*, 1951);
d. infra-red spectra (Braude and Waight, 1954; Huisgen *et al.*, 1954c; Braude and Timmons, 1955; Schubert and Sweeney, 1955; van Veen *et al.*, 1957);
e. Raman spectra (Saunders *et al.*, 1941; Wittek, 1942; Shorygin, 1947, 1948);

f. phosphorescence and fluorescence (*cf* West, 1956; Foster *et al.*, 1956);

g. thermochromism (Rumpf and Chaudé, 1951; Koelsch, 1951; Schönberg *et al.*, 1954);

h. polarographic behaviour (Fields *et al.*, 1949; Bent *et al.*, 1951; Prévost *et al.*, 1953; Huisgen, 1954b);

i. stability of radicals and biradicals (Michaelis *et al.*, 1939; Müller, 1949; Bent *et al.*, 1951);

j. position of basic centre in amino-azo dyes (*cf e.g.* Cilento *et al.*, 1956; Sawicki, 1956; van Loon, unpublished);

k. substantivity of dyes (Hodgson and Marsden, 1944);

l. instability of penicillin (Woodward, 1949);

m. biological activity (Miller *et al.*, 1948; Löfgren, 1948).

CORRELATIONS OF THE CHARACTERISTIC PROPERTIES

In the above discussion, the changes in properties as a result of the presence of steric effects on mesomerism have been scarcely compared with each other. It will have been observed, however, that when a series of compounds is arranged in order of increasing effect, the order is the same for various criteria. A more quantitative correlation can be made for several characteristic properties (Wepster, 1957a, b; *cf* also Baddeley *et al.*, 1954, 1956a, b, c; Huisgen *et al.*, 1954b, c; Taft, 1956); a few of these are shown below, also in view of the fact that they lead to some important inferences.

(i) *Electronic spectra and molecular refractions*—In FIGURE 12 are plotted the extinction coefficients of the 250 mμ band in *iso*octane of NN-dimethylaniline and *ortho*-alkylated derivatives against the ΔMR_D values of the same compounds (*cf* pp. 117 and 123). The approximation to a linear relation between these magnitudes is seen to be very good.

The linearity observed allows a fairly reliable extrapolation to $\varepsilon \simeq 0$, *i.e.* to a point corresponding to $\varphi = 90°$. The ΔMR_D value thus obtained, subtracted from that of NN-dimethylaniline, gives 1·7–1·8 cm^3 as the exaltation due to the mesomeric interaction in the latter compound, in good agreement with the exaltation derived from the molecular refractions of aliphatic and aromatic tertiary amines (average 1·50 cm^3; Vogel, 1948).

(ii) *Electronic spectra and basic strengths*—In FIGURE 13 are plotted the extinction coefficients of the 380 mμ band in ethanol of p-nitro-aniline and derivatives, alkylated in *ortho*-position to the nitro group, as a function of the ΔpK_a values of the same compounds determined

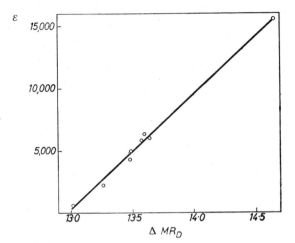

FIGURE 12. Correlation of ultra-violet spectra and molecular refractions of *NN*-dimethylaniline and derivatives

in aqueous solution (TABLE 1 and p. 128). Once more an excellent linear relationship is found to hold.

In this case, extrapolation to $\varepsilon \simeq 0$ yields a ΔpK_a value corresponding to $\varphi = 90°$, which, when subtracted from the ΔpK_a value of *para*-nitroaniline, gives the magnitude of the decrease in basic strength due to the mesomeric *para*-interaction in the latter compound; in this way a value of 1·7 pK_a units, corresponding with 2·3 kcal.mole^{-1} *para*-interaction energy, is obtained.

Further, the extrapolated ΔpK_a value, 1·8 units, is a direct measure of the influence of the inductive effect of the nitro group on the basic strength. Comparison of this value with the pK_a difference between aniline and *m*-nitroaniline, 2·0 units, provides strong corroborative evidence for the thesis that the influence of the inductive effect from the *meta*-position is about the same, and possibly somewhat larger than

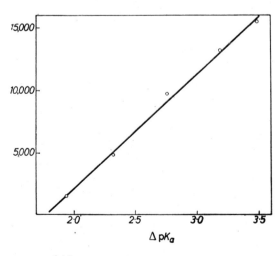

FIGURE 13. Correlation of ultra-violet spectra and basic strengths of *p*-nitroaniline and derivatives

145

from the *para*-position (Rooda *et al.*, 1954). This result will be further evaluated later (p. 152).

There is still another aspect of this correlation. The changes in ΔpK_a are, to a good approximation, determined by the changes in mesomeric *para*-interaction in the free amines. Therefore, from the linearity observed it may be concluded that ε is linearly related to the energy of mesomerism. Again, when accepting the usual cosine square relationship between the mesomeric energy and the angle of twist φ, this also gives a justification of the relation $\varepsilon/\varepsilon_0 = \cos^2 \varphi_a$ which has been adopted by many authors (*cf* Klevens and Platt, 1949; Wepster, 1953; Braude and Waight, 1954; Braude *et al.*, 1955) as also in this review (p. 110).

(iii) *Basic strengths and deacylation rate constants*—When plotting the above-mentioned values of ΔpK_a for *para*-nitroanilines against related values of $\Delta \log k$ for the deacylation of the corresponding *p*-nitro-acetanilides, a very good approximation to a straight line applies (FIGURE 14). The values of $\Delta \log k$ range from 0 to about 3 for $\varphi = 0°$ to $\varphi = 90°$, and also reflect the variation in mesomeric interactions.

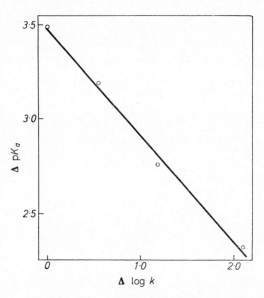

FIGURE 14. Correlation of basic strengths of *p*-nitro-aniline and its derivatives with rates of deacylation of the corresponding *p*-nitro-acetanilides

The linear relationship observed may be interpreted as showing that a certain grouping of substituents *ortho*- to the nitro group gives rise to the same percentage reduction of mesomerism—*i.e.* the same average angle of twist—with the deacylation reaction as with the basic strength. This can be suitably systematized in terms of an extension of the well-known Hammett equation (Hammett, 1940; Jaffé, 1953), in the following way. First, the usual σ value may be regarded as generally composite :

$$\sigma = \sigma_i + \sigma_c$$

in which σ_i reflects the inductive effect, and σ_c the fully operative conjugative effect. Next, by introducing $\sigma_{0°}$ and $\sigma_{90°}$ $(= \sigma_i)$ as the sigma values of the (para-) nitro group (applying to coplanar and perpendicular conformation, respectively) ; and α as a factor measuring the residual mesomerism (and varying from 0 to 1 for $\varphi = 90°$ to $0°$), the following equations may be written :

$$\sigma_\varphi = \sigma_{90°} + \alpha\sigma_c = \sigma_{90°} + \alpha(\sigma_{0°} - \sigma_{90°})$$

so that for the basic strengths :

$$\Delta pK_a - \Delta pK_{a90°} = \rho_1 \cdot \alpha_1(\sigma_{0°}' - \sigma_{90°})$$

and for the deacylation reaction :

$$\Delta \log k_{90°} - \Delta \log k = \rho_2 \cdot \alpha_2(\sigma_{0°}'' - \sigma_{90°})$$

The linear relationship shown in FIGURE 14 implies that $\alpha_1 = \alpha_2$. The numerical values for α which can be derived from FIGURE 14, taking $\Delta pK_{a90°} = 1·8$ (p. 145), are: 4-nitro-3-methyl, 0·8 ; 4-nitro-2 : 3-dimethyl, 0·6 ; 4-nitro-3 : 5-dimethyl, 0·35.

A further extension of this treatment is suggested by the fact that a plot of $\log k$ against pK_a also shows a linear relationship. A similar reasoning as above leads to a generalized Hammett equation :

$$\log k - \log k^0 = \rho[\sigma_{90°} + \alpha(\sigma_{0°} - \sigma_{90°}) + \Sigma\sigma_{os}]$$

in which $\Sigma\sigma_{os}$ stands for the algebraic sum of the sigma values of the other (ortho-)substituents. If $\alpha = 1$ due to the absence of substituents, this equation reduces to the Hammett equation proper ; if $\alpha = 1$ as the result of absence of steric inhibition of mesomerism the equation reduces to the Hammett equation which holds when additivity of sigma values applies (Jaffé, 1953).

A detailed analysis of these results will not be attempted here, since for lack of data it is not possible to establish the scope and limitations of the present procedure. It is worth pointing out, however, that the fact that FIGURE 14 exhibits a linear relationship, notwithstanding the failure of the usual Hammett equation with the deacylation reaction $(\sigma_{p\text{-}NO_2}$ $(= \sigma_{0°}) = 3·2$; Krol, Verkade and Wepster, unpublished), is encouraging with respect to the usefulness of the ideas discussed above (cf also van Berk et al., 1956). On the other hand, the differences in angle of twist φ, calculated for correspondingly substituted nitrobenzenes and p-nitroanilines from spectral data (p. 111), suggest that the values of α will not be strictly constant. That, in spite of this, linearity is observed, can probably be traced back to a compensation of the consequences of differences in mesomeric interaction and in van der Waals repulsion (cf the analysis of ΔpK_a values by Wepster,

147

1957a); with this in mind, α appears as a measure of the sum of electronic and steric strains, rather than of electronic strain only. However this may be, just as the Hammett equation breaks down for certain systems, a significant failure of the present treatment may be foreseen in other cases, although its extent cannot be predicted.

SOME SPECIAL APPLICATIONS

(i) *Separation of isomers*—Nitration of 3-methylacetanilide in mixtures of acetic anhydride and acetic acid yields the 6-, 4- and 2-nitro isomers (LXXXIV–LXXXVI). Treatment of this mixture with Witt-Utermann alkali—a solution of potassium hydroxide in aqueous methanol—leaves the 4-nitro isomer (LXXXV) undissolved; filtration

| LXXXIV | LXXXV | LXXXVI |

gives an alkaline solution containing the other two. This solution, upon standing at room temperature, first separates 3-methyl-6-nitro-aniline in about a day; after filtration, almost pure 3-methyl-2-nitroaniline crystallizes in the course of a fortnight (Wepster and Verkade, 1949b). The basis for this separation is, of course, the fact that the steric inhibition of mesomerism in the 2-nitro isomer (LXXXVI) brings about a decrease in the rate of hydrolysis as compared with the 6-nitro isomer (LXXXIV) in which no such inhibition is present (*cf* TABLE 9).

(ii) *The stereochemistry of the nitrogen atom in amines and amides—*Inspection of molecular models of 2 : 4 : 6-tri-*tert.*-butyl-*N*-methylaniline (LXXXVII) and *N*-acetyl-2 : 4 : 6-tri-*tert.*-butylaniline (LXXXVIII) shows that in both compounds the N—C_{al} carbon atom is virtually

| LXXXVII | LXXXVIII | LXXXIX | XC |

constrained in between the 2- and 6-*tert.*-butyl groups (*cf* p. 118). Hence, in the projection formulae of these compounds, the N—C_{al} bond will appear perpendicular to the plane of the benzene ring, as in LXXXIX or XC. Which of these projections belongs to either compound depends upon whether the nitrogen atom is pyramidal (LXXXIX) or planar (XC). In the first case, the lone pair appears out of the plane of the benzene ring, with an angle of rotation of 60° if sp^3 hybridization applies; in the second case, with sp^2 hybridization, the lone pair is in the plane of the benzene ring. Again, in the first case the N—Ph conjugation is considerably inhibited, in the second case it is eliminated altogether.

With this in mind, it is possible to derive the configurations of the nitrogen atoms in the compounds in question from the ultra-violet spectra shown in FIGURE 15 (Burgers *et al.*, 1957). The intensity of

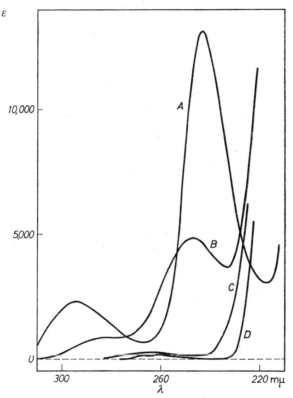

FIGURE 15.   Ultra-violet spectra of: *A.* *N*-methyl-aniline (*isooctane*) ;   *B.* *N*-methyl-2 : 4 : 6-tri-*tert.*-butyl-aniline (*isooctane*) ;   *C.* *N*-acetyl-2 : 4 : 6-tri-*tert.*-butyl-aniline   (ethanol) ;   *D.*   1 : 3 : 5-tri-*tert.*-butylbenzene (ethanol)

absorption of *N*-methyl-2 : 4 : 6-tri-*tert.*-butylaniline (LXXXVII) is considerably less than that of *N*-methylaniline (ε_{max}, 4,900 and 13,200 respectively), but the spectrum retains the characteristic pattern of an aromatic amine, and is still very different from that of 1 : 3 : 5-tri-*tert.*-butylbenzene which it should resemble if the inhibition of mesomerism were complete. It will be clear that these facts form convincing evidence in favour of a pyramidal configuration of the nitrogen atom in LXXXVII, also because the angle of twist, 52°, calculated from $\varepsilon/\varepsilon_0 = \cos^2\varphi_a$, agrees well with projection formula LXXXIX.

As to the spectrum of *N*-acetyl-2 : 4 : 6-tri-*tert.*-butylaniline (LXXXVIII), this shows no resemblance to that of acetanilide (ε_{max} 14,400 at 242 mμ in ethanol; Ungnade, 1954) and is virtually equal to that of 1 : 3 : 5-tri-*tert.*-butylbenzene. Consequently, it may be concluded that the lone pair of the nitrogen atom has its axis of symmetry in the plane of the benzene ring (XC), or more generally that in the amide group the three valencies of the nitrogen atom are in one plane. Thus, these spectral data provide information on the position of the hydrogen atom which is very difficult to obtain otherwise (*cf e.g.* Weinstein, 1954; Kurland, 1955; Richards, 1956).

(iii) *Separation of inductive and mesomeric effects, and the theory of aromatic substitution*—It will be clear from the foregoing that the possibility of sterically influencing mesomerism frequently offers a means of estimating the relative importance of inductive and mesomeric effects to the properties of conjugated systems. Sometimes it is feasible to study the properties of a compound in which the mesomerism is completely eliminated or very nearly so. Alternatively, an attempt can be made to extrapolate the data on a series of compounds with an increasing degree of inhibition, as illustrated above (p. 145).

A simple example is found in the determination of the relative contributions of inductive and mesomeric effects to the basic strength of aromatic amines (Wepster, 1952b). In benzoquinuclidine (XCII) the lone pair of the nitrogen atom has its axis of symmetry in the

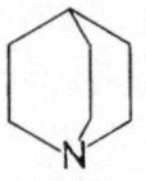

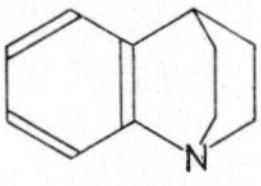

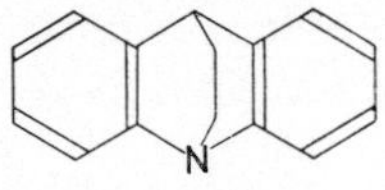

	XCI	XCII	XCIII
p$K_a^{25°}$ (water)	10·58	7·79	4·46

plane of the benzene ring, and, therefore, is not mesomerically related to the benzene ring (*cf* p. 121). Hence, the difference in basic strength between quinuclidine (XCI) and benzoquinuclidine (XCII) forms a direct measure of the influence of the negative inductive effect of the phenyl group. The value found, about 3 pK_a units, is confirmed by the basic strength of dibenzoquinuclidine (XCIII) as compared with benzoquinuclidine (XCII) (van der Krogt and Wepster, 1955). On this basis, the total difference in basic strength between aliphatic and aromatic amines, about 6 pK_a units, can be said to be equally due to inductive and mesomeric effects. It may be noted that these figures yield a value of 4 kcal.mole^{-1} for the mesomeric energy.

Somewhat more complicated is the analysis of the basic strength of a system like that of p-nitrodimethylaniline. Here it is necessary to distinguish between the (dimethyl)aniline mesomerism, the nitro-benzene mesomerism and the *para*-interaction, for which the contributions of structures like XCIV, XCV and XCVI, respectively, are essential. The importance of the aniline mesomerism XCIV has been

| XCIV | XCV | XCVI |

discussed above. The *para*-interaction (XCVI) in p-nitroaniline has been found earlier (p. 145) to correspond with 1·7 pK_a units; it is doubtless of comparable magnitude for the present compound. As to the nitrobenzene mesomerism, the following data (Wepster, 1956) show that it is of little consequence to the basic strength.

	XCVII	XCVIII	XCIX	C
$pK_a^{25°}$, 50% ethanol	4·28	1·63	4·32	1·91
ΔpK_a		2·65		2·41

In all compounds XCVII–C, structures like XCIV and XCVI are without any importance, as shown by electronic spectra (TABLE 3), but whereas the nitrobenzene mesomerism XCV is fully developed in 4-nitro-2-*tert.*-butyldimethylaniline (XCVIII), it is much inhibited in 4-nitro-2 : 5-di-*tert.*-butyldimethylaniline (C; *cf* TABLE 1). Therefore, the difference between the ΔpK_a values given above (2·65 and 2·41) should reflect the greater part of the influence of structures (XCV). From these figures a value of only 0·2 pK_a units can be derived for the mesomeric effect, as against 2·4 pK_a units for the inductive effect. A rather similar view of the comparative unimportance of the mesomeric effect of the nitro group has been derived by Westheimer and Metcalf (1941) from the rates of alkaline hydrolysis of ethyl *para*-nitrobenzoate and ethyl 4-nitro-3 : 5-dimethylbenzoate (p. 140) ; the dissociation constants of the corresponding benzoic acids further confirm this conclusion (Wepster, unpublished).

Summarizing the above data, and disregarding solvent differences, the enormous difference in basic strength between p-nitrodimethylaniline ($pK_a^{25°}$ 0·92; Roberts *et al.*, 1950) and dimethylamine ($pK_a^{25°}$ 10·71; Hall and Sprinkle, 1932) can now be accounted for approximately by the following contributions, expressed in pK_a units:

$-I$ Effect, phenyl group	3
$-M$ Effect, phenyl group	3
$-I$ Effect, nitro group	2·4
$-M$ Effect, nitro group	0·2
para-Interaction	1·7

Extending these comparisons to *meta*-substituted derivatives the following data will be considered (Wepster, 1957b; unpublished).

$pK_a^{25°}$, 50% ethanol	4·39	1·38	4·28	1·55
ΔpK_a		3·01		2·73

Comparison of the ΔpK_a values serves to show that, as expected, *meta*-mesomeric interactions play, at best, a minor part. Further, when comparing with the *p*-nitro derivative (C), it emerges that the influences of the inductive effects are about the same from (and on) the *meta*- and *para*-position, with the *meta*-position slightly predominating (*cf* also p. 145). This is in complete harmony with more direct observations on the influence of the ammonio group (-NH$_3^+$ and -NMe$_3^+$) and the amine oxide group—both groups with only inductive effects—from *meta*- and *para*-position (Roberts *et al.*, 1951; Rooda *et al.*, 1954; Wepster, 1956).

Finally, it will be observed that the ΔpK_a values found for the *m*-nitro derivatives are even somewhat greater than that of 4-nitro-2-*tert.*-butyldimethylaniline (XCVIII) which reflects the sum of the inductive and the mesomeric effect from the *para*-position. On the strength of the argument that the properties of the side chain are determined by the charge on the benzene carbon atom to which they are attached (*cf* Roberts and Semenow, 1955), this may be taken as evidence that in nitrobenzene the partial positive charges on the *meta*- and on the *para*-carbon atom are about equal. The same conclusion may be derived from the small difference in acid strength between, *e.g. m*- and *p*-nitrobenzoic acid, although here the *p*-nitro group has a slightly larger influence. The fact that 6- and 7-nitrobenzoquinuclidine have virtually the same basic strengths (Wepster, 1956) substantiates this view.

The important conclusion is that the strong *meta*-directing effect of the nitro group, with respect to electrophilic reagents, is not inherent in the charge-distribution of the ground state, and, therefore, must be attributed to the electronic requirements of the transition states. A similar reasoning applies to the strong *para*-activating effect of a nitro group with respect to nucleophilic reagents.

Since the nitro group has one of the strongest $-M$ effects the same arguments should hold for most other ' *meta*-directing ' substituents. The *ortho-para*-directing substituents, on the other hand, probably do not show this exception to the ' chemical non-crossing rule ' (R. D. Brown, 1952a). Thus, the fact that *p*-chloroaniline is a stronger base than its *meta*-isomer suggests a charge distribution in chlorobenzene in harmony with the (*ortho*), *para*-directing effect of chlorine. Even here, however, it seems likely that the orientation is determined by (electromeric) polarizability effects, rather than by the polarization present in the ground state.

REFERENCES

Arnold, R. T. and Craig, P. N. (1950) *J. Amer. chem. Soc.* **72**, 2728
— Peirce, G. and Barnes, R. A. (1940) *ibid* **62**, 1627
— and Richter, J. (1948) *ibid* **70**, 3505
Baddeley, G. (1939) *Nature, Lond.* **144**, 444 ; (1942) *ibid* **150**, 178
— and Chadwick, J. (1951a) *J. chem. Soc.* 368
— — and Taylor, H. T. (1954) *ibid* 2405 ; (1956a, b) *ibid* 448, 451
— Holt, G., Smith, N. H. P. and Whittaker, F. A. (1951b) *Nature, Lond.* **168**, 386
— Smith, N. H. P. and Vickars, M. A. (1956c) *J. chem. Soc.* 2455
Badoche, M. (1939) *Bull. Soc. chim. Fr.* (5) **6**, 570
Bartlett, P. D. and Greene, F. D. (1954) *J. Amer. chem. Soc.* **76**, 1088
— and Lewis, E. S. (1950) *ibid* **72**, 1005
Barton, D. H. R. and Cookson, R. C. (1956) *Quart. Rev. chem. Soc., Lond.* **10**, 44
Beaven, G. H., Hall, D. M., Lesslie, M. S. and Turner, E. E. (1952) *J. chem. Soc.* 854
— and Johnson, E. A. (1957) *ibid* 651
Bent, R. L. *et al.* (1951) *J. Amer. chem. Soc.* **73**, 3100
Bentley, J. B., Everard, K. B., Marsden, R. J. B. and Sutton, L. E. (1949) *J. chem. Soc.* 2957
van Berk, P., van Langen, J. O. M., Verkade, P. E. and Wepster, B. M. (1956) *Rec. Trav. chim. Pays-Bas* **75**, 1137
Betts, E. E. and Barclay, L. R. C. (1955) *Can. J. Chem.* **33**, 1768
Biekart, H. J. B., Dessens, H. B., Verkade, P. E. and Wepster, B. M. (1952) *Rec. Trav. chim. Pays-Bas* **71**, 1245
Birtles, R. H. and Hampson, G. C. (1937) *J. chem. Soc.* 10
Braude, E. A. (1955) *Experientia* **11**, 457
— and Forbes, W. F. (1955) *J. chem. Soc.* 3776
— and Sondheimer, F. (1955a, b) *ibid* 3754, 3773
— — and Forbes, W. F. (1954) *Nature, Lond.* **173**, 117
— and Timmons, C. J. (1955) *J. chem. Soc.* 3766
— and Waight, E. S. (1954) *Progress in Stereochemistry*, Vol. 1, Ed. W. Klyne, London, Butterworths
Brooker, L. G. S., White, F. L., Sprague, R. H., Dent, S. G. and van Zandt, G. (1947) *Chem. Rev.* **41**, 325
Brown, F., de Bruyne, J. M. A. and Gross, P. (1934) *J. Amer. chem. Soc.* **56**, 1291
Brown, H. C. (1956) *J. chem. Soc.* 1248

Brown, H. C. and Borkowski, M. (1952) *J. Amer. chem. Soc.* **74,** 1894
— and Cahn, A. (1950) *ibid* **72,** 2939
Brown, R. D. (1952a) *Quart. Rev. chem. Soc., Lond.* **6,** 63 ; (1952b) *J. chem. Soc.* 2231
Brown, W. G., Kharasch, M. S. and Sprowls, W. R. (1939a) *J. org. Chem.* **4,** 442
— and Letang, N. J. (1941) *J. Amer. chem. Soc.* **63,** 358
— and Reagan, H. (1947) *ibid* **69,** 1032
— Widiger, A. H. and Letang, N. J. (1939b) *ibid* **61,** 2597
— Wilzbach, K. E. and Urry, W. H. (1949) *Canad. J. Res.* **B27,** 398
Burawoy, A. and Chamberlain, J. T. (1952) *J. chem. Soc.* 2310
Burgers, J., Hoefnagel, M. A., Verkade, P. E., Visser, H. and Wepster, B. M.
(1957) *Rec. Trav. chim. Pays-Bas* **76,** in the press
Capon, B. and Chapman, N. B. (1957) *J. chem. Soc.* 600
Charlton, J. C. and Hughes, E. D. (1956) *ibid* 850 ; *cf idem ibid* 855
Cilento, G., Miller, E. C. and Miller, J. A. (1956) *J. Amer. chem. Soc.* **78,** 1718
Coggeshall, N. D. and Lang, E. M. (1948) *ibid* **70,** 3283
Coulson, C. A. (1951) cited by L. L. Ingraham (1956), p. 482, footnote 5
— and Jacobs, J. (1949) *J. chem. Soc.* 1983
Craig, D. P. (1951) *ibid* 3175
Craig, L. C. (1933) *J. Amer. chem. Soc.* **55,** 2543
— and Hixon, R. M. (1931) *ibid* **53,** 4367
Cram, D. J. and Knight, J. D. (1952) *ibid* **74,** 5839
Curran, C. and Palermiti, F. M. (1951) *ibid* **73,** 3733
Dauben, W. G. and Pitzer, K. S. (1956) in *Steric Effects in Organic Chemistry,* Ed.
M. S. Newman, New York, Wiley
De la Mare, P. B. D. (1954) *Progress in Stereochemistry,* Vol. 1, Ed. W. Klyne,
London, Butterworths
Dewar, M. J. S. (1952a) *J. Amer. chem. Soc.* **74,** 3345 ; (1952b) *Sci. Progr.,* No. 160
Dippy, J. F. J., Hughes, S. R. C. and Laxton, J. W. (1954) *J. chem. Soc.* 1470
Doub, L. and Vandenbelt, J. M. (1947) *J. Amer. chem. Soc.* **69,** 2714
Everard, K. B. and Sutton, L. E. (1951) *J. chem. Soc.* 2821
Fehnel, E. A. and Carmack, M. (1949) *J. Amer. chem. Soc.* **71,** 84
Fenton, S. W., DeWald, A. E. and Arnold, R. T. (1955) *ibid* **77,** 979
Fields, M., Valle, C. and Kane, M. (1949) *ibid* **71,** 421
Forbes, W. F. and Mueller, W. A. (1955) *Canad. J. Chem.* **33,** 1145
— and Sheratte, M. B. (1955) *ibid* **33,** 1829
Foster, R., Hammick, D. Ll., Hood, G. M. and Sanders, A. C. E. (1956) *J. chem.
Soc.* 4865
Friedlaender, P. (1898) *Mh. Chem.* **19,** 627
Girault-Vexlearschi, G. (1956) *Bull. Soc. chim. Fr.* (5) **23,** 577, 582, 589, 606
Guy, J. (1949) *J. Chim. phys.* **46,** 469
Hall, N. F. and Sprinkle, M. R. (1932) *J. Amer. chem. Soc.* **54,** 3469
Hammett, L. P. (1940) *Physical Organic Chemistry,* New York, McGraw-Hill
Hampson, G. C. and Robertson, J. M. (1941) *J. chem. Soc.* 409
Hawthorne, F. and Cram, D. J. (1952) *J. Amer. chem. Soc.* **74,** 5859
Hedden, G. D. and Brown, W. G. (1953) *ibid* **75,** 3744
Heilbronner, E. and Gerdil, R. (1956) *Helv. chim. acta* **39,** 1996
van Helden, R., Verkade, P. E. and Wepster, B. M. (1954) *Rec. Trav. chim.
Pays-Bas* **73,** 39
Hodgson, H. H. and Marsden, E. (1944) *J. Soc. Dy. Col.* **60,** 210
van Hoek, T. C. (1954) Thesis, Delft
Huisgen, R. and Rapp, W. (1952) *Chem. Ber.* **85,** 826
— — Ugi, I., Walz, H. and Glogger, I. (1954a) *Liebigs Ann.* **586,** 52
— — — — and Mergenthaler, E. (1954b) *ibid* **586,** 1
— Ugi, I., Brade, H. and Rauenbusch, E. (1954c) *ibid* **586,** 30

Huse, G. and Powell, H. M. (1940) *J. chem. Soc.* 1398
Ingham, C. E. and Hampson, G. C. (1939) *ibid* 981
Ingraham, L. L. (1956) in *Steric Effects in Organic Chemistry*, Ed. M. S. Newman, New York, Wiley
Jaffé, H. H. (1953) *Chem. Rev.* **53**, 191
Kadesch, R. G. and Weller, S. W. (1941) *J. Amer. chem. Soc.* **63**, 1310
Kiprianov, A. I. and Zhmurova, I. N. (1953) *J. gen. Chem. U.S.S.R.* **23**, 626; *Chem. Abstr.* (1954) **48**, 6980
Kistiakowski, G. B. (1936) Personal communication quoted by L. W. Pickett, G. F. Walter and H. France (1936) *J. Amer. chem. Soc.* **58**, 2296
Klemm, L. H., Ziffer, H., Sprague, J. W. and Hodes, W. (1955) *J. org. Chem.* **20**, 190
Klevens, H. B. and Platt, J. R. (1949) *J. Amer. chem. Soc.* **71**, 1714
Koelsch, C. F. (1951) *J. org. Chem.* **16**, 1362
Kofod, H., Sutton, L. E., de Jong, W. A., Verkade, P. E. and Wepster, B. M. (1952) *Rec. Trav. chim. Pays-Bas* **71**, 521
— — Verkade, P. E. and Wepster, B. M. (1957) *ibid* **76**, to be published
Kooyman, E. C. and Strang, A. (1953) *ibid* **72**, 329, 342
Kotch, A., Krol, L. H., Verkade, P. E. and Wepster, B. M. (1952) *ibid* **71**, 108
van der Krogt, S. M. H. and Wepster, B. M. (1955) *ibid* **74**, 161
Krol, L. H., Verkade, P. E. and Wepster, B. M. (1952) *ibid* **71**, 545
Kurland, R. J. (1955) *J. chem. Phys.* **23**, 2202
de Lange, J. J., Robertson, J. M. and Woodward, I. (1939) *Proc. roy. Soc.* **A171**, 398
Leonard, N. J. and Blout, E. R. (1950) *J. Amer. chem. Soc.* **72**, 484
Löfgren, N. (1948) Thesis, Stockholm
Magnus, A., Hartmann, H. and Becker, F. (1951) *Z. phys. Chem.* **197**, 75
Michaelis, L., Schubert, M. P. and Granick, S. (1939) *J. Amer. chem. Soc.* **61**, 1981
Miller, J. A., Sapp, R. W. and Miller, E. C. (1948) *ibid* **70**, 3458
Müller, E. (1949) *Fortschritte der chemischen Forschung* **1**. Band, 325; Berlin, Springer-Verlag
Murrell, J. N. (1956) *J. chem. Soc.* 3779
— and Longuet-Higgins, H. C. (1955) *ibid* 2552
Overberger, C. G. and Tanner, D. (1955) *J. Amer. chem. Soc.* **77**, 369
Pauling, L. and Corey, R. B. (1952) *ibid* **74**, 3964
Platt, J. R. (1951) *J. chem. Phys.* **19**, 101
Prelog, V. (1950) *J. chem. Soc.* 420
— Wiesner, K., Ingold, W. and Häfliger, O. (1948) *Helv. chim. acta* **31**, 1325
Prévost, Ch., Souchay, P. and Malen, Ch. (1953) *Bull. Soc. chim. Fr.* (5) **20**, 78
Price, C. C. and Lincoln, D. C. (1951) *J. Amer. chem. Soc.* **73**, 5838
Ramart-Lucas, P. (1954) *Bull. Soc. chim. Fr.* (5) **21**, 1021
— and Hoch, J. (1935) *ibid* (5) **2**, 327
Remington, W. R. (1945) *J. Amer. chem. Soc.* **67**, 1838
Richards, R. E. (1956) *Quart. Rev. chem. Soc., Lond.* **10**, 480
Rieger, M. and Westheimer, F. H. (1950) *J. Amer. chem. Soc.* **72**, 19, 28
Roberts, J. D., Clement, R. A. and Drysdale, J. J. (1951) *ibid* **73**, 2181
— and Semenow, D. A. (1955) *ibid* **77**, 3152
— Webb, R. L. and McElhill, E. A. (1950) *ibid* **72**, 408
Rogers, M. T. (1955) *ibid* **77**, 3681
Rooda, R. W., Verkade, P. E. and Wepster, B. M. (1954) *Rec. Trav. chim. Pays-Bas* **73**, 849
Rumpf, P. and Chaudé, O. (1951) *C.R. Acad. Sci., Paris* **233**, 1274
Saunders, R. H., Murray, M. J. and Cleveland, F. F. (1941) *J. Amer. chem. Soc.* **63**, 3121
Sawicki, E. (1956) *J. org. Chem.* **21**, 605
Schönberg, A., Mustafa, A. and Asker, W. (1954) *J. Amer. chem. Soc.* **76**, 4134

Schubert, W. M. and Sweeney, W. A. (1955) *ibid* **77**, 4172
— — and Latourette, H. K. (1954) *ibid* **76**, 5462
Semerano, G. (1931) *Gazz. chim. Ital.* **61**, 501, 921
Sevast'yanov, N. G., Zhdanov, G. S. and Umanskiĭ, M. M. (1948) *Zhur. Fiz. Khim.* **22**, 1153 ; *Chem. Abstr.* (1949) **43**, 1236
Shorygin, P. P. (1947, 1948) *Chem. Abstr.* (1948) **42**, 2520 ; *ibid* (1949) **43**, 2868
Smith, J. W. (1953) *J. chem. Soc.* 109
Spitzer, W. C. and Wheland, G. W. (1940) *J. Amer. chem. Soc.* **62**, 2995
Taft, R. W. (1956) in *Steric Effects in Organic Chemistry*, Ed. M. S. Newman, New York, Wiley
Thomson, G. (1944) *J. chem. Soc.* 404, 408
Tommila, E. (1941) *Ann. Acad. Sci. Fennicae* **A57**, No. 13, 3
— and Hinshelwood, C. N. (1938) *J. chem. Soc.* 1801
Truce, W. E. and Emrick, D. D. (1956) *J. Amer. chem. Soc.* **78**, 6130
Ungnade, H. E. (1954) *ibid* **76**, 5133
van Veen, A., Verkade, P. E. and Wepster, B. M. (1957) *Rec. Trav. chim. Pays-Bas* **76**, in the press
Verkade, P. E. and Wepster, B. M. (1955) *Industr. chim. belge* **20**, 1281
— and Witjens, P. H. (1943) *Rec. Trav. chim. Pays-Bas* **62**, 201
Vogel, A. I. (1948) *J. chem. Soc.* 1825, 1833
Weinstein, B. K. (1954) *Travaux de l'Institut de Cristallographie*, **10**, 128 ; Editions de l'Académie des Sciences de l'URSS, Moscow
Wenzel, A. (1953) *J. chem. Phys.* **21**, 403 ; (1954) *ibid* **22**, 1623
Wepster, B. M. (1952a, b) *Rec. Trav. chim. Pays-Bas* **71**, 1159, 1171 ; (1953) *ibid* **72**, 661 ; (1954) *ibid* **73**, 809 ; (1956) *ibid* **75**, 1473 ; (1957a, b) *ibid* **76**, 335, 357
— and Verkade, P. E. (1948) *ibid* **67**, 411 ; (1949a, b) *ibid* **68**, 77, 88 ; (1950) *ibid* **69**, 1393
Wesson, L. G. (1948) *Tables of Electric Dipole Moments*, Cambridge, Mass., The Technology Press
West, W. (1956) in *Technique of Organic Chemistry*, Ed. A. Weissberger, Vol. IX, Ed. W. West, New York, Interscience
Westheimer, F. H. (1947) *J. chem. Phys.* **15**, 252
— and Metcalf, R. P. (1941) *J. Amer. chem. Soc.* **63**, 1339
Wheland, G. W. (1955) *Resonance in Organic Chemistry*, New York, Wiley
— Brownell, R. M. and Mayo, E. C. (1948) *J. Amer. chem. Soc.* **70**, 2492
Wilputte-Steinert, L. and Fierens, P. J. C. (1955) *Bull. Soc. chim. Belg.* **64**, 308
Wittek, H. (1942) *Z. phys. Chem.* **B52**, 315
Wolf, K. L. and Trieschmann, H. G. (1934) *ibid* **B27**, 376
Woodward, R. B. (1949) in *The Chemistry of Penicillin*, Ed. H. T. Clarke, J. R. Johnson and R. Robinson, Princeton University Press, pp. 439, 444
Zhdanov, G. S. and Gol'der, G. A. (1955) *Zhur. Fiz. Khim.* **29**, 1248 ; *Chem. Abstr.* (1956) **50**, 7539

5

THE STUDY OF OPTICALLY LABILE COMPOUNDS

M. M. Harris

When the stereochemist prepares a new compound which he considers may be optically active he normally tries to resolve it into its two enantiomeric forms. If it is too unstable optically for resolution* under ordinary conditions, there are still several methods of investigating it which depend upon polarimetry: it is the object of this chapter to describe these methods and, as a cognate matter, to point to the stereochemical significance which may be attached to an observed mutarotation.

The types of molecular architecture which lead to optical instability have been described in a number of past reviews (Ritchie, 1933, 1947; King, 1933; Shriner, Adams and Marvel, 1943; Maitland, 1939; Kenyon, 1942; Mills, 1943; Jamison, 1945; Harris and Turner, 1947; Campbell, 1953) so that this account can proceed straight to a description of the attendant properties. There has been appreciable advance in this field during the last few years.

ASYMMETRIC TRANSFORMATIONS

Asymmetric transformation may be undergone by a substance of which the molecule is capable of optical activity and is also wholly or in part optically labile.

The behaviour of the α- and β-forms of D-glucose, in solution and in crystallizing from it, is the prototype of many of the phenomena of labile optical activity in conjunction with stable optical activity. When Dubrunfaut (1846) first observed the 'birotation' (a word discarded by Lowry in 1899 in favour of 'mutarotation') of glucose solutions he was making an important discovery in sugar chemistry and, as he followed it to the end, he was recording the first example of an asymmetric transformation. There were good reasons why this study did not take its place in the main stream of the earlier stereochemistry of optically labile compounds, notably that the structure of D-glucose was not conclusively proved until the late nineteen-twenties (Haworth), nor was the composition of an equilibrated aqueous solution established until 1940 (Kendrew and Moelwyn-Hughes).

---

* The word *resolution* is used to mean the separation of a racemic compound or mixture into two enantiomers, theoretically 50 per cent of each; it can also be used to describe any part of such a process.

Thus the behaviour of diastereoisomeric salts with one optically labile component, in non-dissociating solvents, was worked out independently of the mutarotation of glucose, and then was found to be obeying similar rules.

In an ideal and complete optical resolution a ($\pm$)-mixture of enantiomers would be separated into 50 per cent of each : in an ideal and complete asymmetric transformation the ($\pm$)-mixture would be converted into one of the isomerides in 100 per cent yield, or the ($+$)- or ($-$)- compound would be converted into the opposite isomeride. Such completion is not in general achieved in an asymmetric transformation in solution, for here an equilibrium is reached in which the free energy difference between the diastereoisomers is not large, but near approach to theoretical yields has often been recorded in asymmetric transformation by crystallization.

These transformations take place in an optically labile compound or group when it comes under the influence of an optically stable, resolved compound or group ; the labile part may be bound to this ' asymmetric influence ' by chemical, ionic or electrostatic bonds, it may be dissolved in it or with it, or the two may form a crystalline adduct. The very simplest category of asymmetric transformation depends upon crystal forces directing the building of a single isomeride on a seed of the same *laevo* or *dextro* pattern.

Asymmetric Transformation by Crystallization

This process, which is often called ' second-order ' asymmetric transformation (*cf* p. 163), is a most useful one for the isolation of optically labile compounds in an optically pure state ; it involves the crystallization of a solid, usually (but by no means always) one of a pair of diastereoisomeric salts, formed of optically labile and optically stable, resolved, component parts :

Crystals	In solution	Crystals
Labile acid		
($+$)A.($-$)B 100% $\xleftarrow{\;a\;}$	($+$)A.($-$)B $\rightleftarrows$ ($-$)A.($-$)B	$\xrightarrow{\;b\;}$ ($-$)A.($-$)B 100%
Labile base		
($+$)B.($-$)A 100% $\xleftarrow{\;a\;}$	($+$)B.($-$)A $\rightleftarrows$ ($-$)B.($-$)A	$\xrightarrow{\;b\;}$ ($-$)B.($-$)A 100%

The crystallization must be carried out under conditions of solvent, temperature and concentration in which the diastereoisomers have a faster rate of partial inversion than of crystallization (Mills and Elliott, 1928; Adams and Gross, 1942; Adams and Sundstrom, 1954). A compound of medium optical stability may undergo such asymmetric transformation at room temperature, faster on heating and negligibly slowly at low temperatures, so that there it is resolvable (Jamison and Turner, 1938; Davidson and Turner, 1945).

Usually only one of the crystallizations (*a*) or (*b*) above can be realised experimentally, but sometimes by the use of alternative solvents (Mills and Bain, 1910; Werner, 1912; Mills and Elliott, 1928; Mills and Breckenridge, 1932) or by appropriate seeding (Meisenheimer and Beisswenger, 1932) it may be possible to get both forms by transformation in either direction. Use of different optically stable components also may allow the separation of both optically labile enantiomers (Thomas, 1921; Stoughton and Adams, 1932; Davidson and Turner, 1945).

If the salts represented by $(\pm)$A.$(-)$B or $(\pm)$B.$(-)$A are completely ionized or otherwise dissociated in solution, then the mother liquor from which crystallization takes place may show no optical activity which can be attributed to the labile acid or base; presumably the condition of diastereoisomerism is absent until the crystal is formed, as in Mills and Breckenridge's work (1932). If, on the other hand, the diastereoisomeric salts are not dissociated or if the asymmetric centres are joined by covalent bonds, then asymmetric transformation controls the composition of the solution. Thus α-D-glucose crystallizes from water (below 35° as α-D-glucose.H_2O) while the solution contains $36\%\alpha$ and $64\%\beta$. D-Mannose (Isbell and Pigman, 1933; Hudson and Yanovsky, 1917), in which the equilibrium is $68\cdot8\%\alpha$ and $31\cdot2\%\beta$, crystallizes from water in the β-form; from a mixture of glacial acetic acid and ethyl alcohol it crystallizes in the α-form. Lactose in water behaves similarly to D-glucose. The ' salt '* brucine 2'-(α-hydroxy*iso*propyl)diphenyl-2-carboxylate, in which the equilibrium proportions in chloroform are $(+)$A.B 58% $(-)$A.B 42%, crystallizes as $(-)$A.B. It will be noted that in all these cases the diastereoisomer which is in smaller proportion in the solution is the one which crystallizes from it, although there seems to be no valid reason why this should be a general rule.

In combination with suitable partners, the following types of optically labile compounds show asymmetric transformation by crystallization as salts:

(i) Substituted diphenyls: Kuhn and Albrecht (1927); Corbellini and Angeletti (1932); Adams *et al.* (1932, 1933, 1943, 1941).

(ii) Related compounds: Meisenheimer and Beisswenger (1932); Hall, Ridgwell and Turner (1954).

(iii) Compounds in which there is restricted rotation about bonds linked to tervalent nitrogen: Mills *et al.* (1928, 1932); Turner *et al.* (1938, 1940, 1955); Adams *et al.* (1950, 1954—two examples, 1956).

---

* The compound formed by dissolving equivalent amounts of a carboxylic acid and a base in chloroform solution is referred to as a salt although it is probably a hydrogen bonded complex or an undissociated ion-pair.

(iv) Similar compound in the antimony series: Campbell (1947).

(v) Other compounds showing restricted rotation in the benzene series: Meisenheimer, Theilacker and Beisswenger (1932); Adams and Gross (1942).

(vi) Compounds owing their optical instability to fugitive formation of a carbon cation (presumably flat) or to keto-enol tautomerism: Pope and Peachey (1900); Leuchs and Wutke (1913); Leuchs (1921); Read and McMath (1925, 1926); Ashley and Shriner (1932); Davidson and Turner (1945).

(vii) Oximino type compounds: Mills and Bain (1910, 1914).

(viii) Coordination complexes: Werner (1912); Thomas (1921).

(ix) Overcrowded molecule: Newman (1947).

As Ritchie (1947) has pointed out, asymmetric transformations of this kind must be of importance in optically selective biosynthesis. For example, the storage of amygdalin, the gentiobioside of (+)-mandelonitrile, and not of *iso*amygdalin, the gentiobioside of (−)-mandelonitrile, may be accounted for by the optical instability of mandelonitrile (Smith, 1931) in conjunction with the greater insolubility of amygdalin in comparison with its diastereoisomer (Krieble, 1912). Kuhn (1936) considered that this is a selective deposition which is not dependent upon enzyme action. The subject has also been discussed by Gause (1941).

Tri-*o*-thymotide (I) (Baker, Gilbert and Ollis; Powell; Newman and Powell; 1952) can exist in enantiomeric conformations related as left- and right-handed three-bladed propellers. The forms are optically labile with an activation energy for racemization, $E_{racem} = 21 \cdot 5^*$ kcal.mole^{-1} in chloroform solution, such stability as they have being due to steric hindrance to interconversion by rotation about single bonds. The compound crystallizes from methyl alcohol as the

I

racemate, but from benzene or from *n*-hexane as a compound of the clathrate type. The unit cell in the latter case is found to hold six molecules of tri-*o*-thymotide and three of *n*-hexane. The tri-*o*-thymotide

* This value is a revision of the originally published one of 16, the calculation of which contained an arithmetical error; the *data* in the paper (Newman and Powell) are correct (personal communication to the writer from Dr. H. M. Powell, 1956).

molecules in one cell are either all *dextro* or all *laevo*, and a single crystal is formed all of one isomer. Although it is not possible to identify the enantiomeric crystals by outward appearance, separation can be achieved by removing a large crystal and testing the optical rotation of a solution of a chip of it. Once a crystal of a single enantiomer is obtained, it can be used to inoculate a solution of tri-*o*-thymotide and it will bring the compound out all in one form, as long as the rate of deposition of crystals is kept slower than the rate of racemization. This might be called a self-induced asymmetric transformation by crystallization. The experimental procedure is very similar to that used by Kipping and Pope (1898) to grow *dextro*rotatory sodium chlorate crystals; in one experiment they grew a *dextro* crystal weighing 17 g. This they chopped up and used to inoculate saturated solutions which then deposited the *dextro* form. Many of the tri-*o*-thymotide adducts show similar behaviour in crystallization.

One group of tri-*o*-thymotide clathrates, crystallizing in the trigonal system, has small, closed asymmetric cavities which may be filled stereospecifically if suitable molecules are available. Powell (1952, 1954) has resolved *sec*-butyl bromide by this means. Tri-*o*-thymotide, itself crystallizing from *sec*-butyl bromide either in the *dextro* or in the *laevo* form, selects one enantiomer from the solvent in order to form the crystal lattice. It would be of great interest to find an optically labile compound which would be the guest molecule in such a crystalline clathrate, but it may be that in order to be optically labile it would have to be too large. The *cyclo*dextrin molecule, which can resolve ethyl mandelate and structurally related esters (Cramer, 1952, 1954) might form a better clathrate for such experiments: mandelic acid and its esters are optically labile under alkaline conditions, so there are interesting possibilities of asymmetric transformation here.

Allylethylmethylphenylammonium iodide crystallizes in the (+)- or the (−)-form only, if care is taken to see that it comes out very slowly indeed, from chloroform with a molecule of the solvent; a single crystal may be grown, a crop being formed all of the same enantio-meride (Havinga, 1941). This depends upon presenting the pattern of one form and giving time for racemization processes (such as MeEtAllylPhN$^+$}I$^- \rightleftarrows$ MeI + EtAllylPhN) to take place in solution. The asymmetric influence is that of the oriented molecules in the crystal on which the solution builds: in such a way must the crystals of *dextro* and *laevo* quartz be laid down, and the sodium chlorate crystals just described, although the constituent molecules themselves are not enantiomorphic.

Among the many interesting optically labile compounds studied by Adams are numerous examples which undergo asymmetric trans-formation: when Adams (1943) says that optically active diphenyls are easy to resolve, he classes together processes of true resolution undergone by salts of the optically stable ones (where the diastereo-isomeric salts often differ markedly in solubility) and of asymmetric transformation. The latter process often led him to obtain an optically pure salt in a single crystallization.

It has lately been discovered that *iso*colchicine (II) exhibits muta-rotation in chloroform solution. Evaporation of such a solution to dryness followed by recrystallization from ethyl acetate yields 99·7 per cent of the original *iso*colchicine which again mutarotates in

chloroform in the same way. Rapoport and Lavigne (1956) have made a thorough study of this interesting case and suggested that in crystalliza-tion only one of a possible pair of diastereoisomers comes out. Since the yield is almost 100 per cent, one of these centres must be labile. The two elements of asymmetry required to explain this behaviour could be provided by the one resolved, optically stable asymmetric carbon atom (C*) and also by restriction of rotation about the bond between rings A and C leading to labile optical activity of the type recognized in bridged diphenyl structures (see later). The original paper should be consulted for further details and discussion.

Examination of stereochemical literature provides numerous cases, new and old, in which asymmetric transformation appears to have been overlooked and a maximum yield of 50 per cent was expected from a crystallization which in favourable circumstances would have provided 100 per cent of one diastereoisomer. For example, 2-(6-methyl-2-nitrophenyl)-3-thenoic acid (III) was dissolved with brucine in a hot ethanol–water mixture (Owen and Nord, 1951) and placed in a refrigerator at $-15°$. About 37 per cent of a crystalline salt was

deposited, $[\alpha]_D^{20}$ changing from $+30\cdot5°$ to $-28\cdot55°$ during 2·5 hours. The salt on decomposition with hydrochloric acid gave an acid $[\alpha]_D^{20}$ $-11\cdot19°$ changing to $0°$ in one hour. Two questions spring to mind: (a) if the solution had been allowed to deposit crystals at room temperature (at which mutarotation takes place) would not the yield of active salt have been larger? ; (b) if the salt had been decomposed much more rapidly would it not have given an acid of larger specific rotation?

Asymmetric Transformation in Solution

Occurrence and Recognition

The distinction between asymmetric transformations in solution and by crystallization may not be a fundamental one in theory, but it is of the utmost importance in practice. It is often not possible to induce a solution of diastereoisomeric substances to deposit crystals, in which case the only means of stereochemical investigation of the labile substance is by observing asymmetric transformation in solution.

This process involves the establishment of an equilibrium between diastereoisomeric pairs, the composition of the equilibrium mixture being different from 50 per cent of each. (It can, of course, occur not only in solution but also in a liquid substance of diastereoisomeric structure, either alone, or under the influence of a suitable catalyst.) Suppose an optically stable, resolved base $(-)B$ (it could be $(+)B$ throughout) is added to one equivalent of a racemic, optically labile acid $(\pm)A$ under conditions which lead to the immediate formation of diastereoisomeric salts (see footnote, p. 159) which are not dissociated in the solvent used. At the moment of addition the quantities of each diastereoisomer will be equal, but, as they have unequal free energies, and A is optically labile, partial inversion will lead to unequal quantities of the two at equilibrium :—

$$(\pm)A + (-)B \longrightarrow \underset{50\%}{(+)A.(-)B} + \underset{50\%}{(-)A.(-)B} \underset{\substack{Asymmetric \\ transformation}}{\longrightarrow} \underset{x\%}{(+)A.(-)B} \rightleftarrows \underset{(100-x)\%}{(-)A.(-)B.}$$

This kind of process has been called ' asymmetric catalytic racemization ', ' optical activation ' or ' first-order asymmetric transformation ' ; the words ' first-order ' are a translation, not altogether fortunate, of ' erster Art ' (Kuhn, 1932; King, 1933; Jamison and Turner, 1942, footnote).

Up to 1947 it seemed that bonding of some formal kind was necessary between the labile and stable centres for the latter to affect the former, but since then it has been shown that an optically active solvent S* can, in certain cases, play a part equivalent to $(-)B$ or $(+)B$:

$$(\pm)A + S^* \longrightarrow \underset{50\%}{(+)A.S^*} + \underset{50\%}{(-)A.S^*} \longrightarrow \underset{x\%}{(+)A.S^*} \rightleftarrows \underset{(100-x)\%}{(-)A.S^*}$$

This must be included as a form of asymmetric transformation.

The only entirely satisfactory way of proving that an observed mutarotation is due to asymmetric transformation is to remove the activating agent and to observe the newly created activity in the labile substance, which may for this purpose be thrown out of solution or extracted by a solvent. The optical activity of the labile substance will then fall to zero according to the first-order kinetic law at a rate dependent upon the solvent in which it is dissolved, the temperature, the concentration, and factors peculiar to itself. Some asymmetric transformations which have yielded active products from an equilibrium mixture will be found in TABLE 1.

When the specific rotation of one of the pure diastereoisomers, $(-)$A.$(-)$B say, is known, then it may be possible to calculate, from the extent of mutarotation starting at $(\pm)$A.$(-)$B, the composition of the equilibrium mixture. The accuracy attainable will depend upon various factors, notably that the rate of mutarotation should not be too fast nor the rate of dissolution of the solid material too slow; also, any calculation assumes that there is no significant dissociation of the diastereoisomeric salts. The calculated equilibrium composition of some systems are included in TABLE 1.

TABLE 2. EQUILIBRIA IN ASYMMETRIC TRANSFORMATIONS BETWEEN COVALENT DIASTEREOISOMERS

Substance	Solvent	Equilibrium composition	
		$(+)$A. ester	$(-)$A. ester
(a) $(-)$-Menthyl $(\pm)$-phenyl-chloroacetate		57%	43%
(b) $(-)$-Menthyl $(\pm)$-phenyl-bromoacetate	EtOH (With a trace of KOH)	47%	53%
(c) $(-)$-Bornyl $(\pm)$-phenyl-chloroacetate		47%	53%
(d) $(-)$-Menthyl $(\pm)$-mandelate		54%	46%
(e) D-Glucose	H_2O	α, 35·8%	β, 64·2%
(f) D-Glucose	MeOH	44·3%	55·7%
(g) D-Glucose	EtOH, 80%	41%	59%
(h) D-Mannose		68·8%	31·2%
(i) D-Lyxose	H_2O	76%	24%
(j) Lactose		36·8%	63·2%

(a), (b), (c) and (d) McKenzie and Smith (1924, 1925); (e) and (f) Andrews and Worley (1927): Isbell and Pigmann (1933): Kendrew and Moelwyn-Hughes (1940); (g) Hudson and Yanovsky (1917); (h), (i) and (j) Isbell and Pigmann (1937), see also Kendrew and Moelwyn-Hughes (1940).

Kacser and Ubblelohde (1950), in an investigation of thermodynamic factors in stereospecific processes, noted that the equilibrium constants K, where they are known, for first-order asymmetric transformations range between 1 (i.e. no stereospecific effect) and 2. This generalization seems to cover most of the equilibria which have been investigated, but not that of $(\pm)$-chlorobromomethanesulphonic acid with $(-)$-hydroxyhydrindamine (see TABLE 1) where K is about 4, nor of the cholesteryl dibromides described below, which are of course stereochemically more complex compounds.

A few examples which involve labile and stable centres within one molecule are listed in TABLE 2; examples (a), (b), (c) and (d) are optically stable in ethyl alcoholic solution until a drop of alcoholic potassium hydroxide is added. Smith (1931) showed that amygdalin, the gentiobioside of (+)-mandelonitrile, behaves similarly to the menthyl phenylchloroacetates (example (a), TABLE 2).

In the sugar series the simple calculation of equilibrium composition from rotation values can be made only for those which exist in two forms, with no significant proportion of a third. The amount of such a third form—for example open chain or furanose ring—in solutions of D-glucose (Andrews and Worley, 1927; Kendrew and Moelwyn-Hughes, 1940; Cantor and Peniston, 1940; Los and Wiesner, 1953), D-xylose, D-mannose or D-lactose is very small indeed. D-Arabinose does not have the simple $\alpha \rightleftarrows \beta$ equilibrium composition, nor do D-ribose, D-galactose and D-talose.

Finally there are cases of shift of equilibrium when an optically labile substance with a single centre of asymmetry is dissolved in an asymmetric solvent (TABLE 3).

TABLE 3. ASYMMETRIC TRANSFORMATIONS IN OPTICALLY ACTIVE SOLVENTS

	Racemic substance	Solvent	Active substance recovered
(a)	Methyl-N-benzoyl-2'-chlorodiphenylamine-2-carboxylate	Ethyl (+)-tartrate	(−)-Compound
(b)	8-Nitro-N-benzenesulphonyl-N-(2-hydroxyethyl)-1-naphthylamine	Ethyl (+)-tartrate	(+)-Compound
(c)	Tris-2-2'-dipyridylnickel chloride	(+)-Tris-ethylenediamine cobalt chloride in H_2O	(−)-Iodide
(d)	Tris-acetylacetone cobalt	(+)-Tris-ethylenediamine cobalt chloride in EtOH aq.	(−)-Compound
		(−) „	(+)-Compound

(a) Buchanan and Graham (1950); (b) Glazer, Harris and Turner (1950); (c) Dwyer (1951); (d) Dwyer (1952).

Structural Factors influencing the Relative Stabilities of Diastereoisomers

It was suggested by W. H. Mills in 1943 that the relative optical stabilities of alkaloidal salts of labile enantiomeric acids could be dependent upon the dipolar attractions between portions of the acid and alkaloid molecules. Since then the study of conformational

TABLE 1. EQUILIBRIA IN ASYMMETRIC TRANSFORMATION OF DIASTEREOISOMERIC SALTS IN NON-DISSOCIATING SOLVENTS

Racemic substance	Activating agent	Solvent	Equilibrium composition		Active substance isolated
a. Bromochloromethanesulphonic acid	(−)-Hydroxyhydrindamine	Acetone	(+)A.B 19%	(−)A.B 81%	
b. N-Benzenesulphonyl-8-nitro-1-naphthylglycine	(i) Cinchonidine (1·0M)	CHCl₃	(+)A.B 38%	(−)A.B 62%	(−)A (in solution)
	(ii) Cinchonidine (0·25M)	CHCl₃/EtOH	(+)A.B predominating		(+)A (in solution)
	(iii) Brucine	CHCl₃	(+)A.B predominating		(+)A (in solution)
c. 2′-(α-Hydroxyisopropyl)diphenyl-2-carboxylic acid	Brucine	CHCl₃	(+)A.B 58%	(−)A.B 42%	
d. 2:5-Dimethoxy-2′-nitrodiphenyl-6′-carboxylic acid	Brucine	EtOH/H₂O	(+)A.B. 53·5%	(−)A.B 46·5%	
e. N-Benzoyl-4:6:6′-tribromodiphenylamine-2-carboxylic acid	Cinchonidine	CHCl₃	(+)A.B 49%	(−)A.B 51%	
f. N-Benzoyl-2′-6-dimethyldiphenylamine-2-carboxylic acid	(i) Cinchonidine	CHCl₃/EtOH	(+)A.B predominating		(+)A (in solution)
	(ii) Quinidine	CHCl₃/EtOH	(−)A.B predominating		(−)A (in solution)
g. N-Benzoyl-4:6-dichlorodiphenylamine-2-carboxylic acid	(i) Cinchonidine (1·0M)	CHCl₃/EtOH	(+)A.B predominating		(+)A solid
	(ii) Cinchonidine (0·5M)	CHCl₃/EtOH	(−)A.B predominating		(−)A solid
h. N-Benzoyl-4:6-dibromodiphenylamine-2-carboxylic acid	Cinchonidine (1·0M)	CHCl₃/EtOH	(+)A.B predominating		(+)A

TABLE 1—*continued*

Racemic substance	Activating agent	Solvent	Equilibrium composition	Active substance isolated
i. 1-Phenylnaphthalene-2′-carboxylic acid	Brucine	$CHCl_3$	(+)A.B predominating	(+)A
j. 1-Phenylnaphthalene-2′:8-dicarboxylic acid	Brucine	$CHCl_3$/EtOH	(+)A.B predominating	(+)A
k. 10-*m*-Aminobenzylideneanthrone	(+)-Camphor-10-sulphonic acid	$CHCl_3$/EtOH	(−)B.A predominating	(−)-Hydriodide
l. *N*-Benzoyl-6-methyldiphenylamine-2-carboxylic acid	Quinidine	$CHCl_3$	(−)A.B predominating	(−)A (in solution)

a, Read and McMath (1925); *b*, Mills and Elliott (1928); Jamison and Turner (1940); *c*, Corbellini and Angeletti (1932); Jamison and Turner (1938); *f* and *h*, Harris, Potter and Turner (1955); *g*, Jamison and Turner (1940); *i* and *j*, Hall, Ridgwell and Turner (1954); *k*, Ingram (1950); *l*, Harris (1955).

analysis has opened a wide field of knowledge which can be applied to the relative stabilities of diastereoisomers, particularly of non-polar compounds (see, for example, Barton and Cookson, 1956). Of a large number of such compounds which might exist in *erythro* (in simple cases *meso*) or *threo* forms, the *erythro* form is found to be the more stable. Assuming that the groups R' and R'' are larger than the group R, the *erythro* form (IV) has a stable, staggered conformation

IV	IV*A*	V
	erythro (*meso*, when R' = R'')	*threo*

(IV*A*) which is energetically preferred over even the most stable conformations (V*A*) of the *threo* isomer (V), all of which involve

V*A*	V*B*	V*C*

greater compressions of the larger groups.

This assertion has been established both by direct equilibration experiments and also by synthesis under conditions which allow equilibration during the formation of the product: the *erythro* form appears in larger quantity.

Barton and Robinson (1954) have made the generalization that the reduction of a keto group to form a new asymmetric centre will give the thermodynamically more stable product if it is carried out in alkaline media; it proceeds by way of a carbanion intermediate. The short-lived carbanion would contain an easily inverted tetrahedral carbon, susceptible to the influence of a stable optically active centre. This generalization covers the cases of reduction of ketones and oximes listed by Cram and Abd Elhafez (1952). Turner and Harris considered in 1948 that asymmetric transformation has a definite role in asymmetric synthesis only if the new asymmetric centre is formed reversibly; in Barton's carbanion-intermediate reductions the new asymmetric centre would be present in the optically unstable carbanion and would be fixed by the subsequent addition of a proton. Additions of Grignard reagents are perhaps another matter. Cram (*ibid*) based his rule of steric control of asymmetric synthesis on the stereochemical

168

result of reactions which he considered to be irreversible and the product composition therefore to be kinetically controlled. Prelog too (1953) assumed a non-reversible Grignard reagent addition to benzoyl-formic esters to account for asymmetric synthesis in this series.

The cholesteryl dibromides provide an interesting case in which the relative stabilities of diastereoisomers influence the position of equilibrium between them (Barton and Miller, 1950; Grob and Winstein, 1952; Barton, 1955). The first product of addition of bromine to cholestene, cholesterol or cholesteryl benzoate is the $5\alpha : 6\beta$ isomer (partial formula VI). This changes to an equilibrium mixture containing excess of the more stable form, VII; the rate of reaction can be followed polarimetrically in various solvents, and closely follows the first-order kinetic law. The mechanism has been shown by Grob and Winstein probably to be intramolecular (see also de la Mare, 1954).

VI (Labile)   VII (Stable)

When R is H, in chloroform, the equilibrium is almost entirely displaced to VII; when R is OH or OBz (cholesterol dibromide or cholesteryl benzoate dibromide) the proportions are roughly one part of VI to four parts of VII.

In changing from VI to VII, the 10-methyl group starts as $a_A a_B$ and becomes $e_A a_B$; the 5-bromine atom changes from $a_A a_B$ to $a_A e_B$; the 6-bromine atom from a to e, all these changes contributing towards the stability of VII. The additional stability afforded to structure VI when R is -OH or OBz is attributed to the conformation of R, which is equatorial in VI and axial in VII. For additional information on interconvertible forms in this field, see Klyne (1954).

The relative stability of the β-form of D-glucose in aqueous solution has been related to the equatorial conformation of the hydroxyl group on the labile carbon atom (Reeves, 1951; cf Klyne, 1954).

Asymmetric Transformations as Reversible First-order Kinetic Processes

The so-called inversion of (−)-menthone (VIII) has been the subject of further kinetic studies which demonstrate that its behaviour fits into the general pattern of asymmetric transformation (Weissberger, 1943).

H_3C- ... a ... b -C_3H_7 $\rightleftharpoons$ H- ... a ... b -C_3H_7
O ... H ... CH$_3$ ... O

VIII (−)-Menthone   IX (+)-*iso*Menthone
(The conformations shown, with the larger *iso*-propyl group equatorial,
are probably the preferred ones)

The molecule has one centre of stable optical activity (*a*) and one of labile (*b*): the labile centre is in the α-position to the CO group, and rearrangement is accompanied by some prototropic change on the other side of this group which does not affect the optical activity. Weissberger confirmed the findings of Tubandt (1905, 1907, 1910) who showed that catalysed mutarotation of (−)-menthone proceeds according to the first-order kinetic law, $dx/dt = kcx - k'c(1-x)$, where *c* is the total concentration of (−)-menthone and (+)-*iso*menthone and *x* and (1−*x*) are the fractions of the isomers present at time *t*. The measured velocity constant k_m is the sum of those for the two partial inversions,

$$k_m = k + k' = \frac{1}{t} \log_e \frac{(\alpha_\infty - \alpha_0)}{(\alpha_\infty - \alpha_t)}$$

where α_0, α_t and α_∞ are the values for the optical rotation of the mixture at the start of the observations, after time *t* and at equilibrium. The composition of the equilibrium mixture of (−)-menthone and (+)-*iso*menthone, has been shown to be identical for all solutions having the same catalyst, concentration, etc. (Read, 1926, 1930), whether the starting material was a menthone of $(\alpha)_D^{20}$ −27·75° or a 'Rechtsmenthon' of $(\alpha)_D^{20}$ + 27·79° or a (+)-*iso*-menthone of $(\alpha)_D^{20}$ +85·6°; the velocity constant for the approach to equilibrium in formic acid was the same in all cases. Tubandt assumed, and Weissberger agrees, that 'Rechtsmenthon', prepared by Beckmann in 1888, is a mixture of (−)-menthone and (+)-*iso*menthone.

The application of the reversed 'unimolecular' law to the equilibration of diastereoisomerides is more remarkable for the wide variety of the examples than for their number. Hudson (1903) showed it for α- or β-lactose in water, Meyer (1908) for α- and β-D-glucose. 'The equation applies alike to the mutarotation of α-D-glucose from +110° to +52°, the mutarotation of the β-form from (+)19° to (+)52°, and to any portion of these changes' (Hudson and Dale, 1917).

Recently Los, Simpson and Wiesner (1956; see also Los and Wiesner, 1953) have determined polarographically at 25° the four velocity coefficients involved when the mutarotation of D-glucose in water is treated according to the equilibrium equation

$$\alpha \underset{k_1'}{\overset{k_1}{\rightleftharpoons}} O \underset{k_2}{\overset{k_2'}{\rightleftharpoons}} \beta$$

where O represents the open chain aldehyde form. The equilibrium concentration of the intermediate free aldehyde was deduced to be 0.0026 ± 0.0002 per cent of the total.

Investigation of cases of optical activation, that is mutarotation observed when a ($\pm$) optically labile acid (or base) is mixed in solution with an optically stable base (or acid) (Read and McMath, 1925; Kuhn and Albrecht, 1927; see also Kharasch *et al.*, 1934; Mills and Elliott, 1928; Pfeiffer and Quehl, 1931; Yuan and Adams, 1932; Stoughton and Adams, 1932; Jamison and Turner, 1938, 1940) led to the demonstration that each is part of the process of equilibration of the diastereoisomeric pair, viewed from the starting point of the ($\pm$) labile material. Thus the salts brucine (+)- and brucine (−)-2′-(α-hydroxy*iso*propyl)diphenyl-2-carboxylic acid undergo mutarotation in chloroform to a larger extent but to the same equilibrium and with the same velocity coefficient as an equimolecular mixture of brucine and the ($\pm$)-acid. Similarly the two salts cinchonidine (+)- and cinchonidine (−)-N-benzoyl-4:6:6′-tribromodiphenyl-amine-2-carboxylate in chloroform solution show mutarotation to the same equilibrium point and with the same velocity coefficient (Jamison and Turner, 1938, 1942). These salts are almost certainly not ionized in solution in chloroform, but are true diastereoisomers of the composition RNH_2,HO_2CR'.

The mutarotations of the diastereoisomeric (−)-menthyl phenyl-chloroacetates follow the same pattern within the limits of the experimental errors involved (McKenzie, 1924, 1925; Turner and Harris, 1947). Grob and Winstein (1952) showed that the mutarotations of $5\alpha:6\beta$-dibromocholestane and of cholesteryl dibromide follow closely the form of reversible first-order reactions. The general rule is that in any one case velocity constants for *partial inversion* are different, but velocity constants for *observed mutarotations* are equal, the latter being the sum of the former two.

Extension of these investigations into the field of optically labile metallic complexes has been attempted using (+)- and (−)-tris-1:10-phenanthrolinenickel iodides (Davies and Dwyer, 1954) dissolved in aqueous ammonium (+)-bromocamphorsulphonate or in aqueous cinchoninium sulphate. The authors set out to show that the rates of racemization of the (+)- and (−)-nickel complexes were different in the presence of an optically stable ion, and they carried out experiments which purported to do this. However, the reactions, observed as mutarotations, finish at an equilibrium which has *not* the composition of the racemic mixture; the relevant overall process is therefore a reversible inversion of which the forward and reverse components are influenced to different degrees by the asymmetry of the environment. The *measured* velocity coefficients would be expected to be equal, if the equilibrium rotation were taken as end-point in

171

the calculation of k. The authors find their measured velocity coefficients different, but they use as their end-rotation a value, separately determined, for the *racemic* iodide in the same solvent. That their logarithmic plots (log α against time) show a drift is therefore not surprising; in fact it confirms the existence of the effect they were seeking. Taken all in all, the authors have demonstrated that a stable, asymmetric ion can influence the rate of inversion of a labile one, but it will be interesting to know whether the behaviour of these solutions would conform to the general pattern for the reversed ' unimolecular ' reaction and so come into line with substantiated asymmetric transformations in solution*. The mechanism of racemization (and inversion) of octahedral complexes containing three chelate groups has been discussed by Nyholm (1954).

Energies of Activation

From time to time the Arrhenius equation, $k = PZe^{-E/RT}$, has been used to calculate a value of E for a process culminating in the establishment of a diastereoisomeric equilibrium. Such calculations often have little value. The two partial inversions, which for simplification may be represented

$$(+)A(-)B \rightarrow (-)A(-)B$$

and

$$(-)A(-)B \rightarrow (+)A(-)B,$$

will in general have different rates (k_+ and k_-) and different activation energies (E_+ and E_-). The measured velocity coefficient obtained from the polarimetric data using the observed infinity reading can be written in the form:

$$k = k_+ + k_- = P_+Z_+e^{-E_+/RT} + P_-Z_-e^{-E_-/RT};$$

use of the simplified expression

$$k = PZe^{-E/RT}$$

could be justified if k_+ were equal to k_- (that is, if the two processes did not involve diastereoisomers, but were straightforward inversions in a non-participating environment, leading to racemization; then E_+ would be equal to E_-). If the diastereoisomers differed greatly in stability, then the difference in k_+ and k_- might be so great as to make the larger of them approximately equal to their sum, and a satisfactory value for the activation energy of the faster process would be obtained. In the case in which k_+/k_- did not vary with temperature, the slope of the line log $k/(1/T)$ would lead to a value of E which was correct for both processes $\{k = k_+[1+(k_-/k_+)]$, where k_-/k_+ is constant; the value of PZ so determined would not be correct$\}$.

* The writer is indebted to Dr. F. P. Dwyer for correspondence on this subject.

It is probable, therefore, that some of the surprisingly low values, recorded for the activation energies of asymmetric transformations, are incorrect because they have been derived, as discussed above, from ' composite ' rate-coefficients. Thus the value of 10·1 kcal.mole^{-1} for the mutarotation of 10-m-aminobenzylideneanthrone $(+)$-camphor-10-sulphonate in chloroform containing 3·25 per cent ethanol (Ingram, 1950) must be incorrect, seeing that the equilibrium composition of the solution varied considerably with temperature. The value of 14·3 kcal.mole^{-1} for the ' inversion ' of menthone (Weissberger, 1943 ; the value quoted in the paper was calculated using Briggsian logarithms) may also be suspect. Kistiakowsky and Smith (1936) suggested that an activation energy of at least 20 kcal.mole^{-1} would be required for resolution, whilst Mills (1943) considered 16 kcal.mole^{-1} to be a lower limit for the observation of unstable optical activity, both in the neighbourhood of room temperature. These opinions depend on the belief that racemizations and mutarotations of the types under consideration will have normal, or smaller than normal, values of the non-exponential term PZ in the Arrhenius equation. This is the general experience for compounds which owe their activity to restricted rotation, as is shown in some of the data summarized by Cagle and Eyring (1951). Some experimental values for related compounds studied recently, are shown in TABLE 4.

On the whole, the Arrhenius parameters bear out the view (*cf* de la Mare, 1954) that these processes usually have values of PZ of *c*. 10^{11} sec^{-1}; those compounds which have particularly low values of E have, of course, very short half-lives at ordinary temperatures. It is only possible to observe optical activity in the substances with low E values because the PZ values are also low ; the low PZ value is probably connected with the necessity for the relative rotation of parts of the molecule to be synchronized before optical inversion can take place.

A recent redetermination of the racemization velocities of 6-nitro-, 4 : 6'-dinitro- and 4 : 6 : 4'-trinitrodiphenic acids (Brooks, Harris and Howlett, 1957) in alkaline solution has led to the interesting result that the *differences* in optical stability (half-lives 28, 91 and 208 min., respectively, at 80°) do not depend upon their activation energies, which all equal 22·6 kcal.mole^{-1}. The differences lie in the PZ values, $10^{10·6}$, $10^{10·1}$, $10^{9·7}$, or, alternatively expressed, in the ΔS^+ values of the absolute reaction rate equation

$$k = \varkappa e \frac{kT}{h} \exp(\Delta S^{\ddagger}/\boldsymbol{R} - E/\boldsymbol{R}T)$$

which are, respectively $-$ 12·2, $-$ 14·7 and $-$ 16·3 e.u.

It should be possible to determine E_+ and E_- for a pair of diastereoisomeric salts ; it has been done for $\alpha \longrightarrow \beta$ and $\beta \longrightarrow \alpha$

Compound	Conditions	E kcal.mole^{-1}	$\log_{10} PZ$	Ref.
	Dioxan Toluene Ethylbenzene	31	13·5*	Hall (1956)
	Ethylbenzene Toluene	31	13·2†	Armarego and Turner (1956)
Tri-o-thymotide	Chloroform	21·4	13·3†	Newman & Powell(1952)
	Chloroform containing 2·5% ethanol	19·3	12·0	Brooks, Harris and Howlett (1957)
	Chloroform containing 6·9% ethanol	16·4	9·7	Potter (1953)
	Chloroform containing 2·5% ethanol	16·2	10·1	Brooks, Harris and Howlett (1957)
		15·7	9·1	
		14·9	8·6	

* Personal communication.   † Calculated from the authors' published data.

D-xylose and for $\alpha \longrightarrow \beta$ and $\beta \longrightarrow \alpha$-D-lactose (for D-glucose the difference between the two values is so slight as to be hardly detectable —Moelwyn-Hughes, 1940). It is necessary for the calculation to measure the optical rotation of (a) one optically pure diastereoisomer (b) the equilibrium mixture and (c) the partial racemate *or* the other diastereoisomer, also optically pure, at each temperature at which k is measured. The measurements (a) and (c) have to be determined by extrapolating back to zero time a logarithmic plot of the muta-rotation, and, unless the salts are instantly soluble in the solvent at that temperature, zero time cannot be stated accurately; error from this source increases as the temperature is lowered and dissolution becomes slower. The extent of mutarotation of the partial racemate in going to equilibrium is usually small and is thus subject to increasing error as the temperature is raised.

Partially Labile Diastereoisomeric Equilibria: Excess of One Component

The effect of adding an excess of optically labile acid, $(\pm)$A, to the equilibrated salts $(+)$A$(-)$B $\rightleftarrows (-)$A$(-)$B in solution has presented a problem for several years. The change in rotation, instantaneous or measurably slow, which usually accompanies addition of $(\pm)$A, has been shown *not* to be due to suppression of dissociation of the salts. The result of adding excess of acid can be so profound that washing out $(-)$B from a solution of one acid : base ratio may give $(+)$A, while from another $(-)$A is recovered (Jamison and Turner, 1938, 1940).

Some progress has been made towards explaining this phenomenon, using as example N-benzoyl-2′ : 4′-dimethyldiphenylamine-2-carbo-xylic acid and cinchonidine (Harris, Potter and Turner, 1955).

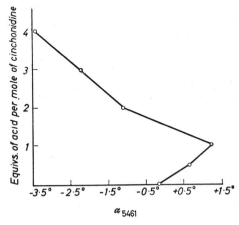

FIGURE 1. Polarimetric measurements

To a solution of cinchonidine (0·1000 g) in bromoform (15 c.c.) were added successive quantities of the $(\pm)$-acid, and the optical rotation was measured after each addition; the results are shown in FIGURE 1.

This is similar to the curves found in chloroform, with this and with some other optically unstable acids, and can be interpreted as showing that, as acid in excess of one equivalent is added, a larger and larger excess of $(-)$A is formed. Side by side with the polarimetric measurements, cryoscopic determinations were made on the same solutions and also on solutions in which naphthalene was added to the cinchonidine salt in bromoform. The results are plotted in FIGURE 2 and show that there is a considerable degree of molecular aggregation in the solutions containing acid and cinchonidine, which does not occur when naphthalene replaces the acid.

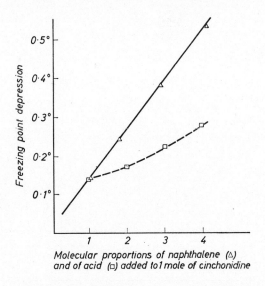

FIGURE 2. Cryoscopic measurements

Without discussing the precise nature of such aggregation and the forces which cause it (see Marryott, 1948) it can be assumed that the molecule of cinchonidine accepts the first equivalent of acid and converts it partially into the *dextro*-isomer. The second molecule of acid which the diastereoisomer then accepts may be influenced in the opposite sense, forming the *laevo*-isomer; this would explain the sharp turn-back of the curve at one equivalent of acid. There are other acids which show not a reversal of direction at this point, but a slope continued in the same sense.

Outside the stereochemical field, association beyond the first acid–base combination has been observed between, for example, myristic acid and tri-*iso*pentylamine in benzene solution by Kaufmann and Singleterry (1952) and between pyridine and trihalogenoacetic acids in chloroform solution by Barrow (1956) together with some other acid–base pairs (see also Bryant and Wardrop, 1957).

Support for the hypothesis that the alkaloid has an influence on more than one equivalent of acid comes from solubility measurements.

10 c.c. of dry chloroform dissolves 0·26 mol. (0·0230 g) of *N*-benzoyl-4′-chlorodiphenylamine-2-carboxylic acid: in the presence of 1·00 mol. of quinine, the same volume of solvent dissolves 2·42 mol. of acid: in the presence of 1·00 mol. of brucine, 1·84 mol. of acid is dissolved.

As a result of reversal of the direction of optical activation by excess of acid, it has been possible to obtain two specimens of acid, (+)- and (−)-rotatory, *without separation of salts*, by decomposition of equilibrated solutions (TABLE 5).

TABLE 5. RESOLUTION OF ACIDS WITHOUT SEPARATION OF SALTS

(±) Acid	Alkaloid		Solvent	Acid obtained free
PhSO₂ CH₂CO₂H NO₂ N (naphthalene ring)	Cinchonidine	1·0M 0·33M 0·25M	CHCl₃ CHCl₃ CHCl₃/EtOH	(−) (±) (+)
Cl Cl (diphenylamine) N CO₂H COPh	Cinchonidine	1·0M 0·5M	CHCl₃ CHCl₃	(+) (−)

Partially Labile Diastereoisomeric Equilibria: Effect of Temperature

It would be surprising if the equilibrium composition of a pair of partially labile diastereoisomers, $(+)A(-)B \rightleftarrows (-)A(-)B$, were not sensitive to change of temperature. The case of D-glucose is probably exceptional: the equilibrium constant

$$K = \frac{k_\alpha}{k_\beta} = \frac{[\beta\text{-D-glucose}]}{[\alpha\text{-D-glucose}]}$$

has been shown to be constant over the range of temperature 0·7°–40° (Hudson and Dale, 1917; Moelwyn-Hughes, 1933); this behaviour is not typical of diastereoisomeric substances.

Certain optically stable simple substances, alone or in solution, show a variation of optical rotation with temperature (Kauzmann, Walter and Eyring, 1940; Hargreaves, 1954) so that if the optical rotation of an equilibrated mixture changes with change of temperature it cannot be said without further proof that the equilibrium composition is changing. However, if the rotation of a solution of a diastereoisomeric mixture is found to change, reversibly, with temperature, the possibility of a shifting equilibrium is worth investigating.

177

The rotation of *N*-benzoyl-6-methyldiphenylamine-2-carboxylic acid (X, optically active and optically labile), and quinidine (1 mol.),

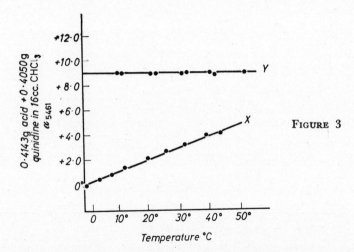

dissolved in chloroform, shows linear variation with temperature between 0° and 50° (FIGURE 3, curve *X*; it will be appreciated that the changes in observed rotation are large). This variation is not shown when the acid is replaced by the optically inactive *N*-benzoyl-diphenylamine-4-carboxylic acid (XI) (FIGURE 3, curve *Y*) (Harris,

FIGURE 3

1955). When solutions of *N*-benzoyl-6-methyl-diphenylamine-2-carboxylic acid and quinidine (1 mol.) are made up at various temperatures and quickly viewed in the polarimeter, mutarotations are observed. Extrapolation to zero time of the logarithmic plot of α against time gives a reading for each solution at the time of mixing. These values (FIGURE 4) show that the rotations of quinidine (±)-*N*-benzoyl-6-methyldiphenyl-amine-2-carboxylate at the moment of mixing are approximately equal at the different temperatures, while at equilibrium the rotations are substantially different. This acid had not previously been obtained in the optically active condition, but decomposition of the equilibrated solutions *A*, *B*, *C*, etc. (FIGURE 5) by shaking with mineral acid gave it in chloroform solution in the *laevo*rotatory form in varying degrees of optical purity. The rotation of these samples decayed to 0°. Also, a solution of the quinidine (±)-acid salt, made up and allowed to stand at 3·5°, when warmed to 21° quickly and then observed in the polarimeter shows mutarotation (FIGURE 6, curve B) towards the same equilibrium value as a solution made up at 21° (FIGURE 6, curve A). Similar phenomena have been observed with the quinidine salts of some other optically labile acids.

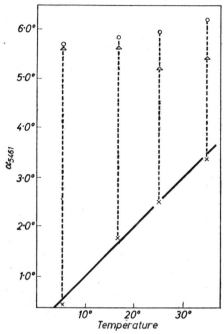

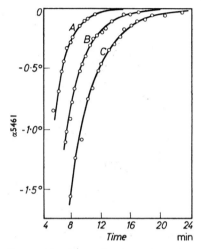

FIGURE 5. Racemization of $(-)$-N-benzoyl-6-methyldiphenylamine-2-carboxylic acid in chloroform at 21°. From asymmetric transformations in solution at (A) 45°, (B) 21°, (C) 0·8°.

FIGURE 4. Asymmetric transformation of N-benzoyl-6-methyldiphenylamine-2-carboxylic acid with quinidine in chloroform at various temperatures.

○ Extrapolated to $t = 0$ × Observed final point   △ Observed first point

FIGURE 7 illustrates the behaviour of the $(+)$-camphor-10-sulphonate of 10-m-aminobenzylideneanthrone (XII) in chloroform solution containing 3·25 per cent of alcohol (Ingram, 1950). The base is optically active as a result of restricted rotation; the degree of hindrance is slight and the base is therefore optically labile. A salt of the $(\pm)$-base with $(+)$-camphor-10-sulphonic acid in chloroform at 30° had immediate $[M_0]_D + 128°$ and, undergoing asymmetric transformation, showed mutarotation to $[M_\infty]_D + 50°$. When this solution was boiled and rapidly cooled to 30° its mutarotation could be observed following the curve B from $[M_0]_D - 55°$ back to the same equilibrium point, $[M_\infty]_D + 50°$ (the half-life periods of these changes are equal). Evidently there is a change in the position of the equilibrium $(+)B(+)A \rightleftarrows (-)B(+)A$ in the *laevo* sense in changing the temperature from 30° to that of boiling chloroform. The range of mutarotation shows that the molecular rotations $[M]_D$ of the 'partial racemate' are nearly independent of temperature, while

179

the equilibrium rotations change with the temperature $(20°*, +135° \to +72°; 30°, +133° \to +50°; 35°, +132° \to +44°)$; it was concluded that the salt of $[M_0]_D$ about 133° was the partial racemate because its rotation lies close to that of pyridine $(+)$-camphor-10-sulphonate.

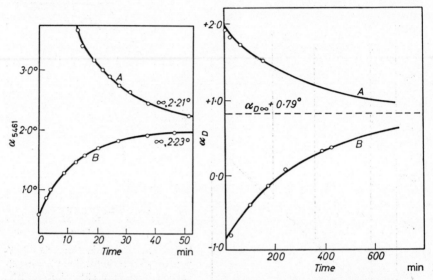

FIGURE 6. *N*-Benzoyl-6-methyldi-phenylamine-2-carboxylic acid with quinidine in chloroform.

A, Asymmetric transformation at 20·2°.

B, Equilibration at 21° of a solution which had been allowed to stand at 3·5°.

FIGURE 7. $(+)$-Camphor-10-sulpho-nate of 10-*m*-aminobenzylidenean-throne in chloroform containing 3·25% of alcohol.

A, Asymmetric transformation at 30°.

B, Equilibration at 30° of a solution which had been heated to boiling and rapidly cooled.

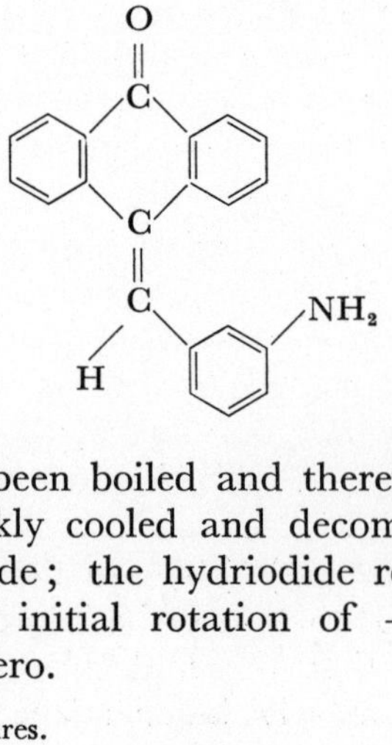

XII

A solution which had been boiled and therefore contained excess of the *laevo* salt was quickly cooled and decomposed by shaking with aqueous potassium iodide; the hydriodide remaining in the chloroform solution had an initial rotation of $-187°$, and underwent mutarotation towards zero.

---

* Temperatures in italic figures.

180

The quinine salt of diphenic acid has an unusually high temperature coefficient of rotation (Lesslie, Turner and Winton, 1941) in chloroform containing ethyl alcohol. Kharasch, Senior, Stanger and Chenicek (1934) have pointed out the dangers of drawing conclusions from the optical rotations of quinine salts, but as diphenic acid mixed with (+)-nor-ψ-ephedrine shows mutarotation at $-30°$, it seems possible that the changes of rotation with temperature are, at least in part, indicative of a shifting equilibrium.

Grob and Winstein (1952) calculated from mutarotation data that the equilibrium constant for the 5 : 6-dibromocholestanes ($[5\beta : 6\alpha]/[5\alpha : 6\beta] = K$) in carbon tetrachloride solution changed from greater than 100 to 27·6 between temperatures 39·98° and 75·05°.

The possibility of using this temperature dependence of equilibrium composition between diastereoisomers to demonstrate new optical activity is very attractive, especially as it would increase the range of optical stability over which polarimetric observations could be made. The phenomenon needs much more thorough investigation before it can be claimed to be diagnostic of optical activity, but it can be reported here that three very interesting acids (recently studied in the laboratories of Bedford College) show a large variation of optical rotation with temperature when observed as their quinidine salts in chloroform solution : 9 : 10-dihydrophenanthrene-2-carboxylic acid

XIII   XIV   XV

(XIII)* might show optical activity on account of a screw arrangement of the bridged diphenyl structure ; Meisenheimer (1924) failed to resolve XIV in which R = CH_3 ; XV is a less hindered triphenylamine. Neglecting the fact that the nitrogen valencies may be pyramidal, the two opposing forces operating about the pivot bonds in XIV and XV are (a) that due to mesomerism involving the nitrogen lone pair and tending to flatness and (b) steric repulsion of the o-atoms or groups. Model requirements show that the molecules cannot be flat, and the possibility arises that they can be arranged as left- or right-handed three-bladed screws (see also Chapters 2 and 6). Simple restricted rotation in absence of the preferred screw conformations could not account for optical activity, however transient, of XV.

* (XIII) D. M. Hall, M. M. Harris and E. E. Turner; (XIV) M. M. Harris; (XV) M. M. Harris and J. W. Brooks (all unpublished).

Asymmetric Environment: Optically Labile Compounds in Asymmetric Solvents

In 1940 Buchanan and Patterson published their finding that the molecular solution volumes of *iso*butyl (+)-tartrate and of *iso*butyl (−)-tartrate are different in (−)-menthyl acetate solution. The difference was only very slight but it was claimed to be outside the experimental error. Ethyl (−)-diacetyltartrate similarly has a larger molecular solution volume than ethyl (+)-diacetyltartrate in the same solvent. This was the first concrete evidence that an asymmetric solvent could behave in any way differently towards two enantiomorphic molecules dissolved in it, apart from the work of McKenzie (1915, 1922, 1923) which will be referred to a little later.

Only recently has ample evidence been gathered of the differences, produced by asymmetric solvents, on the properties, including the solubilities, of optically labile solutes. Buchanan and Graham (1950) found that several optically labile compounds (XVI to XIX for

example) could be obtained with a small optical activity by dissolving the (±)-form in an optically active solvent and crystallizing or precipitating part of it. Successful solvents were ethyl (+)-tartrate and ethyl (−)-tartrate, (−)-menthyl acetate and (+)*sec.*-butyl alcohol; (+)- and (−)-*sec.*-octyl alcohols gave no separation of enantiomorphs. This work established the fact that an asymmetric solvent can affect the composition of an enantiomorphic mixture which is crystallizing or being precipitated from it. It is often difficult to say whether or not the processes are asymmetric transformations since the proportion of total material recovered in a single operation is too small: the observed activity might be due to resolution or to partial precipitation of one form. However, in one case, methyl *N*-benzoyl-2-chlorodiphenylamine-2′-carboxylate, a 95·5 per cent recovered sample showed a rotation α^{19} of −0·10° in chloroform solution.

Nearly quantitative recovery of activated material was achieved (Glazer, Harris and Turner, 1950) in the case of ($\pm$)-methyl N-benzoyl-2′-chloro-6-methyldiphenylamine-2-carboxylate which was dissolved in ethyl (+)-tartrate at 80°, cooled to 25° and left for 30 minutes: precipitation by water gave 98 per cent of the ester, $[\alpha]_{5461}^{25}$ −3·4° in chloroform 2·5 minutes after dissolving. The half-life period of racemization was 9 minutes.

In another experiment, N-benzenesulphonyl-N-(2-hydroxyethyl)-8-nitro-1-naphthylamine (XX) was dissolved in ethyl (+)-tartrate at

XX

$$PhSO_2 \quad CH_2 \cdot CH_2OH$$
$$NO_2 \; N$$

80° and kept at 25° for 2 hours. Addition of excess water led to recovery of 88·5 per cent of the alcohol, $[\alpha]_{5780}^{25°}$ +9·1° in chloroform 2·5 minutes after wetting with solvent, half-life period 27 minutes: the actual observed angle here, α_{5780}, was +0·91°.

These three experiments all indicate that the equilibrium concentrations of (+)enantiomer and (−)enantiomer are displaced from equality in the asymmetric solvents; the effect of the asymmetric solvent seems to be very slight in comparison with that of other modes of connection between a labile centre and an asymmetric influence. Nevertheless, although the observed rotations of the activated materials are small, there is little doubt of their significance, because they decay to zero when left to stand: this test eliminates errors which might be due either to temperature differences or to incomplete removal of the asymmetric solvent. In assessing the value of results which depend upon the crystallization of a specimen which proves to have a small rotation, it is as well to remember the work of Kipping and Pope (1898) who found, on crystallizing sodium chlorate from water, that while the average incidence of *dextro-* and *laevo-* crystals in 46 experiments was 50·08 ±0·11 per cent, the percentage of *dextro*-rotatory crystals in separate experiments varied from 24·14 per cent to 77·36 per cent. Crystallization experiments should therefore be repeatable before they are claimed to be due to more than chance.

Asymmetric Environment: Optically Labile Metal Complexes

The experiments in organic solvents just described could be interpreted on the assumption of an association, possibly by hydrogen bonding, between the solvent and the solute, giving a condition of diastereo-isomerism: such a condition was previously thought necessary in order that the optically stable substance might activate the optically labile one. Dwyer and his collaborators have approached the problem of asymmetric environment from a completely different angle, studying optically labile metal coordination compounds of the type which had already provoked stereochemical interest, on account of their optical lability, in the hands of Werner (1912) and of Pfeiffer (1931, 1932, 1933). The 'solvents' used were dilute aqueous solutions containing optically stable ions; solvent–solute association of any formal kind seems therefore improbable. The results were discussed by Dwyer according to the concept of ' *configurational activity* ' (Dwyer *et al.*, 1951, 1954).

The solubilities of (+)- and (−)-tris-1 : 10-phenanthroline-ruthenium(II) perchlorate (Dwyer and Gyarfas, 1949) have been determined at 25° in ammonium (+)-bromocamphorsulphonate solutions of varying concentrations up to 2 per cent; the curves were found to diverge, the maximum difference of solubility, about 3–3½ per cent, occurring at a concentration of approximately 1–1½ per cent; after that the curves began to converge, the solubility differences diminishing as the ionic strengths became greater.

Analogous results were obtained using aqueous potassium (+)-tartrate solutions as the ' solvent ', only here the (−)-isomeride of the solute was the more soluble. One is reminded a little of Lowry (1904) and of Hudson (1917) using the solubilities of the α- and β-forms of certain sugars to predict their equilibrium compositions in the solvents used.

The solubilities of enantiomeric salts (+)A.X and (−)A.X are of course equal in ordinary solvents, and therefore in saturated solutions their thermodynamic activities are equal. The implication of the above experiment is that the addition of a stable optically active anion or cation to such a solution depresses the thermodynamic activities to different extents, making them unequal; this can lead to the phenomenon of asymmetric transformation.

For example, the tris-2 : 2′-dipyridylnickel(II) ion was already known to be optically labile in solution in the form of its iodide (half-life period, 15 minutes at 17°; Morgan and Burstall, 1931) and to behave as if it were undergoing asymmetric transformation in presence of the (+)-camphorsulphonate ion or of the (+)-α-bromocamphor-π-sulphonate ion in aqueous solution (Pfeiffer and Nakatsuka, 1933). When the racemic chloride was dissolved in ammonium (+)-bromo-camphorsulphonate solution (1½ per cent) and immediately precipitated in fractions by adding sodium iodide, the first fractions were *dextro*-rotatory and the latter were *laevo*-rotatory. If the solution was left for a day at 20°, during which time its rotation became more negative, and then precipitated similarly, the first fractions were optically inactive and the final were *laevo*-rotatory. This shows that at the moment of mixing the activity of the (−)-ion was less than that of the (+)-ion and therefore, the concentrations being equal, the

(+)-ion was precipitated first: in the sample which had been left for a day the activities became equal, the concentration of the (−)-ion increasing. Precipitation then brought out racemate first (activities of (+)- and (−)-ions being equal) and the excess of (−)-ion at the end. This is convincing evidence in favour of asymmetric transformation. Quinine bisulphate and (+)-trisethylenediaminecobalt(III) also worked as activating agents for this ion. Pfeiffer's results can be described satisfactorily in these terms: the absence of observable optical activity on precipitation in his cases could well be due to very low optical stability.

Following on this work, Dwyer and Gyarfas (1951) have demonstrated asymmetric transformation in a solution of a non-electrolyte, trisacetylacetonecobalt(III) (XXI), using (+) or (−)-trisethylenediaminecobalt(III) (XXII) in aqueous alcohol as activating agent. There could hardly be any direct chemical combination here between the optically active compound and the activating agent.

XXI   XXII

The experiments described above give support to the conclusions, reached in other cases (Pfeiffer and Quehl, 1931; Pfeiffer and Nakatsuka, 1933; Brandt, Dwyer and Gyarfas, 1954) that asymmetric transformations were involved when a substantial increase in optical activity follows the addition of a racemic metal complex to a resolved optically active material in solution.

It is not easy to decide how the asymmetric 'solvents', solutions containing a few per cent of (+)-bromocamphorsulphonate anion or cinchoninium cation, can exert the 'diastereoisomeric' effect upon the solubility or the rate of inversion of dissolved cations. The formally uncharged trisacetylacetonecobalt complex can be influenced by cation or anion equally. Dwyer and his co-workers have expressed the view that the configurational activity effect is due to the large asymmetric electric fields of the large complex ions. Even trisacetylacetonecobalt(III), on account of its structure, may be expected to carry a slight negative charge asymmetrically distributed over its outer surface.

Bailar and Das Sarma (1955) have accomplished the optical activation of cis-dichlorotriethylenetetraminecobalt(III) chloride using (+)-antimonyl tartrate ions: the mechanism of this transformation is not yet clear.

Dwyer's precipitation experiments, particularly those which he carried out *before* allowing asymmetric transformation to take place, have something in common with observations by McKenzie and his collaborators (1915, 1922, 1923) on optically stable substances. In these, when $(-)$-malic acid was added to aqueous potassium racemate solution, a *dextro*-rotatory product of a mixture of potassium hydrogen racemate and potassium hydrogen $(+)$-tartrate crystallized. Similarly, crystallization of the potassium hydrogen racemate from aqueous $(-)$-malic acid solution gave potassium hydrogen $(+)$-tartrate mixed with potassium hydrogen racemate. Fifteen other optically active acids were tried in place of $(-)$-malic acid and failed to give its asymmetric effect, but $(+)$-malic acid gave an analogous result in the opposite sense.

OPTICAL STABILITY AND RESTRICTED ROTATION

The factors which influence the optical stability of compounds which owe their activity to restricted rotation about single bonds are still imperfectly understood, although since 1933, when Adams based his stability series on ' interference values ', other influences have been recognized.

Formulae XXIII, XXIV and XXV each represent a pair of stereo-isomers which are interconvertible* by passing through a symmetrical (effectively planar) transition state. Two main opposing factors determine the optical stability : (i) conjugation across the pivot bond *a* tending to bring bonds *a*, *b* and *c* into a plane, leading to optical instability ; (ii) repulsive forces due to size or polar character opposing rotation about the pivot bond and hence tending to optical stability.

XXIII   XXIV   XXV

Among many examples Adams (1942, 1948, 1950, 1956, 1957) has shown that the molecule (XXIII) is much less stable when R is Cl than

---

* It is arguable whether pairs of enantiomorphs of this type should be described as differing in conformation or in configuration. They may be interconvertible without breaking bonds, in which case conformation is obviously the suitable term. If they are so highly hindered that only rupture of the molecule could lead to formation of the mirror image, then configuration seems the better word. However, a change of nomenclature for a property as it differs in degree is hardly satisfactory. Nevertheless, the term configuration has long been in use to describe two substituted diphenyls, related as object and mirror image. This may be a point of nomenclature which is better settled by usage than by definition. Braude and Timmons (1956) have suggested an arbitrary distinction.

when R is H, establishing thus that an electron-attracting group in ring *A* favours the ' passing position ' about bond *a*. Buchanan and Graham (1950) have come to similar conclusions in the series (XXIV). Harris, Potter and Turner (1955) have shown that electron-attracting groups (such as halogen) in ring *B* of molecule (XXV) make the molecule *more* stable optically whereas electron-repelling groups (such as methyl) lower the optical stability. Substituents in ring *B* evidently affect the availability of electrons for conjugation with ring *A*. (The arrangement of the N*abc* structure as a low pyramid is neglected for simplicity in this description.)

XXVI   XXVII

p-Carboxyphenyl-2-diphenylphenylstibine (XXVI) has been resolved (Campbell, 1955) and found to be optically stable, even in boiling xylene : Campbell contrasts this stability with Meisenheimer's inability to obtain evidence of resolution in *N*-α-naphthyl-*N*-phenylanthranilic acid (XXVII). It is suggested that the optical stability of the stibine may be due to the fact that greater energy is required to flatten the pyramidal molecule in this than in the nitrogen case (see also Chapter 6).

XXVIII   XXIX   XXX

XXXI   XXXII

The amount of conjugation (spectroscopically assessed) between the two coaxial rings of *ortho*-bridged diphenyls (XXVIII to XXXII, in some cases with *o*- or *m*-substituents) has been discussed in relation to the angle between the planes of the rings (estimated from scale models) by Beaven, Hall and Turner and their colleagues (1952, 1954, 1955, 1956). Braude (1955) has applied the empirical relationship $\cos^2\theta = \varepsilon/\varepsilon_0$ (Braude and Sondheimer, 1955) to some of these compounds, where θ is the mean interplanar angle in the ground state, and ε and ε_0 are the molecular extinction coefficients for the absorption resulting from inter-nuclear mesomerism in the compound and in fluorene respectively; this expression is perhaps too simple for its use to be warranted, and, in any case, fluorene differs from the other bridged diphenyls studied in that its rings are not collinear (Brown and Bartner, 1954; Burns and Iball, 1954).

' Bridging ' appears to lessen optical stability in some sulphur compounds studied by Armarego and Turner (1956, 1957). Whereas molecules XXXIII*A*, *B* and *C* are not racemized under the most stringent conditions tried, XXXIV in which the sulphur atoms— which must make the greatest contribution to the steric hindrance —are bonded, can be racemized in boiling toluene or ethylbenzene $(E = 31 \text{ kcal.mole}^{-1})$.

XXXIII*A*   XXXIII*B*   XXXIII*C*

XXXIV

Hall and Turner (1955) have drawn attention to the considerable increase in optical stability that occurs when the bridging ring in a 2 : 2′-diphenyl system is enlarged from six to seven atoms. 2 : 7-Dihydro-4′ : 1″-dimethoxy-3 : 4-5 : 6-dibenzazepinium-1-*spiro*-1‴-piperidinium iodide and 2 : 7 - dihydrodinaphtho - (2′ : 1′-3 : 4)(1″ : 2″-5 : 6)aze-pinium-1-*spiro*-1‴-piperidinium bromide (XXXV) are much more stable optically than 9 : 10-dihydro-3 : 4-5 : 6-dibenzophenanthrene (TABLE 4, first formula); this difference cannot be due to steric interference, for this is identical in the latter two compounds, but must reflect the greater distortion required to enable the seven-membered ring to pass through the transition state of optical inversion. The preparation of 1 : 1-di(ethoxycarbonyl)-3 : 4-5 : 6-dibenzo*cyclo*hepta-3 : 5-diene (XXXVI) in an optically active form by Iffland and Siegel (1956) lends strong support to this view; this compound has no sterically interfering groups in the two *o*-positions of the diphenyl skeleton which are not involved in the bridge.

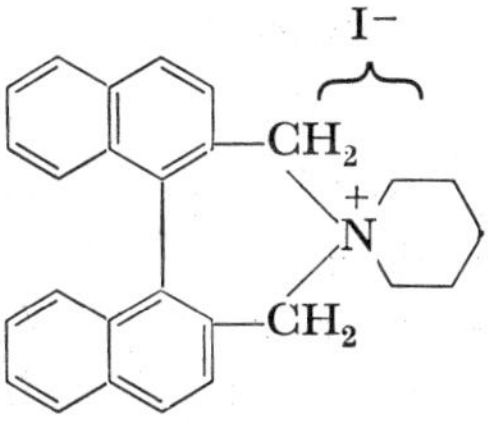

XXXV 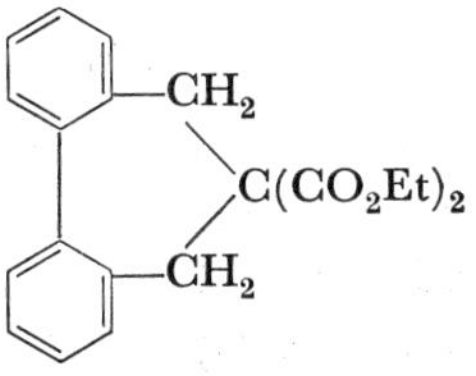   XXXVI

Steric hindrance in the symmetrical transition state can presumably be relieved to some extent by bond bending *in* the plane of the attached ring (a movement in the opposite direction to that forced by buttressing) or by bending *out* of the plane of the attached ring. Presumably the methyl group bonds are bent out in the normal structures of the optically active molecules XXXVII (M. S. Newman and Hussey, 1947) and XXXVIII (M. S. Newman and Wise, 1956).

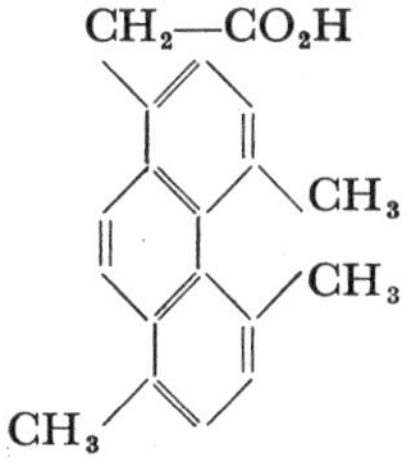

XXXVII 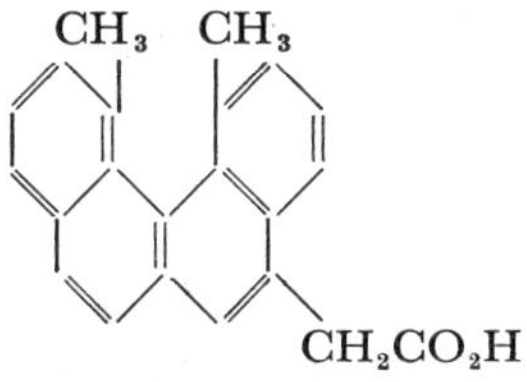   XXXVIII 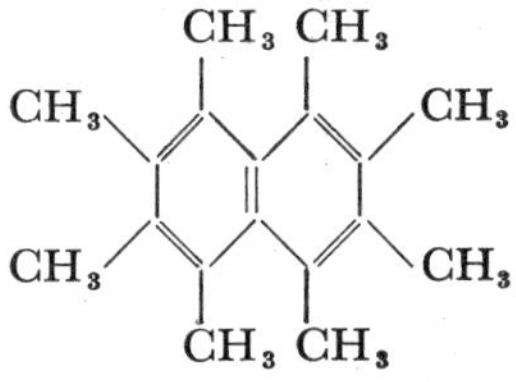   XXXIX

Donaldson and Robertson (1953) have shown that in the octamethyl naphthalene (XXXIX) the α-methyl groups are displaced 0·73 Å and the β-methyl groups 0·25 ±0·4 Å in the opposite direction out of the main plane: the naphthalene nucleus is also possibly distorted to a smaller extent (*cf* Speakman, Chapter 1). The degree of contortion which an aromatic framework may tolerate can be illustrated by considering the molecule XL; this was resolved by M. S. Newman, Lutz and Lednicer (1955), and is a helical structure in which the non-bonded carbon atoms at the ends of the helix lie over each other (Fitts and Kirkwood, 1955, taking the distance between these carbon atoms as 3·80 Å, calculated $[\alpha]_D$ as $-3640°$, a good agreement with the measured $[\alpha]_D$ $-3010°$). McIntosh, Robertson and Vand (1952)

189

by x-ray crystallography, found a distance of 3·0 Å between the nearest non-bonded carbon atoms in 3 : 4 - 5 : 6-dibenzphenanthrene (XLI) which implies a degree of twist brought about by carbon and hydrogen repulsion. Such a force must be operative, although with

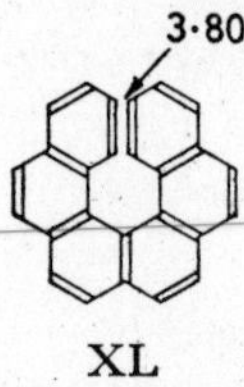

3·80Å

XL 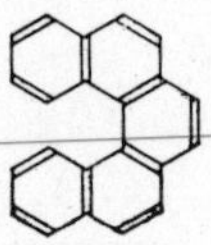   XLI

freedom from the aromatic bridge across the 9 : 10 positions (numbering as in the dibenzphenanthrene), in members of the diquinolyl, di-*iso*-quinolyl and dinaphthyl series. Crawford and Smyth (1952, 1954a) quoted the following order of stabilities for diquinolyls and di-*iso*-quinolyls :

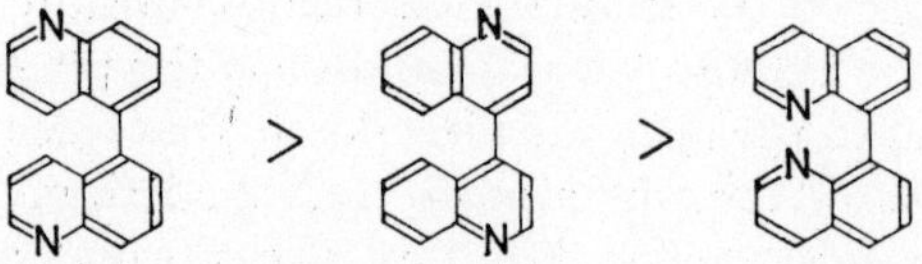

XLII   >   XLIII   >   XLIV

(XLIV was found inactive by Bell and Morgan, 1950)

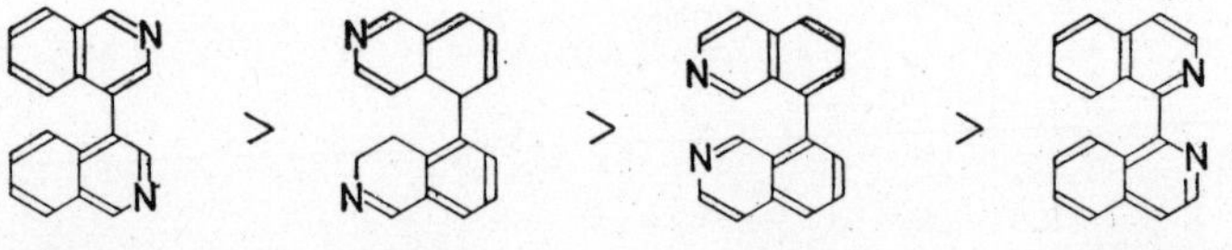

XLV   >   XLVI   >   XLVII   >   XLVIII

(These drawings show one of the two possible passing positions). One regularity in the results is that replacement of CH by N in a blocking position leads to a lessening of optical stability.

Ten structurally related acids (with one ester included) were placed in order of optical stability by Hall, Ridgwell and Turner (1954) (XLIX, most stable—LVII and LVIII, no optical activity). LVII and LVIII showed no response to any of the tests for optical activity attempted. An interesting point is that acid XLIX is very stable optically in sodium hydroxide solution, whereas acid LIII is extremely unstable in the same circumstances; it would be expected that, in alkali, the carboxylate ion groups would repel each other and the passing positions alternative to the ones shown would be used. Scale models show identical interference in these two, but the degree of flexibility of the bonds may well be different.

190

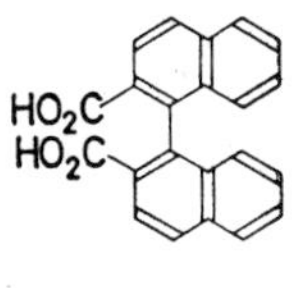

XLIX    L 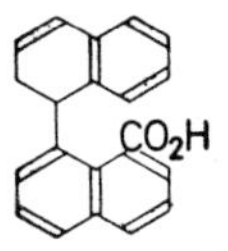   LI 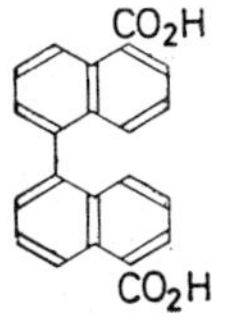   LII

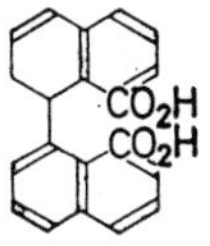

LIII 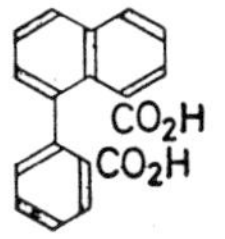   LIV 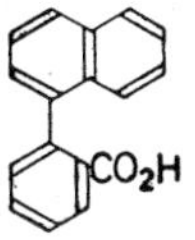   LV 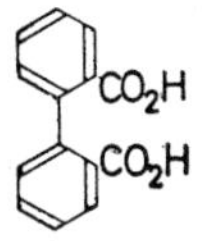   LVI

Baddeley (1946) proposed a special type of structural influence for the inversion of substituted diphenyls. Discussing figures given by Adams and his co-workers (1939) showing that LIX, LX and LXI are in increasing order of stability, and LXII, LXIII and LXIV similarly, he suggested that out-of-plane bending, depending for its

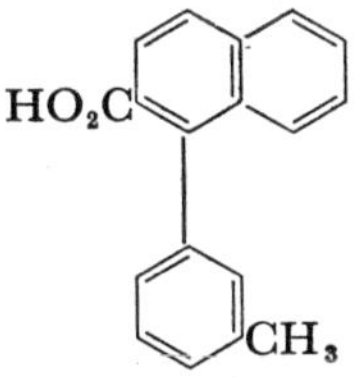

LVII 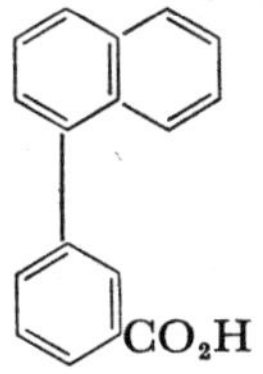   LVIII

operation on electron availability to make C^- at the junction (LXV), was an adjustment which could lower the energy required for racemization. The electron densities in the upper rings of all these compounds are in the same order as the rates of racemization. Crawford and Smyth (1954) considered that an electrophilic attack

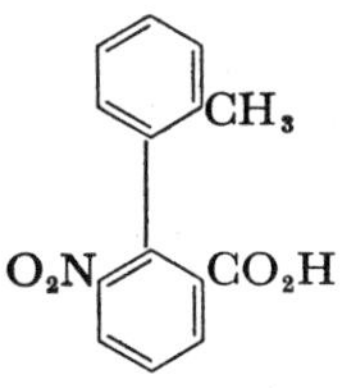

LIX 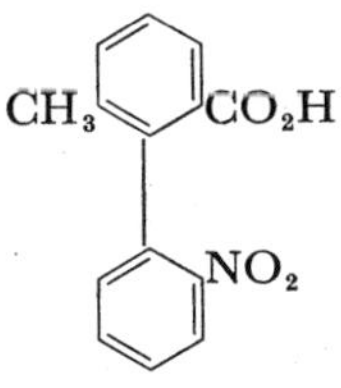   LX 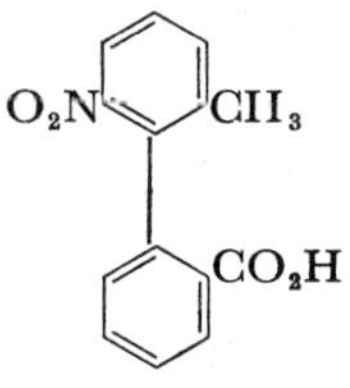   LXI

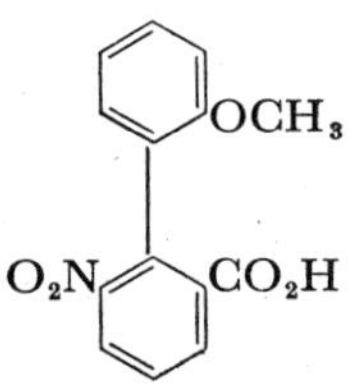

LXII 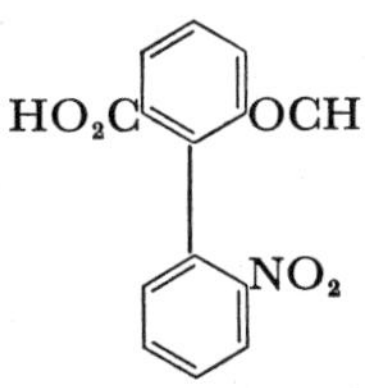   LXIII 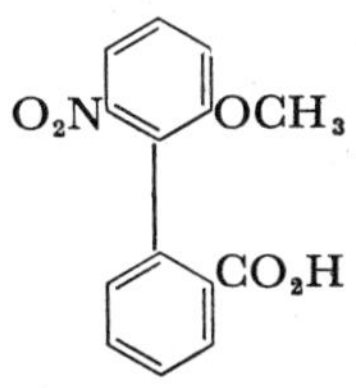   LXIV

191

by hydrogen might develop an intermediate complex, resembling that proposed for aromatic substitution, and favourable to optical inversion (LXVI). These two proposals have not found general acceptance.

LXV   LXVI

REFERENCES

Adams, R. and Albert, A. A. (1942) *J. Amer. chem. Soc.* **64**, 1475
— Blomstrom, D. C. and Sundstrom, K. V. Y. (1954) *ibid* **76**, 5478
— and Brower, K. R. (1956) *ibid* **78**, 663
— and Finger, G. C. (1939) *ibid* **61**, 2828
— and Gibbs, H. H. (1957) *ibid* **79**, 170
— and Gordon, J. R. (1950) *ibid* **72**, 2454, 2458
— and Gross, W. J. (1942) *ibid* **64**, 1786
— and Hale, J. B. (1939) *ibid* **61**, 2825
— and Kornblum, N. (1941) *ibid* **63**, 188
— and Sundholm, N. K. (1948) *ibid* **70**, 2667
— and Sundstrom, K. V. Y. (1954) *ibid* **76**, 5474
— and Yuan, H. C. (1933) *Chem. Rev.* **12**, 261
Andrews, J. C. and Worley, F. P. (1927) *J. phys. Chem.* **31**, 1880
Armarego, W. L. F. and Turner, E. E. (1956) *J. chem. Soc.* 3668 ; (1957) *ibid* 13
Ashley, W. C. and Shriner, R. L. (1932) *J. Amer. chem. Soc.* **54**, 4410
Baddeley, G. (1946) *Nature, Lond.* **157**, 694
Bailar, J. C., jr. and Sarma, B. (1955) *J. Amer. chem. Soc.* **77**, 5480
Baker, W., Gilbert, B. and Ollis, W. D. (1952) *J. chem. Soc.* 1443
Barrow, G. M. (1956) *J. Amer. chem. Soc.* **78**, 5802
Barton, D. H. R. (1955) *Experientia*, Suppl. **2**, 121
— and Cookson, R. C. (1956) *Quart. Rev. chem. Soc., Lond.* **10**, 44
— and Miller, E. (1950) *J. Amer. chem. Soc.* **72**, 1066
— and Robinson, C. H. (1954) *J. chem. Soc.* 3045
Beaven, G. H., Bird, G. R., Hall, D. M., Johnson, E. A., Ladbury, J. E., Lesslie, M. S. and Turner, E. E. (1955) *ibid* 2708
— and Hall, D. M. (1956) *ibid* 4637
— — Lesslie, M. S. and Turner, E. E. (1952) *ibid* 854
— — — — and Bird, G. R. (1954) *ibid* 131
Beckmann, E. (1888) *Liebigs Ann.* **250**, 322
Bell, F. and Morgan, W. H. D. (1950) *J. chem. Soc.* 1963
Brandt, W. W., Dwyer, F. P. and Gyarfas, E. C. (1954) *Chem. Rev.* **54**, 959
Braude, E. A. (1955) *Experientia* **11**, 457
— and Forbes, W. F. (1955) *J. chem. Soc.* 3776
— and Sondheimer, F. (1955) *ibid* 3754
— and Timmons, C. J. (1956) *ibid* 3766
Brooks, J. W., Harris, M. M. and Howlett, K. E. (1957) *ibid* 1934, 2380
Brown, G. M. and Bartner, M. H. (1954) *Acta. cryst., Camb.* **7**, 139
Bryant, P. J. R. and Wardrop, A. W. H. (1957) *J. chem. Soc.* 895
Buchanan, G. and Graham, S. H. (1950) *ibid* 500

Burns, D. M. and Iball, J. (1954) *Nature, Lond.* **173,** 635
Cagle, H. W. and Eyring, H. (1951) *J. Amer. chem. Soc.* **73,** 5628
Campbell, I. G. M. (1947) *J. chem. Soc.* 4; (1953) *Annu. Rep. Progr. Chem.* 152; (1955) *J. chem. Soc.* 3116
Cantor, S. M. and Peniston, Q. P. (1940) *J. Amer. chem. Soc.* **62,** 2113
Chien, S. L. and Adams, R. (1934) *ibid* **56,** 1787
Corbellini, A. and Angeletti, A. (1932) *R.C. Atti. Accad. Lincei* **15,** 639
Cram, D. J. and Fathy Ahmed Abd Elhafez (1952) *J. Amer. chem. Soc.* **74,** 5828
Cramer, F. (1952) *Angew. Chem.* **64,** 136; (1954) *Einschlussverbindungen,* Berlin, Springer
Crawford, M. and Smyth, I. F. B. (1952) *J. chem. Soc.* 4133; (1954a) *ibid* 3464; (1954b) *Chem. & Ind.* 346
Davidson, E. M. and Turner, E. E. (1945) *J. chem. Soc.* 843
Davies, N. R. and Dwyer, F. P. (1954) *Trans. Faraday Soc.* **50,** 24
de la Mare, P. B. D. (1954) *Progress in Stereochemistry,* Vol. 1, London, Butterworths
Donaldson, D. M. and Robertson, J. M. (1953) *J. chem. Soc.* 17
Dubrunfaut, A. P. (1846) *C.R. Acad. Sci., Paris* **23,** 38
Dwyer, F. P. and Gyarfas, E. C. (1949) *J. roy. Soc. N.S.W.* **83,** 170; (1951) *Nature, Lond.* **168,** 29
—— —— and O'Dwyer, M. R. (1951) *ibid* **167,** 1036
Eisenlohr, F. and Meier, G. (1938) *Ber. dtsch. chem. Ges.* **71,** 997
Fitts, D. D. and Kirkwood, J. G. (1955) *J. Amer. chem. Soc.* **77,** 4940
Gause, G. F. (1941) *Optical Activity and Living Matter,* Biodynamica Normandy (Missouri)
Glazer, J., Harris, M. M. and Turner, E. E. (1950) *J. chem. Soc.* 1753
Grob, C. A. and Winstein, S. (1952) *Helv. chim. acta* **35,** 782
Hall, D. M. (1956) *J. chem. Soc.* 3674
—— Ridgwell, S. and Turner, E. E. (1954) *ibid* 2498
—— and Turner, E. E. (1955) *ibid* 1242
Hargreaves, M. K. (1954) *ibid* 1781
Harris, M. M. (1955) *J. chem. Soc.* 4152
—— Potter, W. G. and Turner, E. E. (1955) *ibid* 145
Havinga, E. (1941) *Chem. Weekbl.* **38,** 642
Haworth, W. N. (1929) *The Constitution of the Sugars,* London, Arnold
Hudson, C. S. (1903) *Z. phys. Chem.* **44,** 487
—— and Dale, J. K. (1917) *J. Amer. chem. Soc.* **39,** 320
—— and Yanovsky, E. (1917) *ibid* **39,** 1013
Iffland, H. and Siegel, D. C. (1956) *J. org. Chem.* **21,** 1056
Ingram, V. M. (1950) *J. chem. Soc.* 2318
Isbell, H. S. and Pigman, W. (1933) *J. Res. nat. Bur. Stand.* **10,** 337; (1937) *ibid* **18,** 141
Jamison, M. M. (1945) *Trans. Faraday Soc.* **41,** 696
—— and Turner, E. E. (1938) *J. chem. Soc.* 1646; (1940) *ibid* 264; (1942) *ibid* 437
Kacser, H. and Ubbelohde, A. R. (1950) *ibid* 2152
Kaufman, S. and Singleterry, C. R. (1952) *J. phys. Chem.* **56,** 604
Kauzmann, W. J., Walter, J. E. and Eyring, H. (1940) *Chem. Rev.* **26,** 339
Kendrew, J. C. and Moelwyn-Hughes, E. A. (1940) *Proc. roy. Soc.* **A176,** 352
Kenyon, J. (1942) *Annu. Rep. Progr. Chem.* **39,** 125
Kharasch, M. S., Senior, J. K., Stanger, D. W. and Chenicek, J. A. (1934) *J. Amer. chem. Soc.* **56,** 1646
King, H. (1933) *Annu. Rep. Progr. Chem.* **30,** 261
Kipping, F. S. and Pope, W. J. (1898) *Nature, Lond.* **59,** 53
Kistiakowsky, G. B. and Smith, W. R. (1936) *J. Amer. chem. Soc.* **58,** 1043
Klyne, W. (1954) *Progress in Stereochemistry,* Vol. 1, London, Butterworths

Krieble, V. K. (1912) *J. Amer. chem. Soc.* **34**, 716 ; *cf* also Walker, J. W. and
Krieble, V. K. (1909) *J. chem. Soc.* 1437
Kuhn, R. (1932) *Ber. dtsch. chem. Ges.* **65**, 49
— and Albrecht, O. (1927) *Liebigs Ann.* **455**, 272
Kuhn, W. (1936) *Angew. chem.* **49**, 215 ; (1936) *Ergeb. Enzymforsch*, **5**, 1
Lesslie, M. S., Turner, E. E. and Winton, E. R. (1941) *J. chem. Soc.* 257
Leuchs, H. (1921) *Ber. dtsch. chem. Ges.* **54**, 830
— and Wutke, J. (1913) *ibid* **46**, 2420
Li, C. C. and Adams, R. (1935) *J. Amer. chem. Soc.* **57**, 1565
Los, J. M., Simpson, L. B. and Wiesner, K. (1956) *ibid* **78**, 1564
— and Wiesner, K. (1953) *ibid* **75**, 6346
Lowry, T. M. (1899) *J. chem. Soc.* 211
— and Robertson, W. (1904) *ibid* 1541
McIntosh, A. O., Robertson, J. M. and Vand, V. (1952) *Nature, Lond.* **169**, 322
McKenzie, A. (1915) *ibid* 440
— and Plenderleith, H. J. and Walker, N. (1923) *ibid* 2875
— and Smith, I. A. (1924) *ibid* 1582 ; (1925) *Ber. dtsch. chem. Ges.* **58**, 894
— and Walker, N. (1922) *J. chem. Soc.* 349
Maitland, P. (1939) *Annu. Rep. Progr. Chem.* **36**, 247
Marckwald, W. (1904) *Ber. dtsch. chem. Ges.* **37**, 349
Maryott, A. A. (1948) *J. Res. nat. Bur. Stand.* **41**, 1
Meisenheimer, J., Angermann, L., Finn, O., Vieweg, E. (1924) *Ber. dtsch. chem.
Ges.* **57**, 1744
— and Beisswenger, O. (1932) *ibid* **65**, 32
— Theilacker, W. and Biesswenger, O. (1932) *Liebigs Ann.* **495**, 249
Meyer, J. (1908) *Z. phys. chem.* **62**, 59
Mills, W. H. (1943) *J. chem. Soc.* 194 (Presidential Address)
— and Bain, A. M. (1914) *ibid* 64
— and Breckenridge, J. G. (1932) *ibid* 2209
— and Elliott, K. A. C. (1928) *ibid* 1291
— and Kelham, R. M. (1937) *ibid* 274
Moelwyn-Hughes, E. A. (1933) *The Kinetics of Reactions in Solution*, Oxford,
Clarendon, p. 45 ; (1940) 2nd ed.
Morgan, G. T. and Burstall, F. H. (1931) *J. chem. Soc.* 2213
Newman, A. D. C. and Powell, H. M. (1952) *ibid* 3747 ; see footnote, p. 160
Newman, M. S. and Hussey, A. S. (1947) *J. Amer. chem. Soc.* **69**, 3023
— Lutz, W. B. and Lednicer, D. (1955) *ibid* **77**, 3420
— and Wise, R. M. (1956) *ibid* **78**, 450
Nyholm, R. S. (1954) *Progress in Stereochemistry*, Vol. 1, London, Butterworths,
p. 322, see p. 356
Owen, L. J. and Nord, F. F. (1951) *J. org. chem.* **16**, 1864
Patterson, T. S. and Buchanan, C. (1940) *J. chem. Soc.* 290, also *cf* Patterson, T. S.
and Lamberton, A. H. (1937) *ibid* 1453
Pfeiffer, P. and Nakatsuka, Y. (1933) *Ber. dtsch. chem. Ges.* **66**, 415
— and Quehl, K. (1931) *ibid* **64**, 2667 ; (1932) *ibid* **65**, 560
Pope, W. J. and Peachey, S. J. (1900) *J. chem. Soc.* (Proceedings) **16**, 42, 116
Potter, W. G. (1953) Thesis, University of London
Powell, H. M. (1952) *Nature, Lond.* **170**, 155 ; (1954) *J. chem. Soc.* 2658 (Tilden
Lecture) ; (1956) *Endeavour*, XV, **57**, 20
Prelog, V. (1953) *Helv. chim. acta* **36**, 308 ; *ibid* 320 ; *ibid* 325
Rapoport, H. and Lavigne, J. B. (1956) *J. Amer. chem. Soc.* **78**, 2455
Read, J. (1930) *Chem. Rev.* **7**, 1
— and McMath, A. M. (1925) *J. chem. Soc.* 1572 ; (1926) *ibid* 2183
— and Robertson, G. J. (1926) *ibid* 2209

Reeves, R. E. (1951) *Advanc. carbohydr. chem.* **6,** 108

Reiger, M. and Westheimer, F. H. (1950) *J. Amer. chem. Soc.* **62,** 19

Ritchie, P. D. (1933) *Asymmetric Synthesis and Asymmetric Induction,* London, Humphrey Milford; (1947) *Advanc. Enzymol.* **7,** 65

Searle, N. E. and Adams, R. (1933) *J. Amer. chem. Soc.* **55,** 1649

Shriner, R. L., Adams, R. and Marvel, C. S. (1943) in *Organic Chemistry,* Ed. Gilman, H., 2nd ed.

Smith, I. A. (1931) *Ber. dtsch. chem. Ges.* **64,** 427; *ibid* 1115

Stoughton, R. W. and Adams, R. (1932) *J. Amer. chem. Soc.* **54,** 4426

Thomas, W. (1921) *J. chem. Soc.* 1140

Tubandt, C. (1905) *Liebigs Ann.* **339,** 41; (1907) *ibid* **354,** 259; (1910) *ibid* **377,** 284

Turner, E. E. and Harris, M. M. (1947) *Quart. Rev. chem. Soc., Lond.* **1,** 299

Weissberger, A. (1943) *J. Amer. chem. Soc.* **65,** 102

Werner, A. (1912) *Ber. dtsch. chem. Ges.* **45,** 3061

Yuan, H. C. and Adams, R. (1932) *J. Amer. chem. Soc.* **54,** 2966, 4434

6

THE STEREOCHEMISTRY OF THE GROUP V ELEMENTS

F. G. Mann

THE following discussion of the progress in our knowledge of the stereochemistry of the Group V elements has in general been limited to work recorded during the last fifteen years, although it has often been necessary to refer briefly to rather earlier investigations which have formed the immediate foundation of the work about to be described, or have formed a connecting link between this work and the more classical studies. Consequently certain very interesting subjects, such as the stereochemistry of the oximes, have been omitted because the chief points in the elucidation of their stereochemistry had been established before the main period covered by this account. Considerations of space have also enforced a very brief discussion of other more recent but also very interesting topics. Furthermore, the stereochemistry of nitrogen and the Group VB elements is exceedingly rich and varied, whilst that of the Group VA elements is remarkably meagre: for this reason, and again for lack of space, the Group VA elements (vanadium, niobium and tantalum) have been omitted.

For convenience of treatment, the material is divided into four sections, namely, derivatives of the 3-covalent, the 4-covalent, the 5-covalent and the 6-covalent elements. The ambiguity which now attaches to the term ' 4-covalent element' when applied to certain classes of compound is briefly discussed on p. 207, where the classes included in this section are listed.

DERIVATIVES OF THE 3-COVALENT ELEMENTS

Each of these derivatives can be regarded as a substituted ammonia, phosphine, arsine, etc., and the physical properties of these three hydrides in particular are therefore of considerable importance. The molecules of ammonia, phosphine and arsine are known to be pyramidal (I; where $X = N$, P or As), and to be in a state of oscillation, in which the three hydrogen atoms can be regarded as oscillating between the extreme positions IA and IB. The rate of this oscillation has a direct bearing on the stereochemistry of tertiary amines, phosphines and arsines. In TABLE 1, the interatomic X—H length, the intervalency angle, and the height of the pyramidal molecule are those determined by Sutherland, Lee and Wu (1939), using spectroscopic methods, and the times of inversion are the corrected values given by Costain and Sutherland (1952).

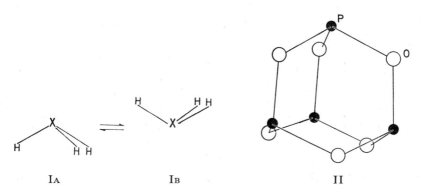

I_A   I_B   II

These striking results for the time of inversion of AsH_3 and AsD_3 indicate, as these authors pointed out, that a suitably substituted tertiary arsine should be resolvable into optically active forms. Earlier, Kincaid and Henriques (1940), on the basis of approximate calculations of activation energy from spectroscopic data, had decided that 'no compound of the type $NR^1R^2R^3$ can be resolved into active forms at room temperature', but they considered that a similar tertiary phosphine might be resolved: their work unfortunately did

TABLE 1

	X—H (Å)	H—X—H angle	Height of pyramidal molecule (Å)	Time of inversion
NH_3	1·02	111°	0·30	$2·5 \times 10^{-11}$ sec
PH_3	1·46	99°	0·67	$2·3 \times 10^{-6}$ sec
AsH_3	1·56	97°	0·75	1·4 years
AsD_3				$3·5 \times 10^7$ years

not extend to arsenic compounds. Weston (1954) has reviewed the methods available for determining the above constants, and supports those employed by Costain and Sutherland: he has expressed his results concerning the oscillation of the molecules in terms of the temperature at which the half-time for racemization would be 2 hours, and obtained the values: NMe_3 −168°; PMe_3 +7°; $AsMe_3$ +107°; $SbMe_3$ +67°. These again emphasize the decreasing speed of oscillation from nitrogen to arsenic.

Before discussing the bearing of these properties upon the stereochemistry of the more complex organic derivatives, it should be emphasized that, in addition to the spectroscopic evidence, there is considerable other physical evidence for the pyramidal disposition of the valencies of phosphorus, arsenic and antimony in compounds of

197

type XR_3. This disposition is implicit in the values, given in TABLE 2, of the intervalency angles at the Group V atoms determined by electron diffraction or micro-wave spectrum studies of their gaseous compounds.

TABLE 2

Compound	Angle	Ref.	Compound	Angle	Ref.
PF_3	$104° \pm 4°$	a	AsF_3	$102° \pm 2°$	f
PCl_3	$100·1° \pm 0·3°$	b	$AsCl_3$	$98·4° \pm 0·5°$	b
PBr_3	$106° \pm 3°$	c	$AsBr_3$	$100·5° \pm 1·5°$	d
PI_3	$102° \pm 2°$	d	AsI_3	$101° \pm 1·5°$	d
PMe_3	$100° \pm 4°$	e	$AsMe_3$	$96° \pm 5°$	e
$SbCl_3$	$99·5° \pm 1·5°$	g	SbI_3	$99° \pm 1°$	d
$SbBr_3$	$97° \pm 2°$	d	$BiCl_3$	$100° \pm 6°$	h

References: a Pauling and Brockway (1935) ; b Kisliuk and Townes (1950) ; c Williams and Gordy (1950) ; d Allen and Sutton (1949) ; e Springall and Brockway (1935) ; f Kisliuk and Geschwind (1953) ; g Kisliuk (1954) ; h Skinner and Sutton (1940).

By similar methods, it has been established that the phosphorous anhydride (P_4O_6) molecule has the four phosphorus atoms at the apices of a regular tetrahedron, each oxygen atom linking two phosphorus atoms and being in line with, but extended beyond, the edge of the tetrahedron (II), the O—P—O angle being $99° \pm 1°$. Arsenious oxide (As_4O_6) has the same structure, with the O—As—O angle $100° \pm 1·5°$ (Hampson and Stosick, 1938): the corresponding sulphide, obtained in the vapour state by the sublimation of orpiment (As_4S_6) has a closely similar structure (Lu and Donohue, 1944). X-ray crystal analysis shows that in crystalline black phosphorus the average value for the P—P—P angle is $102°$ (Hultgren, Gingrich and Warren, 1935) and in crystalline arsenic is $97°$ (Bradley, 1924: cf Chatt and Mann, 1940a). These intervalency angles are thus all in the neighbourhood of $100°$. A curious exception is provided by the P_4 and As_4 molecules in the vapour state, in which electron diffraction studies indicate a regular tetrahedral structure with however an intervalency angle of c $60°$ in each molecule (Maxwell, Hendricks and Moseley, 1935: cf also Thomas and Gingrich, 1938, for a comparable result for the liquid yellow P_4 molecule by x-ray investigation).

The prediction of Kincaid and Henriques (1940) concerning compounds of type $NR^1R^2R^3$ still holds good, for no compound is known the optical activity of which is due to an ' unhindered ' asymmetric trivalent nitrogen atom. To avoid ambiguity on this point, however, attention should be drawn to two long series of investigations, one by Jamison and Turner, and the second by Adams and his co-workers, which have one essential feature in common. Jamison (now Harris) and Turner (1938, 1940, 1955) have investigated a number of substituted benzoyldiphenylamine-2-carboxylic acids (III).

They showed that certain members, *e.g.* (III ; $R^1 = R^2 = Cl$; $R^3 = H$)
and (III ; $R^1 = R^2 = Me$; $R^3 = H$), when treated in solution with
an equivalent of an optically stable active base, showed asymmetric
transformation in solution or ' first-order asymmetric transformation '
(*cf* Chapter 5), *i.e.* that in these circumstances the acids were showing
optical activity, but that since this activity was not stable the two
diastereoisomerides, $(+)$acid-$(+)$base and $(-)$acid-$(+)$base, were not
formed in solution in equal quantity. The acid (III ; $R^1 = R^2 = R^3 =$
Br) furthermore, when treated in acetone solution with cinchonidine,

III IV V

VI

showed asymmetric transformation by crystallization (or ' second-order
asymmetric transformation '), the optically pure cinchonidine-$(+)$acid
being precipitated : this salt when dissolved in chloroform underwent
mutarotation. In their last paper (1955) they reviewed the behaviour
of fourteen similar acids, and emphasized that the optical activity is
due to restricted rotation within the acid molecule (or anion) and not
to the asymmetric trivalent nitrogen atom : optical activity was never
shown in acids of type III which lacked *ortho*-substituents. They
considered that rotation about all three N—C bonds is possible,
provided there is *synchronized* movement of the various parts, but that
these ' favourable rotating positions ' must be relatively rarely attained.
    Adams and Daukert (1940) reported the optical resolution of
N-methyl-*N*-succinyl-bromomesidine (IV), which had considerable
optical stability, and also adduced evidence that the dissymmetry of
such arylamines was caused by restricted rotation rather than by a
' formally ' asymmetric nitrogen atom. This paper formed the first
of a series of eighteen on this subject, in the last of which, Adams,
Blomstrom and Sundstrom (1954) stated their conclusions regarding
these optically active arylamines : (i) all aromatic amines showing
optical activity have been of type Aryl-NR^1R^2 ; (ii) no such molecule
in which R^1 or R^2 is a hydrogen atom has been observed to possess
restricted rotation and thus to be resolvable ; (iii) substituent groups

in each of the *ortho* positions in the aryl group are usually essential for the restricted rotation : occasionally one large *ortho* is adequate, but the compound is optically unstable ; (iv) in all instances (of the arylamines), at least one of the groups R^1 or R^2 have been acyl or sulphonyl groups, which provide substantially greater blocking effect than alkyl or carboxymethyl groups.

These general conclusions are supported by the fact that Meisenheimer *et al.* (1924) failed to resolve *N*-phenyl-*N*-*p*-tolylanthranilic acid (V) but Patterson and Adams (1933) resolved 9-*o*-carboxyphenyl-3-nitrocarbazole (VI), where the two *o*-phenylene rings, rigidly held in one plane, restrict the rotation of the *o*-carboxyphenyl group. Essentially, the work of Jamison and Turner, and of Adams and his colleagues, represents a detailed and very valuable study of the general phenomenon of restricted rotation about a trivalent nitrogen atom, initiated by the isolation in optically active forms of benzenesulphonyl-(8-nitro-1-naphthyl)glycine (VII) by Mills and Elliott (1928).

VII   VIII

Another compound, which probably falls into this general class, is *p*-carboxyphenyl-2-diphenylylphenylstibine (VIII) which has been recently resolved into optical active forms by Campbell (1955). This compound shows marked optical stability : its solution in pyridine was unchanged after 3 months at room temperature, and solutions in toluene and *p*-xylene were unaffected by 1 and 2 hours' boiling respectively. Consequently Campbell considered that in this compound the dissymmetry may be due to restricted rotation involving the 2-diphenylyl group rather than to the configuration of the antimony atom. It should be pointed out that if restricted rotation did occur in compounds of type III, IV and VIII, optical activity might occur even if the three N—C or Sb—C bonds were coplanar. This however is very unlikely, for the C—N—C angle in triphenylamine has been calculated as 114° (Leonard and Sutton, 1948) and the C—Sb—C angle in triphenylstibine as 112–113° (Campbell, 1955).

The practical realization of optical activity due quite certainly to an unhindered asymmetric trivalent atom in Group V has recently been obtained by Campbell and Poller (1956), who have resolved 9-*p*-carboxyphenyl-2-methoxy-9-arsafluorene (IX) and 2-amino-9-phenyl-9-arsafluorene (X) into optically active forms. The compound IX has $[\alpha]_D$ $\pm 160°$ in pyridine solution, and shows considerable optical stability, for the rotation of this solution after 30 days at room temperature had fallen by only 7·5 per cent. The compound X has

200

even greater optical stability, for its rotation in ethanol ($[\alpha]_D$ —255°) was unaffected by 1 hour's heating at 110°, and at room temperature remained unchanged apparently indefinitely. The attribution of the

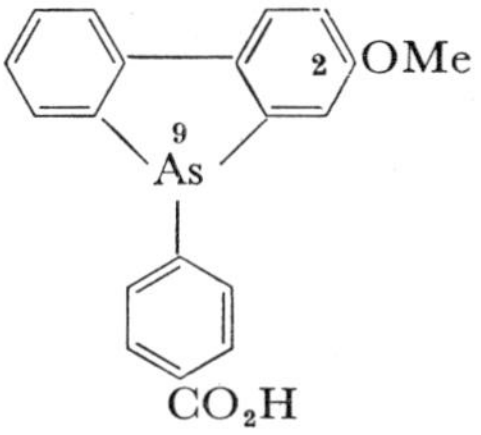

IX 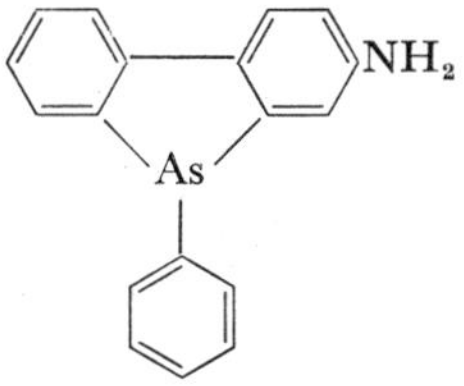   X 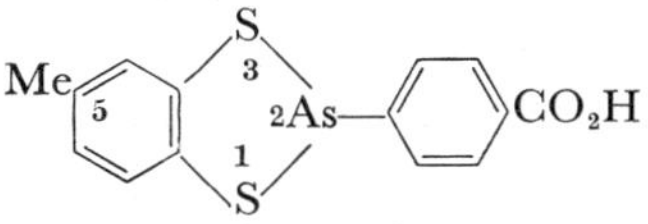   XI

activity of these compounds to the trivalent arsenic atom would of course be invalidated if the tricyclic arsafluorene system were itself non-planar, *i.e.* if the molecules were 'twisted' so that the two *o*-phenylene rings were set at an angle to one another. Campbell and Poller adduced considerable and convincing evidence that this system is in fact rigidly planar.

Miss Campbell (1956) has more recently resolved 2-*p*-carboxyphenyl-5-methyl-1 : 3-dithia-2-arsa-indane (XI), which has $[\alpha]_D$ —8·7° and +8·9° in chloroform solution : this compound also has high optical stability, for the rotation of an ethanolic solution was unaffected by heating at 110° for 2 hours. Here again, there is strong reason to believe that the 1 : 3-dithia-2-arsa-indane system is flat, and that the optical activity is due, as in the compounds IX and X, to the pyramidal configuration of the arsenic atom.

In the antimony field, the resolution of 2-carboxy-9-*p*-tolyl-9-stibiafluorene (XII; R = CO_2H) and its 2-amino analogue (XII; R = NII_2) had been earlier realized by Campbell (1950, 1952), and subsequently three other similar derivatives were resolved by Campbell

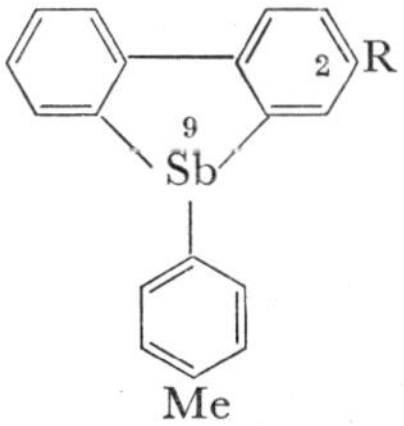

Me

XII

and Morrill (1955) in order to study their racemization under various conditions. Evidence is also adduced that the tricyclic stibiafluorene ring system is planar. It is noteworthy in this connection that attempts to resolve various stibiafluorenes having no substituents in the two *o*-phenylene rings uniformly failed, although, had the stibiafluorene ring system possessed a stable 'skew' configuration, the presence of such substituents should not be necessary for optical activity.

Another class of heterocyclic compound, having almost undoubtedly a distinctive structural feature, should be considered. It has been pointed out by Campbell, Le Fèvre, Le Fèvre and Turner (1938) that a tricyclic system of type XIII, in which A and B are *ortho*-phenylene rings, will be planar only if the intervalency angles α and β subtended

XIII   XIV   XV

by the atoms X and Y are either 120° or approach closely to this value. If the angles α and β are appreciably less than 120°, the molecule must be 'folded' about the X–Y axis, *i.e.* if the atoms X and Y are in the plane of the paper, the groups A and B can be regarded as sloping upwards towards the observer. With these considerations in mind, Lesslie and Turner (1934) had earlier synthesized and investigated 10-methylphenoxarsine-2-carboxylic acid (XIV; R = Me). If in this compound the intervalency angles at the oxygen and arsenic atoms (corresponding to α and β) have their normal value of c 100°, the molecule must be folded about the O–As axis and thus be dissymmetric. Lesslie and Turner were able to resolve this compound, $[\alpha]_{5461}^{20°}+111\cdot5°$ and $-111\cdot7°$ in ethanol, and found that its rotation was unaffected even when its solution is N-NaOH solution was heated at 100° for 6 hours. Later (1935) the 10-ethyl and 10-phenyl analogues (XIV: R = Et and Ph) were prepared and resolved. Two possible explanations of these results have been discussed by Lesslie and Turner (1934). (a) If the molecule is folded about the O–As axis as described above (*i.e.* if it is of the 'butterfly' type), it will possess molecular dissymmetry irrespective of the disposition of the group R about the arsenic atom. (b) If the tricyclic phenoxarsine system is planar, optical activity will be shown only if the group R is above or below this plane. Similar considerations apply to 10-*p*-carboxyphenyl-2-methylphenoxstibine (XV), which Campbell (1947) synthesized and resolved into optically active forms, and which proved to have an optical stability lower than that of the phenoxarsine derivatives. There appears to be little doubt that both these types of compound (XIV and XV) are 'folded' as described in (a), and it is to this structural feature that they owe their optical activity.

A rather different approach to these 'folded' molecules was made by Chatt and Mann (1940a), who investigated 5 : 10-di-*p*-tolyl-5 : 10-dihydroarsanthrene (XVI), a compound which for this purpose has the advantage of possessing two identical heterocyclic atoms. This compound should similarly be folded about the As–As axis, and in consequence it should exist in geometric isomers. This is shown diagrammatically in XVIA and XVIB, in which the two arsenic

atoms are depicted as being in the plane of the paper, with one *ortho*-phenylene group (in thick lines) projecting above this plane and towards the observer, and the second such group (in thin lines) projecting below this plane: the *p*-tolyl groups (represented by ' Tol ') are both in the plane of the paper. A model constructed to scale, with all the C—As—C angles 100°, shows a *cis* form (XVIA) in which both tolyl groups are in the angle subtended by the two *ortho*-phenylene groups,

and a *trans* form (XVIB) in which the upper tolyl group is in the same position as before, but the lower tolyl group now projects upwards on the opposite side of the angular molecule. (A third form, represented by XVIc, cannot exist, because the two tolyl groups now become almost coincident in space.) Fractional crystallization of this compound ultimately separated it into an α form, m.p. 178–179°, and a β form, m.p. 179–181°, a mixture of equal quantities having m.p. 144–158°. Both forms showed a normal molecular weight in boiling acetone, but they differed in many chemical properties. The isolation of two geometric isomers is thus in accordance with theoretical prediction, but it is not known which form corresponds to XVIA and which to XVIB.

It is noteworthy that the compound XVI gave a dibromide, which had the properties of a salt and not those of a tertiary arsine dibromide, and which Chatt and Mann depicted as (XVII; R = *p*-tolyl). This conclusion was strongly supported by a detailed study of the 5 : 10-dimethyl analogue (XVII; R = Me) by Jones and Mann (1955c), and the ring structure in XVII represents a novel ' aromatic ' system which would of course be stabilized by resonance (*cf* anthracene).

The compounds IX–XVI discussed above have one structural feature in common, namely, that the constituent trivalent Group V element has two valencies bound in a ring system, whilst the third valency carries a single group theoretically capable of oscillating about the pyramidal position. Two other classes of compound, also possessing this structural feature, deserve discussion. Prior to 1938, it had been recognized that azobenzene, Ph—N : N—Ph, should be capable of existing in two geometric (*cis-trans*) isomers, but the isolation of a second form had not been achieved. Hartley (1938) showed that normal samples of azobenzene consisted almost solely of the *trans* form (XVIIIA), which, however, when dissolved in organic solvents and exposed to daylight gave an equilibrium mixture of the *trans* ⇌ *cis* forms. An acetic acid solution so exposed was then diluted with sufficient water (in the dark) to precipitate the less soluble *trans* form; further aqueous dilution then precipitated the *cis* form (XVIIIB), which was obtained crystalline by rapid evaporation of its chloroform extract. The dipole moments of the pure *trans* and *cis* forms were zero and 3·0 D respectively. The crystalline *cis* form was stable in the dark, but in organic solvents was converted entirely to the *trans* form: these solutions on exposure to light re-established the original equilibrium. The structure of the two forms was proved by an x-ray

XVIIIA	XVIIIB	XIXA	XIXB

crystal investigation by Robertson (1939) and Hampson and Robertson (1941), who determined in particular the interatomic distances and intervalency angles for the C—N=N—C unit in each isomer.

Other examples of *cis-trans* isomerism have been established for substituted azobenzenes by Cook *et al.* (1938, 1939) and, in the case of 2 : 2′- and 3 : 3′-azopyridine, by Le Fèvre (1951), and by Campbell, Henderson and Taylor (1953): in most of these examples, the *cis* form reverted readily to the more stable *trans* form. In heavier molecules, such as the substituted azo-3-indoles (Huang-Hsinmin and Mann, 1949), this conversion has not been detected, each isomer retaining its identity.

It is noteworthy that the ultra-violet and visible absorption spectra of *cis-* and *trans-*azobenzene are very similar in general type to those of o-chlorobenzene-*syn-* and -*anti-*diazosulphonates respectively, and also to those of p-chlorobenzene-*syn-* and -*anti-*diazocyanides (Freeman and Le Fèvre, 1951). This provides strong confirmatory evidence that the essential difference between the two diazosulphonates and also between the two diazocyanides is one of configuration and not of constitution.

Badger, Buttery and Lewis (1953) have shown that *cis*- and *trans*-azobenzene, when oxidized with perbenzoic acid in the dark, give *cis*- and *trans*-azoxybenzene (XIXA and B) respectively: in this series also, the *cis* compound is readily converted into the *trans* compound, especially in sunlight.

Arsenobenzene, a colourless crystalline compound obtained by the reduction of phenylarsonic acid or by the action of sodium on phenyl-dichloroarsine, was for many years regarded (as its name implies) as the arsenic analogue of azobenzene, of formula Ph—As : As—Ph. It is however considerably associated in organic solvents (for a summary of these properties, see Lyon and Mann, 1945) and there is some evidence that the arsenic atoms form a ring in the more complex molecule. The more volatile arsenomethane has been investigated in greater detail. In one of the most recent studies, Waser and Schomaker (1945) stated that (a) vapour density measurements indicate the existence of different degrees of association corresponding to $n = 3$–5 in the formula $(AsMe)_n$; (b) electron diffraction measurements rule out the simple structure Me—As : As—Me, but are compatible with a puckered 5-membered ring of arsenic atoms, with an average intervalency angle As—As—As of 90°. This class of compound is clearly entirely different in structure from the azo compounds.

A curious factor arises in the configuration of certain 1 : 4-di-substituted piperazines. It will be clear that 1 : 4-dimethylpiperazine (XX; R = H) should be able to exist as the C (or 'boat') form (XXA; R = H) and in the Z (or 'chair') form (XXB; R = H),

| XX | XXA | XXB | XXI | XXII |

in each of which the methyl groups could oscillate about the pyramidal position as shown. This compound behaves normally as a di-tertiary amine in that it will readily form a dimethobromide and a dimeth-iodide; it will also unite similarly with ethylene dibromide to form triethylenediamine dimethobromide (XXI) (Mann and Mukherjee, 1949; Mann and Baker, 1957), a reaction which must involve the boat form (XXA; R = H).

1 : 2 : 2 : 4 : 5 : 5-Hexamethylpiperazine (XX; R = Me) also readily forms a dimethobromide and a dimethiodide, but all attempts to induce cyclization by 'diquaternization' with ethylene, trimethylene or *o*-xylylene dibromide yielded the dihydrobromide of the base (Mann and Senior, 1954; McElvain and Bannister, 1954). The reason for this striking difference in the behaviour of dimethyl- and

hexamethyl-piperazine is uncertain, but it would appear that the presence of the two pairs of *gem*-dimethyl groups in the latter ' locks ' the molecule in the chair form (XXB; R = Me), which would of course prevent this type of cyclization. Hexamethylpiperazine is a liquid : an x-ray crystal investigation of its dinitrate by Cochran (*cf* Mann and Senior, 1954) has shown however that the cation of this salt has a centre of symmetry and must therefore have the chair form.

Similar properties are shown by 1 : 4-diphenyl-1 : 4-diars*acyclo*hexane (XXII), recently synthesized by Jones and Mann (1955a). This crystalline di-tertiary arsine also readily undergoes di-quaternization with simple alkyl bromides and iodides, but will not do so with the above three alkylene dibromides, with which it forms apparently amorphous products. Nyburg and Hilton (1955) have shown by x-ray analysis that this diarsine also has a centre of symmetry and thus has the chair form. These crystallographic results are of great interest, but of course they afford no evidence that the free hexamethylpiperazine and the diarsine may not be capable of assuming the boat form when molten or in solution.

Although the frequency of inversion in the ammonia molecule is so high, it will clearly be completely arrested if all the three valencies of the nitrogen are ' locked ' in a suitable polycyclic system. This must occur in triethylenediamine (XXIII), which can be obtained by the thermal decomposition of the dimethobromide (XXI) (Hromatka and Kraupp, 1951 ; Mann and Baker, 1957), and which, like the analogous quinuclidine (Meisenheimer, 1920), is a remarkably volatile crystalline base. This arrested oscillation will also apply to compounds such as diethylene-*o*-phenylenediarsine (XXIV) (Mann and Baker, 1952) and to tri-*o*-phenylenediarsine (XXV) (McCleland and Whitworth, 1927 ; Chatt and Mann, 1940a). Consideration of the structure of these three

XXIII   XXIV   XXV

molecules shows how well they accord with the pyramidal configuration of the nitrogen and the arsenic atoms.

A very interesting example of this type of molecule is ' Troger's Base ', which is prepared by the condensation of formaldehyde and *p*-toluidine, and which was shown by Spielman (1935) to have the structure XXVI. It will be seen that the ' locked ' pyramidal configuration of the nitrogen atoms should enable this compound to exist in enantiomorphic forms (XXVIA and B, in which the groups $\cdot N \cdot CH_2 \cdot N \cdot$ are depicted in the plane of the paper, while the ring systems in thick and thin lines project respectively above and below this plane). Early attempts to resolve it using optically active acids proved unsatisfactory. Complete resolution was ultimately achieved (Prelog and Wieland, 1944) by chromatographic separation of the base in petroleum solution on a column of specially prepared powdered (+)-lactose hydrate. The two forms were thus obtained having $[\alpha]_D +287 \pm 7°$ and $-278° \pm 7°$ respectively in hexane solution.

XXVI   XXVIA   XXVIB

Mahler and Burg (1957), in a preliminary note, have recently recorded an apparently unique type of 3-covalent phosphorus compound, of formula $[F_3C \cdot P]_4$, prepared by the action of mercury on trifluoromethyl-di-iodophosphine, F_3CPI_2, and by other methods. This compound has a ring of four phosphorus atoms. It melts at 65°, and is apparently readily volatile, for on storage in a vacuum the crystal form " varies, plates, needles, hexagons, lozenges ". This ready sublimation recalls that shown by triethylenediamine and quinuclidine (p. 206). The structure and reactions of this compound are being studied : the authors stated that it is reasonable to suppose that the four-phosphorus ring " is stabilized by extra bonding which involves the lone electron pair on each phosphorus atom with the $3d$ orbitals of adjacent phosphorus atoms, much as the chlorine molecule is stabilised by $3p$-$3d$ π bonding ".

DERIVATIVES OF THE 4-COVALENT ELEMENTS

The modern development of the theory of valency in correlation with that of experimental techniques for the molecular structure determination has largely destroyed the simple valency classification of compounds which formed, for example, a striking feature of Sidgwick's classical *Electronic Theory of Valency* (1927). Consequently it is no longer possible to assign a simple number to the valency of phosphorus and arsenic (in particular) in many compounds in which they were earlier regarded as 4-covalent. No ambiguity occurs in quaternary salts of type $[R_4El]X$, where El, representing the elements nitrogen, phosphorus, arsenic or antimony, is here clearly 4-covalent : nor in the tertiary amine oxides, $R_3N \to O$, where the available electrons of the nitrogen atom are insufficient to form other than a single bond, which has however a markedly polar character.

The reason for the uncertainty arose initially from measurements of interatomic distances in compounds such as phosphorus oxychloride, which Sidgwick formulated as $Cl_3P{\rightarrow}O$. Electron-diffraction and micro-wave spectrum measurements indicated, however, that in the phosphorus oxyhalides the P—O distance ranged between 1·41–1·55 Å (TABLE 3), whereas the calculated lengths for single, double and triple bonds between these atoms are 1·76, 1·57 and 1·43 Å respectively. Similarly the P—S distance in phosphorus thiohalides, likewise determined, is 1·86–1·89 Å, the calculated lengths for single, double and triple bonds being 2·14, 1·94 and 1·80 Å respectively. The P—O and P—S distances are therefore apparently too short to allow these atoms to be bound by a single bond. Phillips, Hunter and Sutton (1945), in an excellent and critical survey of the whole subject, have obtained additional evidence from the dipole moments of many compounds that the bonds between phosphorus and oxygen, and between phosphorus and sulphur, in the above and other comparable compounds, have far more double bond than single bond character. The precise *nature* of this bond remains uncertain: Jensen (1943b) has found the dipole moments (in Debye units) of the compounds Ph_3PO, Ph_3PS, Ph_3PSe, Ph_3AsO, and Ph_3SbS to be 4·31, 4·74, 4·83, 5·50 and 5·40 respectively, and considered that these high values indicate the presence of a semipolar binding.

TABLE 3

Compound	P—O Distance (Å)	Ref.	Compound	P—S Distance (Å)	Ref.
POF_3	$\begin{cases}1\cdot48 \\ 1\cdot45 \pm 0\cdot03\end{cases}$	a e	PSF_3	$\begin{cases}1\cdot86 \\ 1\cdot87 \pm 0\cdot03\end{cases}$	a e
$POClF_2$	1·55 ± 0·03	b	$PSCl_3$	1·85 ± 0·02	e
$POCl_2F$	1·55 ± 0·03	b	$PSBr_3$	1·89 ± 0·06	d
$POCl_3$	1·45 ± 0·03	c, e	$PSFBr_2$	1·87 ± 0·05	d
$POBr_3$	1·41 ± 0·07	d	PSF_2Br	1·87 ± 0·05	d

References: *a* Hawkins, Cole and Roski (1952); *b* Brockway and Beach (1938); *c* Badgley and Livingston (1954); *d* Secrist and Brockway (1944); *e* Williams, Sheridan and Gordy (1952).

For earlier values for PSF_3 and $PSCl_3$, see Stosick (1939); Beach and Stevenson (1938).

It may be added, moreover, that Hampson and Stosick (1938) have shown by electron-diffraction studies that phosphoric anhydride (P_4O_{10}) has the structure I*, *i.e.* it has the tricyclic structure of P_4O_6 (formula II, p. 197) with an extra oxygen atom denoted as O^1 tetrahedrally projecting from each phosphorus atom. In the P_4O_6 structure, single bonds should link each phosphorus atom to the three neighbour-

* In order to avoid large Roman numbers, a fresh series of formula-numbers begins for each principal section of this chapter.

ing oxygen atoms, but this P—O distance is 1·65 Å. In the P_4O_{10} structure, this P—O distance in the cyclic system is 1·62 Å, but the P—O¹ distance falls to the remarkably low value of 1·39 Å, *i.e.* that to be expected of a P≡O link. Similar results have been obtained by x-ray analysis of the crystalline compound (de Decker and Mac-Gillavry; de Decker, 1941).

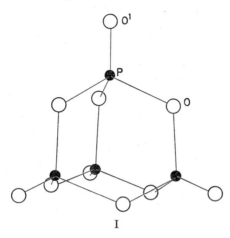

I

The solid compound P_4S_{10} is reported to have a structure analogous to I, with the sulphur atoms tetrahedrally arranged around each phosphorus atom (Vos and Wiebenga, 1954).

It should be added that Wells (1949) in a detailed discussion of 'Bond Lengths in Some Inorganic Molecules and Complex Ions' considered that the arguments for formulating oxy-ions of phosphorus, sulphur, and chlorine with double bonds are not acceptable, and that "the apparent abnormal shortness of many bonds cannot be satisfactorily explained in the present state of our knowledge."

It would appear from these considerations that the bond between the Group V element and oxygen in compounds of type R_3PO, R_3AsO and R_3SbO is a resonance hybrid having single (coordinate) and double bond contributions, in which the double bond contribution probably increases as one proceeds down the Group. This bond retains marked polar qualities, however, and tertiary arsine oxides, for example, readily combine with acids: with nitric acid they often form highly crystalline hydroxynitrates, $[R_3AsOH]NO_3$, and their slightly soluble hydroxypicrates, $[R_3AsOH]O·C_6H_2(NO_2)_3$ are of great value in practical work. Tertiary phosphine oxides seldom give these slightly soluble picrates, but they will combine with such weak acids as toluene-*p*-sulphonamide to give crystalline hydroxy-toluene-*p*-sulphonamides, $[R_3P·OH]HN·SO_2·C_6H_4·Me$ (Mann and Chaplin, 1937). These polar properties, however, are not shared by the corresponding sulphides and selenides of the tertiary phosphines and arsines: these two types of derivatives, incidentally, are not formed by tertiary amines. Similarly there is at present some uncertainty regarding the precise nature of the bond which links tertiary phosphines, arsines and stibines to metals in coordination compounds such as $[(R_3P)_2PdCl_2]$, but this bond may also possess a marked double bond contribution.

For simplicity of classification, therefore, the quaternary salts, and the oxides, sulphides and metallic coordination compounds of the tertiary derivatives will be considered to contain the Group V element formally in the 4-covalent condition, since in all these classes this element has the tetrahedral configuration. Also for simplicity, the resonance bond discussed above will be formally represented as in $Ph_3P{\rightarrow}O$.

Quaternary Salts

The initial optical resolution of a quaternary ammonium salt, of type [abcdN]X, by Pope and Peachey (1899) did not provide decisive evidence for the configuration of the 4-covalent nitrogen atom, which could have had the tetrahedral or the (less likely) ' Bischoff pyramidal ' configuration. Decisive evidence for the tetrahedral configuration was provided by the optical resolution of 4-phenyl-4'-carbethoxy-bispiperi-dinium-1 : 1'-spirane bromide (Mills and Warren, 1925), and in the corresponding arsenic field by the x-ray crystal-structure investigation of tetraphenylarsonium iodide, $[Ph_4As]I$, by Miss Mooney (1940). Nevertheless, Pope and Peachey's work on the ammonium salts encouraged many chemists to attempt the synthesis and resolution of similar phosphonium and arsonium salts, as it was obviously highly unlikely that there was any fundamental difference in the configuration of the three elements in the 4-covalent condition. For nearly forty-five years, however, failure attended these attempts to obtain optically stable phosphonium and arsonium salts.

There is very little doubt that the main factor in this failure is the following, put forward, with considerable experimental evidence, by Burrows and Turner (1921), based on an earlier suggestion of Pope and Harvey (1901). If, for example, one of the four groups in an arsonium salt were an alkyl group, the arsonium halide in solution would give rise to a ' dissociation equilibrium ', $[abcdAs]X \rightleftarrows abcAs + dX$, thus causing rapid racemization of the optically active salt. Since, for synthetic reasons, all such salts contained at least one alkyl group, a satisfactory resolution was obviously very difficult to achieve.

An intermediate stage was attained by Chatt and Mann (1939a) who separated ethylene-1 : 2-bis(n-butyl-methyl-phenylarsonium) di-picrate (II) into two forms, the more soluble α-form having m.p. 113–115°, and the β-form having m.p. 139·5–140·5°. The isomerism of this compound is obviously of the tartaric acid type, for each arsenic atom is linked to the same set of four unlike groups. Consequently the compound will exist as a racemic and a *meso* form, although it is not known which of the two isomers is the former and

$$\begin{array}{c} \overset{+}{H_2C{\cdot}AsBuMePh} \\ | \overset{+}{} \\ H_2C{\cdot}AsBuMePh \end{array} \left\{ {\cdot}O{\cdot}C_6H_2(NO_2)_3 \right\}_2^{-}$$

$$\begin{array}{cc} OEt & OEt \\ | & | \\ Ph_3C{\cdot}P{-}O{-}P{\cdot}CPh_3 \\ \downarrow & \downarrow \\ O & O \end{array}$$

II   III

which the latter. No interconversion of the picrates in boiling ethanol was observed: this was not unexpected, because the picrate ion would suppress dissociation and hence racemization.

A compound which, although not a quaternary salt, possesses similar stereochemical features, is ethyl triphenylmethylpyrophosphate (III), which Hatt (1933) separated into two forms, m.p. 222–223° and 228–231° respectively: again one of these forms must have been the *meso* and one the racemic compound. Hydrolysis of each compound gave the same acid, for the phosphorus atoms would become symmetric in the resonance anion of the acid.

The difficulty of optical resolution of a quaternary salt was ultimately overcome by Holliman and Mann (1943), who showed that *o*-2-bromo-ethylbenzyl bromide (IV) would condense with phenyldichloroarsine in the presence of sodium to give 2-phenyl-1 : 2 : 3 : 4-tetrahydro-*iso*-arsinoline (V), which contained a very stable heterocyclic ring system. This compound in turn readily quaternized with *p*-chlorophenacyl

IV   V   VI

bromide to give 2-*p*-chlorophenacyl-2-phenyl-1 : 2 : 3 : 4-tetrahydro-*iso*arsinolinium bromide (VI), a salt in which the phenacyl group appeared to be very strongly bound to the asymmetric arsenic atom, and which therefore was unlikely to give a 'dissociation-equilibrium' in solution. The cation of the compound (VI) was in fact readily resolved as its (+)-bromocamphorsulphonate, and its picrate was isolated having $[M]_D + 457°$ and $-450°$, and its iodide having $[M]_D -354°$, all in chloroform solution. The rotation of the iodide remained unchanged for 5 days at room temperature, although the attainment of a dissociation-equilibrium usually occurs particularly readily in chloroform solution.

The first spirocyclic arsonium salt, in which the ring system contained solely carbon atoms and the central arsenic atom, was prepared by

Lyon and Mann (1945). This opened the way for a further development in the stereochemical studies of arsenic, for Holliman and Mann (1945), in an adaptation of this synthesis, quaternized 2-methyl-1 : 2 : 3 : 4-tetrahydro-*iso*arsinoline with *o*-2-bromoethylbenzyl bromide to give the quaternary salt (VII), which when heated in a vacuum smoothly lost methyl bromide with the formation of the highly

VII   VIII

crystalline As-*spiro*-bis-1 : 2 : 3 : 4-tetrahydro-*iso*arsinolinium bromide (VIII). This compound possesses molecular dissymmetry, and was also resolved as the (+)-bromocamphorsulphonate, the corresponding iodide being isolated having $[M]_D$ +342° and −344° in chloroform solution, in which no racemization was detected at room temperature during four weeks.

The correlation of chemical and optical stability in each of the salts (VI) and (VIII) affords strong confirmation that racemization does occur by a dissociation mechanism. It should be added however that Mann and Watson (1947) failed to resolve a number of salts of type [abcdAs]X, where a,b,c and d were unlike *aryl* groups, and in which this dissociation presumably could not occur: this failure, however, was probably due to manipulative difficulties, particularly that of crystallization.

Examples of a quaternary di-arsonium salt in which the tricyclic cation has a unique 'pseudo-aromatic' structure analogous in type to that of anthracene have already been briefly discussed (p. 203).

Synthetic work in the phosphorus field is, for various reasons, more difficult and more laborious than that in the arsenic field. It must suffice here to record that 2-phenyl-2-*p*-hydroxyphenyl-1 : 2 : 3 : 4-tetrahydro-*iso*phosphinolinium bromide (IX) was optically resolved by

IX   X   XI

Holliman and Mann (1947) and P-*spiro*-bis-1 : 2 : 3 : 4-tetrahydro-phosphinolinium iodide (X) by Hart and Mann (1955), the former compound having $[M]_D$ +32·9° in aqueous ethanol and the latter

having $[M]_D$ +66° and −65° in chloroform, neither compound
showing any racemization at room temperature. The salt (X) is
the only known spirocyclic phosphonium salt having the rings around
the phosphorus atom composed entirely of carbon atoms. As an
indication of the greater complexity of synthesis in the phosphorus
field, it may be mentioned that the spirocyclic arsonium salt (VIII)
was synthesized in three stages from o-2-bromoethylbenzyl bromide,
and the spirocyclic phosphonium salt (X) in nine stages from o-bromo-
benzyl bromide.

It will be clear that geometric isomerism could occur if two
quaternary nitrogen atoms were members of a ring system. This
was realized by Hanby and Rydon (1945), who converted 1:4-
dimethylpiperazine into various di-quaternary salts of type XI, which
in turn were separated into *cis* and *trans* isomeric forms. In the case
of the compound (XI; $R = CH_2CH_2Cl$; $X = I$), x-ray crystal
evidence showed that the cation of the higher-melting, less soluble form
had a centre of symmetry: it was therefore the *trans* form, and the
ring system moreover had the chair conformation, as in the cation
produced by 1:2:2:4:5:5-hexamethylpiperazine (p. 206).

A unique type of geometric isomerism in the quaternary field
becomes possible in 1:4-dimethyl-o–phenylene-o-xylylenediarsine dimethobromide (XII), which is readily formed by the union of

XII

o-phenylenebis(dimethylarsine) and o-xylylene dibromide (Jones and
Mann, 1955b). A scale model shows that the distances apart of the
two arsenic atoms, and of the two methylene groups, are almost
identical, and hence the two As—CH_2 bonds must be very nearly
parallel. If the left-hand benzene ring P and the two arsenic atoms
of the cation are depicted in the plane of the paper, the tetrahedral
disposition of the arsenic atoms will cause these two parallel bonds
to be directed, for example, below this plane to the methylene groups
C^1 and C^2 (*cf* XIIIA and B in which all the hydrogen atoms and also
the benzenoid double bonds are omitted for simplicity). The methyl
groups C^3 and C^4 however will now lie almost exactly in this plane,
but the methyl groups C^5 and C^6 will project as shown towards the
observer. The tetrahedral configuration of the carbon atoms at the
methylene groups C^1 and C^2 will now allow the benzene ring Q to
assume one of two non-interconvertible positions. It may either
(XIIIA) adopt a position almost parallel to, but necessarily below the

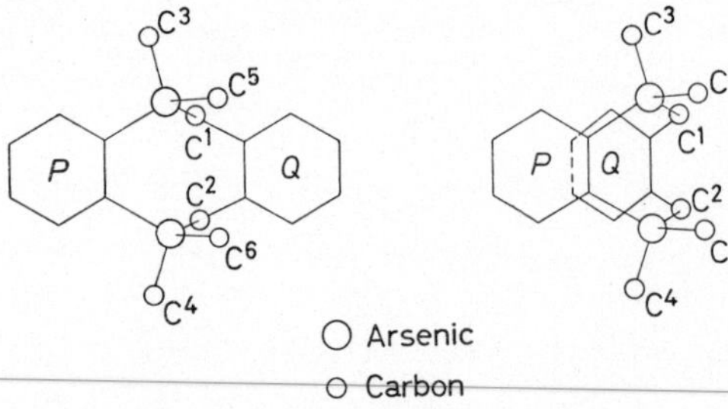

○ Arsenic
○ Carbon

XIIIA   XIIIB

planc of, the benzene ring P, or (XIIIB) it may be bent backwards behind the arsenic atoms to form an angle with the ring P. (The conformations of the two eight-membered rings, each fused to two benzene rings, in XIIIA and XIIIB are thus formally analogous in type to those of the ' chair ' and ' boat ' forms of *cyclo*hexane.) The compound XII has been isolated in only one form, which x-ray analysis indicates is almost certainly XIIIA.

The compound XII undergoes a remarkable thermal decomposition, producing *o*-phenylenebis-(2-*iso*arsindoline) (XIV). This compound

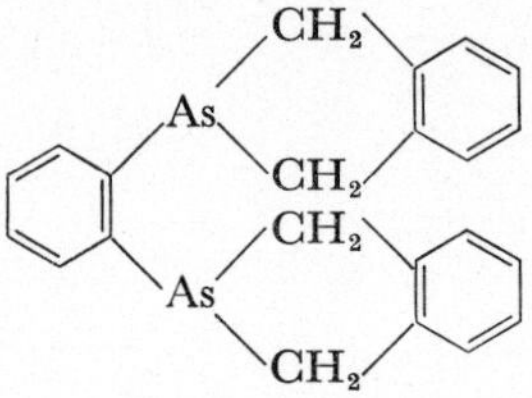

XIV 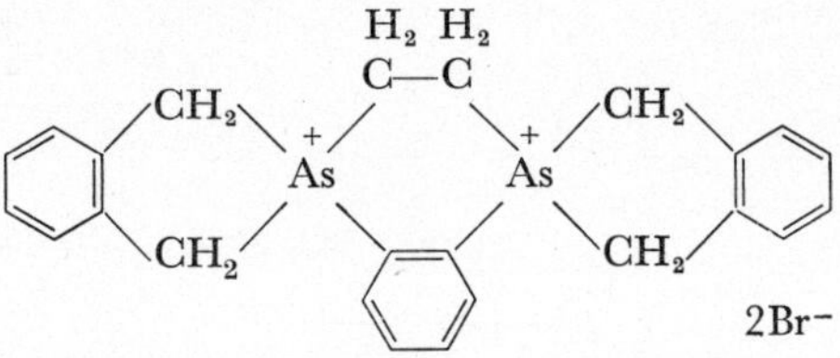   XV

in turn combines with ethylene dibromide to form bis(*iso*arsindoline)-(As-*spiro*-)ethylene-*o*-phenylenediarsonium dibromide (XV), which is unique in the arsenic field in having a double spirocyclic structure.

Oxides of the Tertiary Derivatives

It may be recorded that Meisenheimer (1908) first resolved a tertiary amine oxide, MeEtPhN→O (in the form of its salts), into optically

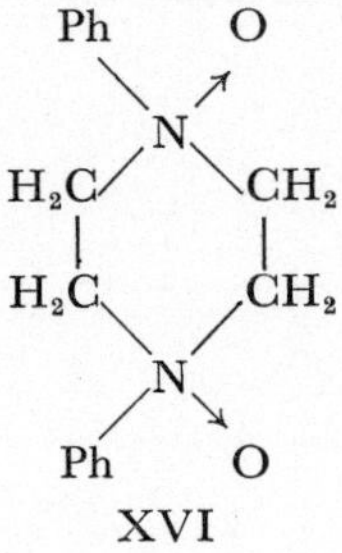

XVI

214

active forms. Only recently, however, has geometric isomerism, dependent on the tetrahedral arrangement of such oxides, been detected. Bennett and Glynn (1950) have separated 1 : 4-diphenyl-piperazine dioxide (XVI) into two forms, which give quite distinct series of salts : it is probable that the less soluble dioxide has the *trans*-configuration.

The work of Meisenheimer and his co-workers (1911, 1926) on the resolution of a tertiary phosphine oxide has certain points that warrant brief comment. Meisenheimer converted methylethylphenylphosphine oxide (XVII) to its (+)-bromocamphorsulphonate (XVIII) which after repeated recrystallization had in aqueous solution $[M]_D$ $+313°$,

$$\text{MeEtPhP} \rightarrow \text{O} \qquad [\text{MeEtPhPOH}]^+(+)[\text{O}_3\text{SC}_{10}\text{H}_{14}\text{OBr}]^- \qquad (\text{PhCH}_2)\text{MePhP} \rightarrow \text{O}$$

$$\text{XVII} \qquad\qquad\qquad \text{XVIII} \qquad\qquad\qquad\qquad \text{XIX}$$

which fell to $+306°$ on the addition of one equivalent of sodium hydroxide : since the bromocamphorsulphonate ion has $[M]_D$ $+267°$ at this concentration in water, he argued that the cation in XVIII had $[M]_D$ $+39°$. When the sulphonate in benzene solution was treated with ammonia, the insoluble ammonium bromocamphor-sulphonate was deposited, and the filtrate gave the (+)phosphine oxide (XVII), which could be distilled without racemization. The oxide had $[M]_D$ $+38°$ in aqueous solution, $+40°$ in water containing one equivalent of hydrochloric acid, and $+47°$ in benzene solution. Meisenheimer argued that the rotation in the hydrochloric acid was that of the salt [MeEtPhPOH]Cl, which confirmed the value for the cation calculated from the sulphonate salt.

He also resolved benzylmethylphenylphosphine oxide as its (+)cam-phorsulphonate, and showed that the optically pure (−)phosphonium (+)camphorsulphonate when treated even in hot aqueous solution with an excess of ammonia deposited the crystalline (−)phosphine oxide (XIX) : no indication was obtained that the dihydroxide, [(PhCH$_2$)MePhP·OH]OH, was an intermediate in this liberation of the oxide.

These results may have some bearing on the complete failure which has so far attended all attempts to resolve analogous tertiary arsine oxides, of type $R^1R^2R^3As \rightarrow O$. This failure may be due solely to manipulative difficulties. The attempts have however apparently all been based on salt formation at the As—O link with optically active acids, as in Meisenheimer's phosphine oxide work. A possible explanation (Mann, 1945) may emerge from the nature of the series of compounds which can be formed by the action of alkalies on, for example, tertiary arsine dibromides. The latter (XX) are usually orange covalent compounds, having a structure presumably similar to that of the corresponding stibine derivatives (formula II, p. 221), *i.e.*

consisting of a trigonal bipyramid in which the three groups R lie in a triangular plane around the arsenic atom, with the bromine atoms

$$R_3AsBr_2 \rightarrow R_3AsBrOH \rightarrow R_3As(OH)_2 \rightarrow R_3As(OH)\cdot O\cdot(OH)AsR_3 \rightarrow R_3AsO$$

XX	XXI	XXII	XXIII	XXIV

on an axis passing through the arsenic atom at right angles to this plane. The action of alkalies on the dibromide XX is dependent largely on the nature of the groups R. The first action is to form the bromo-hydroxide XXI which may then give the dihydroxide XXII. The stability of this compound varies considerably : it may be reasonably stable, or lose water to give the ' sesqui ' compound XXIII, or pass so rapidly to the oxide XXIV that the dihydroxide cannot be isolated. If, in the course of the attempted resolution, the recrystallized salt of the arsine oxide and the optically active acid when treated with alkali gave the dihydroxide XXII and if this also should have the trigonal bipyramid structure, racemization must at once occur, even if the dihydroxide had only a transient existence as it underwent dehydration to the oxide XXIV. Meisenheimer's experiments indicate strongly that the corresponding phosphorus compounds are ionized bases, $[R_3POH]OH$, to which this mechanism of racemization would not apply. It would be of interest to decompose the diastereoisomer in the arsenic series also with ammonia in anhydrous conditions to avoid the intermediate formation of the dihydroxide and thus possibly preserve the optical activity.

It may be noted that triphenylarsine hydroxychloride, $Ph_3As(OH)Cl$, similar to the general type XXI, has a high dipole moment of 9·2 D, which Jensen (1943b) attributed to the contribution of the canonical forms Ph_3As^+—O^-—H—Cl and $[Ph_3As^+$—$OH]Cl^-$ [cf also Mann (1945) for a discussion of the compounds XXI to XXIII].

Sulphides of the Tertiary Derivatives

Confirmation of the tetrahedral disposition of the arsenic valencies in a tertiary arsine sulphide was obtained by Mills and Raper (1925), who resolved p-carboxyphenylethylmethylarsine sulphide (XXV) into optically active forms, having $[M]_{5780}$ +51° and −52° respectively in ethanolic solution. An aqueous solution of the sodium salt of this acid

XXV	XXVI	XXVII

216

was optically unaffected by prolonged boiling, and the acid has therefore considerable optical stability.

In view of this result, it is noteworthy that two forms of ethylene-1 : 2-bis(*n*-butylphenylarsine sulphide) (XXVI), having m.p. 113–116° and 121° respectively, were isolated by Chatt and Mann (1939a). In this case, the lower-melting isomer, when heated alone or in boiling ethanol, passed readily over to the higher-melting form. Since the two isomers must have been a *meso* and racemic pair, this conversion necessarily entailed a change in configuration at only one of the arsenic atoms in the lower-melting form. The mechanism of this conversion is unknown. It is possible, however, that in the corresponding monosulphide (XXVII), the positive charge on the arsenic atom joined to the sulphur tends to deactivate the second arsenic atom, and in consequence the disulphide (XXVI), when molten or in solution, exists in equilibrium with a very small proportion of the monosulphide (XXVII) and sulphur. In support of this suggestion, the apparently complete absence of interconversion of the two forms of the comparable palladium compound (p. 219), in which this type of dissociation could not occur, should be noted : on the other hand, the As→S link in the monosulphide XXVII must give this arsenic atom a positive charge so small that its inductive effect on the second arsenic atom should be very weak indeed.

In the phosphorus field, the optical resolution of *n*-butyl-*p*-(carboxymethoxy)phenyl-phenylphosphine sulphide (XXVIII) has been accom-

$$HO_2C \cdot CH_2O \cdot \left\langle\underline{}\right\rangle \cdot \overset{Bu}{\underset{Ph}{P}} \to S$$

XXVIII

plished by Davies and Mann (1944). This compound had $[M]_D$ +9·6° and −9·7° in benzene solution, and neither the acid in benzene, nor its ammonium salt in water, underwent racemization.

Three other classes of compounds containing formally 4-covalent phosphorus may conveniently be mentioned here : the optical resolution of one member of each class has recently been announced.

Aaron and Miller (1956), in a preliminary note, have recorded the resolution of *O*-ethylethylphosphonothiolic acid (XXIX) by the fractional crystallization of its quinine salt. The optically active free acids were not isolated, but the two diastereoisomerides were converted into the di-*cyclo*hexylamine salts, one having m.p. 158–160°, and

$$\begin{array}{cc}
\overset{Et}{\underset{EtO}{\diagdown}} \overset{O}{\underset{SH}{P}} & \overset{Me}{\underset{Ph}{\diagdown}} \overset{O}{\underset{OH}{P}} \\
\text{XXIX} & \text{XXX}
\end{array}$$

$[\alpha]_D^{25}$ $+6\cdot85°$ in methanol, and the other having m.p. 158–160·5°, and $[\alpha]_D^{25}$ $-7\cdot11°$: the racemic di-*cyclo*hexylamine salt had m.p. 166–168°. Although the observed rotations were small ($+0\cdot221°$ and $-0\cdot153°$), there appears no doubt concerning the actual resolution. This optically active compound is of considerable interest, for earlier attempts to resolve, for example, phosphinic acids such as methyl-phenylphosphinic acid (XXX) by Pope and Gibson (1912) had of course failed because ionization of these acids gave a resonance anion in which the phosphorus was no longer asymmetric. Even if the anion formed by ionization of the acid XXIV showed similar resonance, *i.e.* if the negative charge were distributed between the oxygen and sulphur atoms, the phosphorus atom would still remain asymmetric.

Coyne, McEwen and VanderWerf (1956) have resolved the methiodide of methyl methyl-*p*-dimethylaminophenylphosphinate

Me   O   Ph   O
  \ ↗   \ ↗
   P   P
  ⁄ \   ⁄ \
MeO   C₆H₄NMe₃ I⁻   PhO   NHCH₂CH₂NMe₃ I⁻

      XXXI   XXXII

(XXXI) by recrystallization of the $(+)$- and $(-)$-dibenzoyl hydrogen tartrates. The $(+)$iodide had m.p. 155·6–156·4°, $[\alpha]_D^{25}$ $+28°$, and the $(-)$iodide had m.p. 155·8–156·4°, $[\alpha]_D^{25}$ $-29\cdot0°$ in methanol: the picrates had $[\alpha]_D^{25}$ $+22°$ and $-22°$ respectively. The difficulty with which Pope and Gibson were unconsciously striving does not arise in this compound, for it is an ester of a phosphinic acid.

The resolution of the methiodide of *N*-2-dimethylaminoethyl-*O*-phenyl-*P*-phenylphosphonamidate (XXXII) has been accomplished by Marsi, VanderWerf and McEwen (1956), using fractional crystallization of the $(+)$camphorsulphonate. The $(+)$iodide had m.p. 160·0–160·5°, $[\alpha]_D^{24}$ $+4\cdot44°$, and the $(-)$iodide had m.p. 160·0–160·8°, $[\alpha]_D^{24}$ $-6\cdot42°$. The $(+)$iodide was isolated from the more soluble diastereoisomeride, and was thus not quite optically pure.

Metallic Coordination Compounds

There is a steadily increasing volume of x-ray-crystallographic evidence that when a tertiary phosphine or arsine coordinates with a metal, the three organic groups and the metallic atom are, as expected, tetrahedrally arranged around the central phosphorus or arsenic atom. This arrangement has thus been found, for example, in tetrakis(mono-iodotriethylarsinecopper), $[Et_3As{\rightarrow}CuI]_4$, in tetrakis(monoiodotri-*n*-propylarsinesilver), $[nPr_3As{\rightarrow}AgI]_4$, and almost certainly in mono-chlorotriethylarsinegold, $[Et_3As{\rightarrow}AuCl]$ (Mann, Purdie and Wells, 1936, 1937).

The tetrahedral configuration for both coordinated phosphorus and arsenic has been demonstrated by x-ray analysis in bis(*o*-diethyl-phosphinophenyldiethylarsine)aurous iodide (XXXIII) and the iso-morphous cuprous iodide (Cochran, Hart and Mann, 1957). This

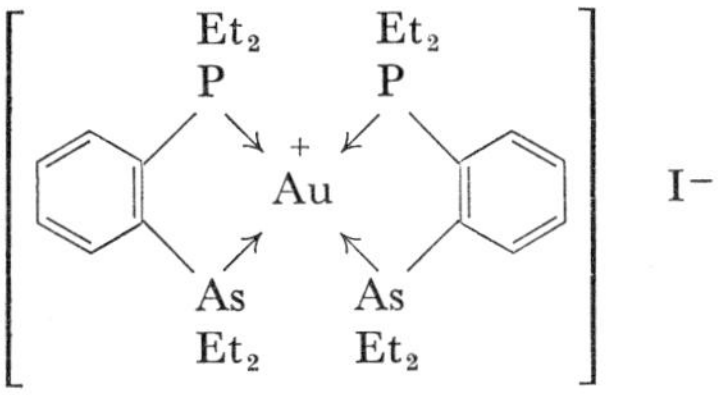

XXXIII

configuration has also been found in the two types of 'bridged' molecules, dibromobis(trimethylarsine)-$\mu\mu$-dibromodipalladium (XXXIV) (Mann and Wells, 1938; Wells, 1938a) and dibromobis-(triethylphosphine)-$\mu\mu$-dibromodicadmium (XXXV) (Evans, Mann, Peiser and Purdie, 1940): it is of interest incidentally that in these

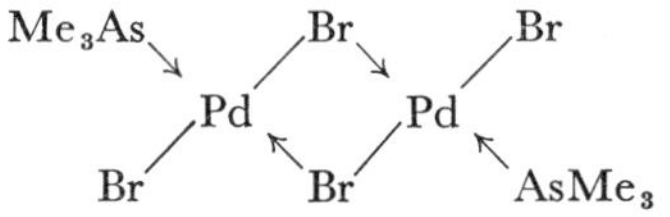

XXXIV 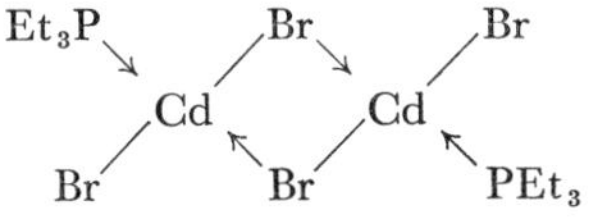   XXXV

compounds the 4-covalent palladium and the cadmium atoms have the planar and tetrahedral configuration respectively, and each molecule has a centre of symmetry. A final example, analysed in considerable detail, is tribromotriethylphosphinegold, [Me$_3$P→AuBr$_3$], (Perutz and Weiss, 1946).

It is clear that an asymmetric tertiary phosphine or arsine, when thus coordinated to a metal, could give a molecule capable of optical resolution by virtue of the asymmetric 4-covalent phosphorus or arsenic atom which it contains. This has not apparently been realized in practice. The compound, dichloro-ethylene-1 : 2-bis(*n*-butylphenyl-arsine)palladium (XXXVI), has been isolated in the two forms, m.p. 172–174° and 185–186° respectively (mixed m.p. 137–150°), which

XXXVI

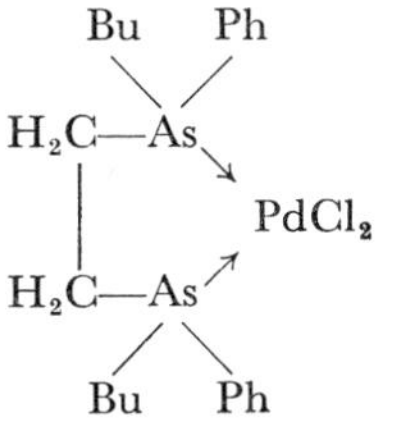

again represent a *meso* and racemic pair (Chatt and Mann, 1939b). In this compound, the very powerful chelating action of the diarsine gives a highly stable 5-membered ring, and the two asymmetric arsenic atoms are thus 'locked' in position, and no conversion (which would involve change of configuration at one arsenic atom) could be detected.

DERIVATIVES OF THE 5-COVALENT ELEMENTS

The Pentahalides

The phosphorus compounds, of empirical formula PX_5, where X is the halogen, are conveniently discussed under the above heading: they show however a very interesting variety of structures, in which the covalency of the phosphorus atom ranges from four to six. Phosphorus pentafluoride has been shown by Brockway and Beach (1938) by electron diffraction measurements to have a trigonal bipyramid molecule (I), in which all the P—F distances are equal, and which has zero dipole moment. The same structure was determined independently by Braune and Pinnow (1937).

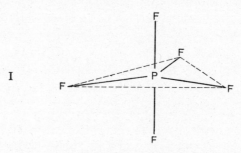

Phosphorus dichloride-trifluoride, PCl_2F_3, also has a trigonal bipyramid molecule (as I), with the fluorine atoms occupying the three horizontal (or equatorial) positions and the chlorine atoms the vertical (or axial) positions (Brockway and Beach, 1938).

Crystalline phosphorus pentachloride, however, has been shown by x-ray analysis to have an ionic structure, $[PCl_4]^+[PCl_6]^-$, in which the four chlorine atoms are arranged around the phosphorus in the cation as a rather irregular tetrahedron (Cl—P—Cl angles being 111° and 119°), and the six chlorine atoms are octahedrally arranged around the phosphorus in the anion (Powell, Clark and Wells, 1940; Clark, Powell and Wells, 1942). There is evidence that this ionic structure is retained in various solvents, such as acetonitrile (Payne, 1953). In the gaseous form, however, the molecules revert to the 5-covalent bipyramid structure (as I) (Rouault, 1938), although of course they readily dissociate.

Phosphorus pentabromide is also a salt, of structure $[PBr_4]^+Br^-$, in which the four bromine atoms form an almost regular tetrahedron around the phosphorus atom (Powell and Clark, 1940; van Driel and MacGillavry, 1943). In acetonitrile solution, however, phosphorus pentabromide gives rise to the ions $[PBr_4]^+$ and $[PBr_6]^-$ (Harris and Payne, 1956).

Arsenic forms only one pentahalide, the fluoride, AsF_5, which has b.p. $-53°$, and which tends to dissociate.

Antimony pentachloride has been shown, by Raman spectra studies of the vapour (Jensen, 1943a) and by x-ray analysis of the crystal (Ohlberg, 1954), also to have a trigonal bipyramid molecule (as I).

Arsenic and antimony in particular form three series of compounds, which may be exemplified as $RAsCl_4$, R_2AsCl_3 and R_3AsCl_2 (where R is an alkyl or aryl group) ; these can usually be readily formed by the addition of a molecule of chlorine to the corresponding compounds $RAsCl_2$, R_2AsCl, and R_3As, and similar compounds containing bromine, and sometimes iodine, can also be prepared. The last and most stable class, of type R_3ElX_2, can be obtained when El = P, As, Sb and Bi. Wells (1938b) has shown that the three compounds Me_3SbX_2, where X = Cl, Br and I, are isomorphous and that the dibromide, for example, has the trigonal bipyramid structure (II), with the methyl groups occupying the equatorial positions and the two bromine atoms the polar positions. The Sb—Br distance is intermediate between that expected for a covalent and for an ionic arrangement and almost certainly indicates a hybrid bond. Jensen (1943a) has found that the compounds Ph_3SbCl_2 and Ph_3BiCl_2 have

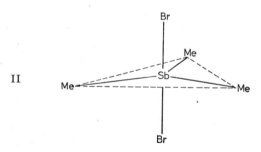

zero dipole moments in benzene solution but unusually large atomic polarization, and he considers that they also have a structure analogous to (II) : the compound $Ph_3Sb(OH)_2$ has zero dipole moment and therefore presumably the same structure.

A compound having formally 5-covalent phosphorus, and of great stereochemical interest is one of the various products of general formula $(PNCl_2)_n$ obtained by the action of chlorine on phosphorus nitride. A more recent and convenient method of preparation, due to Steinman, Schirmer and Audrieth (1942), utilizes the interaction of phosphorus pentachloride and ammonium chloride, whereby in particular the two polymers, of formula $(PNCl_2)_3$ and $(PNCl_2)_4$ respectively, can be isolated. Electron diffraction studies (Brockway and Bright, 1943) show that the former compound, $P_3N_3Cl_6$, has the

III

IV

structure (III), where the ring consists of a regular planar hexagon in which the P—N distance is 1·65 Å throughout, and the projecting P—Cl distance is uniformly 1·97 Å. The calculated interatomic distances for phosphorus and nitrogen when joined by a single and a double bond are 1·80 and 1·60 Å, respectively: for phosphorus and chlorine they are similarly 2·09 and 1·89 Å respectively. It is clear therefore that we have here an inorganic ring which is stabilized by resonance, and is thus closely similar in general type to that in benzene: in this case, however, the P—Cl distance indicates that the resonance also affects the phosphorus–chlorine bond.

The structure of the higher polymer, of formula $P_4N_4Cl_8$, has been investigated by Ketelaar and de Vries (1939) using x-ray crystal analysis. They found that the molecule has a puckered eight-membered ring (IV), in which the intervalency P—N—P and N—P—N angles are 123° and 117° respectively, and the P—N distances throughout the ring are 'essentially the same', namely 1·67 Å : hence this ring also has some degree of resonance. Each phosphorus atom has two nitrogen and two chlorine atoms arranged tetrahedrally around it. These workers say that although the chlorine atoms can be hydrolysed, the stability of the ring system is shown by the fact that it is not affected by boiling aqua regia. The existence of the puckered eight-membered ring in the corresponding dihydrated acid, $P_4N_4(OH)_8, 2H_2O$, has been confirmed by Corbridge (1953) by x-ray analysis.

A remarkable series of compounds, of general formula Ph_5El, where El is phosphorus, arsenic, antimony and bismuth, has recently been prepared and studied by Wittig and his co-workers. The first member is obtained from tetraphenylphosphonium iodide: quaternary salts of this type can be obtained by the interaction of (a) triphenylphosphine and phenylmagnesium bromide (Dodonow and Medox, 1928), (b) triphenylphosphine and bromobenzene in the presence of aluminium chloride (Chatt and Mann, 1940b; Lyon and Mann, 1942), (c) triphenylphosphine oxide and phenyl-lithium (Gilman and Brown, 1945). Method (b) can also be used to prepare the corresponding arsonium and stibonium salts.

222

Wittig and Rieber (1949) showed that tetraphenylphosphonium iodide reacts with phenyl-lithium to give the crystalline pentaphenyl-phosphorus, m.p. 124°. Wittig and Claus (1952a) showed that pentaphenyl-arsenic, m.p. 149–150°, can be similarly prepared, whilst pentaphenyl-antimony, m.p. 169–170·5°, can be prepared by the action of phenyl-lithium on tetraphenylstibonium bromide or (better) on triphenylstibine-dibromide. Pentaphenyl-bismuth, violet crystals, which explode at c 105°, is formed by the interaction of phenyl-lithium and triphenylbismuth-dichloride at −75° (Wittig and Claus, 1952b) : it contrasts in colour markedly with its colourless phosphorus, arsenic, and antimony analogues.

It should be added that the above four pentaphenyl compounds are sometimes termed pentaphenyl-phosphorane, -arsorane, -stiborane, and -bismuthorane respectively.

Phenyl-lithium also reacts with methyl-triphenylphosphonium iodide to give the pale yellow crystalline methylenetriphenyl-phosphorus, $CH_2 : PPh_3$, with benzyl-triphenylphosphonium chloride to give the orange-red compound $PhCH : PPh_3$, and with the allyl analogue to give the deep red compound $CH_2 : CH \cdot CH : PPh_3$ (Wittig and Geissler, 1953 ; Wittig and Schöllkopf, 1954). These compounds are similar in type to the red compound, $Ph_2C : PPh_3$, prepared much earlier by Staudinger and Meyer (1919).

Very little is known at present regarding the stereochemistry of the above pentaphenyl compounds, or of these derivatives having a group linked formally by a double bond to the phosphorus atom. The marked difference in colour between the two series of 5-covalent phosphorus compounds may indicate a fundamental difference in structure : the trigonal bipyramid structure (as I) is presumably possible for the pentaphenyl compounds, but would almost certainly be impossible for the double-bonded compounds.

It may be added that these double-bonded compounds are proving invaluable to the organic chemist, as they afford a method whereby in one operation the oxygen atom of a carbonyl group can be replaced by a methylene or substituted methylene group (Wittig and Geissler, 1953 ; Wittig and Schöllkopf, 1954). Thus the above compounds $CH_2 : PPh_3$, $PhCH : PPh_3$ and $CH_2 : CH \cdot CH : PPh_3$ react readily with benzaldehyde to give styrene $(PhCH : CH_2)$, *trans*-stilbene $(PhCH : CHPh)$, and ω-vinyl-styrene $(PhCH : CH \cdot CH : CH_2)$ respectively, with the formation of triphenylphosphine oxide in each case. Ketones react similarly.

DERIVATIVES OF THE 6-COVALENT ELEMENTS

Few compounds in which the Group V element shows a covalency of six are at present known, but there is little doubt that both a greater number and a greater variety will come to light in due course.

One would expect this covalency to occur most readily in the halogen derivatives. Lange and von Krueger (1932) have claimed that sodium, potassium and ammonium fluorides react with phosphorus pentachloride to give salts of type $M[PF_6]$. The existence of the $[PCl_6]^-$ anion in crystalline phosphorus pentachloride and the existence of the $[PBr_6]^-$ anion in solutions of the pentabromide have already been discussed (p. 220). Wittig and Geissler (1953) have shown that pentaphenyl-phosphorus reacts with phosphorus penta-chloride in accordance with the reaction :

$$Ph_5P + 2PCl_5 = [Ph_4P][PCl_6] + PhCl + PCl_3$$

The salt thus obtained forms colourless crystals.

Furthermore, pentaphenyl-antimony combines with phenyl-lithium to give the salt $Li[SbPh_6]$, which can be crystallized from tetrahydro-furan (Wittig and Claus, 1952). We know from the x-ray evidence that the six chlorine atoms are octahedrally arranged around the phosphorus atom in the $[PCl_6]$ anion in phosphorus pentachloride, and it is highly probable that the same arrangement occurs in the other hexahalides, and in the above hexaphenylantimonate.

I   II

An entirely different type of compound, in which the octahedral arrangement must occur, is tripyrocatechylarsenic acid (I), which is readily obtained by the interaction of pyrocatechol and arsenic acid, H_3AsO_4, in boiling aqueous solution. This acid crystallizes as a pentahydrate, from which only four molecules of water can be detached : the acid and all its known salts have this extra one molecule of water. For this reason, Reihlen, Sapper and Kall (1925) considered that the acid has the structure II.

The acid has been resolved into optically active forms by Rosenheim and Plato (1925), the two forms having $[M]_D$ +2002° and −2187° respectively in aqueous acetone. The acid is optically stable in alkaline solution (*i.e.* as its salts), undergoes slow racemization in neutral solution, and immediate racemization in acidic solution.

If the acid had the structure II, with the unchelated pyrocatechyl group and the coordinated molecule of water in the *cis* or 1 : 2 position, it would of course still be susceptible to optical resolution. For a more detailed discussion of the structure of this compound and of the corresponding antimony compound, which has not been optically resolved, see Mann (1950).

REFERENCES

Aaron, H. S. and Miller, J. T. (1956) *J. Amer. chem. Soc.* **78,** 3538
Adams, R., Blomstrom, D. C. and Sundstrom, K. V. Y. (1954) *ibid* **76,** 5478
— and Dankert, L. J. (1940) *ibid* **62,** 2191
Allen, P. W. and Sutton, L. E. (1950) *Acta cryst., Camb.* **3,** 46
Badger, G. M., Buttery, R. G. and Lewis, G. E. (1953) *J. chem. Soc.* 2143
Badgley, G. R. and Livingston, R. L. (1954) *J. Amer. chem. Soc.* **76,** 261
Beach, J. Y. and Stevenson, D. P. (1938) *J. chem. Phys.* **6,** 75
Bennett, G. M. and Glynn, E. (1950) *J. chem. Soc.* 211
Bradley, A. J. (1924) *Phil. Mag.* **47,** 657
Braune, H. and Pinnow, P. (1937) *Z. phys. Chem.* **B35,** 256
Brockway, L. O. and Beach, J. Y. (1938) *J. Amer. chem. Soc.* **60,** 1836
— and Bright, W. M. (1943) *ibid* **65,** 1551
Burrows, G. J. and Turner, E. E. (1921) *J. chem. Soc.* **119,** 426
Campbell, I. G. M. (1947) *ibid* 4 ; (1950) *ibid* 3109 ; (1952) *ibid* 4448 ; (1955)
  ibid 6372 ; (1956) *ibid* 1976
— Le Fèvre, C. G., Le Fèvre, R. J. W. and Turner, E. E. (1938) *ibid* 404
— and Morrill, D. J. (1955) *ibid* 1662
— and Poller, R. C. (1956) *ibid* 1195
Campbell, N., Henderson, A. W. and Taylor, D. (1953) *ibid* 1281
Chatt, J. and Mann, F. G. (1939a) *ibid* 610 ; (1939b) *ibid* 1622 ; (1910a) *ibid*
  1184 ; (1940b) *ibid* 1192
Clark, D., Powell, H. M. and Wells, A. F. (1942) *ibid* 642
Cochran, W., Hart, F. A. and Mann, F. G. (1957) *ibid* 2816
Cook, A. H. (1938) *ibid* 876
— and Jones, D. G. (1939) *ibid* 1309
— — and Polya, J. B. (1939) *ibid* 1315
Corbridge, D. E. C. (1953) *Acta cryst., Cop.* **6,** 104
Costain, C. C. and Sutherland, G. B. B. M. (1952) *J. Amer. chem. Soc.* **56,** 321
Coyne, D. M., McEwen, W. E. and VanderWerf, C. A. (1956) *ibid* **78,** 3061
Davies, W. C. and Mann, F. G. (1944) *J. chem. Soc.* 276
de Decker, H. C. J. (1941) *Rec. Trav. chim. Pays-Bas* **60,** 413
— and MacGillavry, C. H. (1941) *ibid* 153
Dodonow, J. and Medox, H. (1928) *Ber. dtsch. chem. Ges.* **61,** 907
Evans, R. C., Mann, F. G., Peiser, H. S. and Purdie, D. (1940) *J. chem. Soc.* 1209
Freeman, H. C. and Le Fèvre, R. J. W. (1951) *ibid* 415
Gilman, H. and Brown, G. E. (1945) *J. Amer. chem. Soc.* **67,** 824
Hampson, G. C. and Robertson, J. M. (1941) *J. chem. Soc.* 409
— and Stosick, A. J. (1938) *J. Amer. chem. Soc.* **60,** 1814
Hanby, W. E. and Rydon, H. N. (1945) *J. chem. Soc.* 833
Harris, G. S. and Payne, D. S. (1956) *ibid* 4617
Hart, F. A. and Mann, F. G. (1955) *ibid* 4107
Hartley, G. S. (1938) *ibid* 633
Hatt, H. H. (1933) *ibid* 776
Holliman, F. G. and Mann, F. G. (1943) *ibid* 547, 550 ; (1945) *ibid* 45 ; (1947)
  ibid 1634
Hromatka, O. and Kraupp, O. (1951) *Mh. Chem.* **82,** 880
Huang-Hsinmin and Mann, F. G. (1949) *J. chem. Soc.* 2903
Hultgren, R., Gingrich, N. S. and Warren, B. E. (1935) *J. chem. Phys.* **3,** 351
Jamison, M. M. and Turner, E. E. (1938) *J. chem. Soc.* 1646 ; (1940) *ibid* 264 ;
  (1955) *ibid* 145
Jensen, K. A. (1943a) *Z. anorg. Chem.* **250,** 257 ; (1943b) *ibid* **250,** 268

225

Jones, Emrys R. H. and Mann, F. G. (1955a) *J. chem. Soc.* 401 ; (1955b) *ibid* 405 ; (1955c) *ibid* 411
Ketelaar, J. A. A. and de Vries, T. A. (1939) *Rec. Trav. chim. Pays-Bas* **58**, 1081
Kincaid, J. F. and Henriques, F. C. jun. (1940) *J. Amer. chem. Soc.* **62**, 1474
Kisliuk, P. (1954) *J. chem. Phys.* **22**, 86
— and Geschwind, S. (1953) *ibid* **21**, 828
— and Townes, C. H. (1950) *ibid* **18**, 1109
Lange, W. and Krueger, G. von (1932) *Ber. dtsch. chem. Ges.* **65**, 1253
Le Fèvre, R. J. W. (1951) *J. chem. Soc.* 1814
Leonard, N. J. and Sutton, L. E. (1948) *J. Amer. chem. Soc.* **70**, 1564
Lesslie, M. S. (1949) *J. chem. Soc.* 1183
— and Turner, E. E. (1934) *ibid* 1170 ; (1935) *ibid* 1051, 1268 : *cf* also Lesslie, M. S. (1949) *ibid* 1183
Lu, C. S. and Donohue, J. (1944) *J. Amer. chem. Soc.* **66**, 818
Lyon, D. R. and Mann, F. G. (1942) *J. chem. Soc.* 666 ; (1945) *ibid* 30
McCleland, N. P. and Whitworth, J. B. (1927) *ibid* 2753
McElvain, S. M. and Bannister, L. W. (1954) *J. Amer. chem. Soc.* **76**, 1126
Mahler, W. and Burg, A. B. (1957) *ibid* **79**, 251
Mann, F. G. (1945) *J. chem. Soc.* 65 ; (1950) *The Heterocyclic Derivatives of Phosphorus, Arsenic, Antimony, Bismuth, and Silicon*, New York, Interscience
— and Baker, F. C. (1952) *J. chem. Soc.* 4142 ; (1957) *ibid* 1881
— and Chaplin, E. J. (1937) *ibid* 527
— and Mukherjee, D. P. (1949) *ibid* 2298
— Purdie, D. and Wells, A. F. (1936) *ibid* 1503 ; (1937) *ibid* 1828
— and Senior, A. (1954) *ibid* 4476
— and Watson, J. (1947) *ibid* 505
— and Wells, A. F. (1938) *ibid* 702
Marsi, K. L., VanderWerf, C. A. and McEwen, W. E. (1956) *J. Amer. chem. Soc.* **78**, 3063
Maxwell, L. R., Hendricks, S. B. and Moseley, V. M. (1935) *J. chem. Phys.* **3**, 699
Meisenheimer, J. (1908) *Ber. dtsch. chem. Ges.* **41**, 3966 ; (1920) *Liebigs Ann.* **420**, 190
— Angermann, L., Finn, O. and Vieweg, E. (1924) *Ber. dtsch. chem. Ges.* **57**, 1744
— Casper, J., Höring, M., Lauter, W., Lichtenstadt, L. and Samuel, W. (1926) *Liebigs Ann.* **449**, 224
— and Lichtenstadt, L. (1911) *Ber. dtsch. chem. Ges.* **44**, 356
Mills, W. H. and Elliott, K. A. C. (1928) *J. chem. Soc.* 1291
— and Raper, R. (1925) *ibid* **127**, 2479
— and Warren, E. H. (1925) *ibid* **127**, 2507
Mooney, R. C. L. (1940) *J. Amer. chem. Soc.* **62**, 2955
Nyburg, S. C. and Hilton, J. (1955) *Acta cryst. Cop.* **8**, 358
Ohlberg, S. (1954) *ibid* **7**, 600
Patterson, W. I. and Adams, R. (1933) *J. Amer. chem. Soc.* **55**, 1069
Pauling, L. and Brockway, L. O. (1935) *ibid* **57**, 2684
Payne, D. S. (1953) *J. chem. Soc.* 1052
Perutz, M. F. and Weiss, O. (1946) *ibid* 438
Phillips, G. M., Hunter, J. S. and Sutton, L. E. (1945) *ibid* 146
Pope, W. J. and Gibson, C. S. (1912) *ibid* **101**, 740
— and Harvey, A. W. (1901) *ibid* **79**, 831
— and Peachey, S. J. (1899) *ibid* **75**, 1127
Powell, H. M. and Clark, D. (1940) *Nature, Lond.* **145**, 971
— — and Wells, A. F. (1940) *ibid* **145**, 149
Prelog, V. and Wieland, P. (1944) *Helv. chim. Acta* **27**, 1127
Reihlen, H., Sapper, A. and Kall, G. A. (1925) *Z. anorg. Chem.* **144**, 218

Robertson, J. M. (1939) *J. chem. Soc.* 232
Rosenheim, A. and Plato, W. (1925) *Ber. dtsch. chem. Ges.* **58**, 2000
Rouault, M. (1938) *C.R. Acad. Sci., Paris* **207**, 620
Secrist, J. H. and Brockway, L. O. (1944) *J. Amer. chem. Soc.* **66**, 1941
Sidgwick, N. V. (1927) *The Electronic Theory of Valency*, Oxford
Skinner, H. A. and Sutton, L. E. (1940) *Trans. Faraday Soc.* **36**, 681
Spielman, M. A. (1935) *J. Amer. chem. Soc.* **57**, 583
Springall, H. D. and Brockway, L. O. (1938) *ibid* **60**, 996
Staudinger, H. and Meyer, J. (1919) *Helv. chim. Acta* **2**, 635
Steinman, R., Schirmer, F. B. and Audrieth, L. F. (1942) *J. chem. Soc.* **64**, 2377
Stosick, A. J. (1939) *J. Amer. chem. Soc.* **61**, 1130
Sutherland, G. B. B. M., Lee, E. and Wu, C. K. (1939) *Trans. Faraday Soc.* **35**, 1373
Thomas, C. D. and Gingrich, N. S. (1938) *J. chem. Phys.* **6**, 659
van Driel, M. and MacGillavry, C. H. (1943) *Rec. Trav. chim. Pays-Bas* **62**, 167
Vos, A. and Wiebenga, E. H. (1954) *Proc. k. ned. Akad. Wet.* **B57**, 497
Waser, J. and Schomaker, V. (1945) *J. Amer. chem. Soc.* **67**, 2014
Wells, A. F. (1938a) *Proc. roy. Soc.* **A167**, 169; (1938b) *Z. Kristallogr.* **99**, 367;
(1949) *J. chem. Soc.* 55
Weston, R. E. (1954) *J. Amer. chem. Soc.* **76**, 2645
Williams, Q. and Gordy, W. (1950) *Phys. Rev.* **79**, 225
— Sheridan, J. and Gordy, W. (1952) *J. chem. Phys.* **20**, 164
Wittig, G. and Claus, K. (1952a) *Liebigs Ann.* **577**, 26; (1952b) *ibid* **578**, 136
— and Geissler, G. (1953) *ibid* **580**, 44
— and Rieber, M. (1949) *ibid* **562**, 187
— and Schöllkopf, V. (1954) *Chem. Ber.* **87**, 1318

7

STERIC FACTORS IN IMMUNOCHEMISTRY

J. R. Marrack and Eva S. Orlans

THE reactions between antigens and antibodies are extremely specific. The early work of Nuttall and Strangeways (1904) showed that the proteins of closely related species, such as men and apes, could be distinguished by the amounts of precipitate formed with antisera; many similar instances of this high specificity have been found since then. Most of the antigens studied in early years were proteins, and it has been conclusively shown during the last 25 years that antibodies are serum globulins. These proteins are all made up of the same relatively few amino acids and the compositions of antibodies against different antigens differ little, if at all, one from another. We cannot, as yet, invoke any special group in a protein antigen or an antibody to account for their specific reactions. Ehrlich used the lock-and-key simile; but the exact significance of this simile among immunologists was not clear; most took refuge in a smoke-screen of nebulous terms invoking " colloid " reactions. A revolution in the approach to the specificity of these reactions began when Landsteiner (Landsteiner and Lampl, 1917) developed a method of making antisera against groups of known composition and structure, at an opportune time, when x-ray analysis was beginning to show that organic molecules actually had the shapes predicted by structural formulae; any consideration of the specificity of antigen–antibody reactions must commence with Landsteiner's work.

ARTIFICIAL ANTIGENS

The method used by Landsteiner can be illustrated by his first experiments on these lines. He diazotized p-aminophenylarsonic acid $(NH_2 \cdot C_6H_4 \cdot AsO_3H_2)$ and coupled the diazo compound to sheep serum protein; the diazonium salt combines mainly with the tyrosyl and histidyl residues of proteins forming a coloured compound. If such a compound is injected repeatedly into a rabbit, antibodies appear in the serum of the rabbit; these antibodies will form precipitates with the compounds formed by coupling the diazotized p-aminophenylarsonic acid with proteins unrelated to sheep serum proteins (the reaction is not dependent on the protein used) and, as shown later, these antibodies combine specifically with phenylarsonic acid compounds. The degree of specificity of the antibodies formed varies; the degree that may be expected is illustrated by TABLE 1*.

In much of his work Landsteiner depended on the visual estimation of the amount of precipitate formed by an antiserum with a test antigen and represented the amount by a varying number of + signs† ; these estimates are rough and may depend very much on the observer;

TABLE 1. REACTIONS OF HOMOLOGOUS AND HETEROLOGOUS ANTIGENS

[Amounts of precipitate formed by homologous and heterologous antigens with antiserum against diazotized *m*-aminophenylsulphonic acid coupled to horse serum protein. The protein of the test antigens was chicken serum protein (Landsteiner and van der Scheer, 1936).]

Test antigen made from	Position of group G in test antigen		
	N=N— ⬡G	N=N— ⬡G	N=N— ⬡ G
Amino-phenylsulphonic acid $G = SO_3H$	$+\pm$	$+++$	$\pm$
Amino-phenylarsonic acid $G = AsO_3H_2$	0	$+$	0
Amino-benzoic acid $G = CO_2H$	0	$+$	0

accurate analytical methods were introduced later. Also the amount of precipitate depends on the ratio of antigen to antibody present in the serum; if tests are not made with a series of different amounts of antigen, the amount of precipitate observed may not be the maximum that can be formed with this particular antigen. But this method may be open to a more serious objection. It is only during recent years that it has been realized that small impurities in an antigen may give rise to disproportionately large amounts of antibody; thus, the amount of antibody against ovalbumin in the serum of a horse that had been immunized with crystalline ovalbumin was less than the amount of antibody against conalbumin, that was present as an impurity in the ovalbumin (Cohn *et al.*, 1949). Likewise the antiserum obtained by immunizing with antigens formed from a (−)isomer, contaminated

* It is convenient to give the name, *determinants*, to the groups that are attached to the proteins and confer a new specificity. The compound used for immunizing and the compound, made from another protein, that is used for testing, are called *immunizing* and *test* antigens. An antibody against such an immunizing antigen and a test antigen containing the same determinant are said to be *homologous* one to the other.

† ± represents a trace.

with a very small amount of the $(+)$isomer, may contain a considerable amount of antibody against the $(+)$isomer. The antibody against the $(-)$isomer will appear less specific than it actually is, since this antibody against the $(+)$isomer will form a precipitate with test antigens formed from the $(+)$isomer.

This complication can be avoided by using an inhibition method. Substances of low molecular weight that contain the specific determinant group (phenylarsonic acid in the instance quoted) combine with the antibody but do not form precipitates. They compete with test antigens for the antibody and, therefore, inhibit the formation of a precipitate by antiserum and test antigen. Such inhibiting compounds are called *haptens*. The affinity of a hapten for antibody may be estimated by the degree to which a given amount inhibits the formation of precipitate by homologous test antigen with antiserum, or by the amount of hapten required to reduce the precipitate by a given amount. In such experiments the presence of a small amount of impurity in the hapten or the presence in the serum of antibodies against an impurity of the immunizing antigen will not appreciably affect the result.

TABLE 2. IMMUNOLOGICAL REACTIONS OF TARTARIC ACID ISOMERS

A. Amounts of precipitate formed by tartaric acid antigens with homologous and heterologous antisera.

B. Degree of inhibition by homologous and heterologous haptens.

(Landsteiner and van der Scheer, 1929)

A. Precipitates

	Antigen		
	$(-)$	$(+)$	*meso*
Antiserum $(-)$	+++	f.tr.*	+
$(+)$	0	+++	+
meso	f.tr.*	0	+++

B. Inhibition

	Hapten			No hapten (Control)
	$(-)$	$(+)$	*meso*	
$(-)$ Antigen and anti$(-)$ serum	0	+	±	++
$(+)$ Antigen and anti$(+)$ serum	+±	0	±	++±
meso Antigen and anti (*meso*)-serum	++±	++	0	++±

* f.tr. = faint trace.

A particularly interesting study (Landsteiner and van der Scheer, 1929) is a good example of the use of inhibition by haptens, although the amounts of precipitate were estimated visually (TABLE 2A). The three isomers of tartaric acid (I, II, III) were attached to proteins by coupling the latter with diazonium salts derived from the diastereo-isomers of p-aminotartranilic acid ($NH_2 \cdot C_6H_4 \cdot NH \cdot CO \cdot CH(OH) \cdot CH(OH) \cdot CO_2H$) and the resulting products were used for immunizing rabbits. In this case the amounts of precipitate that were compared were those formed with the optimum amounts of the antigens. The experiments show the advantage of the inhibition method in demonstrating the affinity for antibody of a particular configuration. For one might suppose that each of the determinants is attached to the corresponding four sites, P, Q, R and S of the homologous antibody (e.g. I–III). The $meso$-tartaric determinant (III) could then be

$$
\begin{array}{ccc}
\overset{\textcircled{S}}{-O_2C}\overset{H}{\underset{\textcircled{R}}{\underset{OH}{\overset{|}{C}}}} & \overset{\textcircled{S}}{-O_2C}\overset{OH}{\underset{\textcircled{R}}{\underset{H}{\overset{|}{C}}}} & \overset{\textcircled{S}}{-O_2C}\overset{OH}{\underset{\textcircled{R}}{\underset{H}{\overset{|}{C}}}} \\
& & \\
\underset{\textcircled{P}}{HO}\underset{H}{\overset{|}{C}}\underset{\textcircled{Q}}{CONH} & \underset{\textcircled{P}}{H}\underset{OH}{\overset{|}{C}}\underset{\textcircled{Q}}{CONH} & \underset{\textcircled{P}}{HO}\underset{H}{\overset{|}{C}}\underset{\textcircled{Q}}{CONH} \\
(-) & (+) & meso \\
I & II & III
\end{array}
$$

attached at three points, P, Q, S, and the $(+)$tartaric determinant (II) at two points only (Q and S) to the $(-)$tartaric antibody site. It would be expected, then, that the $meso$-tartaric acid determinant would have considerable affinity for the $(-)$tartaric site; and although the $meso$-tartaric test antigen formed only a trace of precipitate with the $(-)$tartaric antiserum, a $meso$-tartaric hapten had a considerable inhibitory effect as shown by the reduction of the amount of precipitate formed by $(-)$tartaric test antigen with $(-)$tartaric antiserum (TABLE 2B).

We shall consider, in the main, the inhibition experiments in which the amount of precipitate was measured accurately and refer to the great volume of work on the subject done by Landsteiner only to illustrate certain special points. Another of his investigations may, however, be introduced here as it illustrates the sources of error in the simple precipitation experiment in which the amount of precipitate was estimated visually. Rabbits were immunized with an antigen formed by coupling with protein the diazonium salt of p-toluidine [p-Me$\cdot$C$_6$H$_4 \cdot$N$\equiv$N]$^+$Cl$^-$ (Landsteiner and van der Scheer, 1927). The resulting antisera formed the same amounts of precipitate, estimated visually, with test antigens made from p-chloro- and p-bromo-aniline, and with those made from p-anisidine ($NH_2 \cdot C_6H_4 \cdot OCH_3$) and p-iodo-aniline, in which the group attached was considerably larger than the methyl group of toluidine. It is highly probable that, if the precipitates had been estimated accurately, considerable differences would have been found. The antiserum also formed a precipitate with an *o*-toluidine test antigen; it is possible that antibodies had been formed against traces of *o*-isomer in the *p*-toluidine, and that the precipitate formed with the *o*-toluidine test antigen was largely due to this antibody.

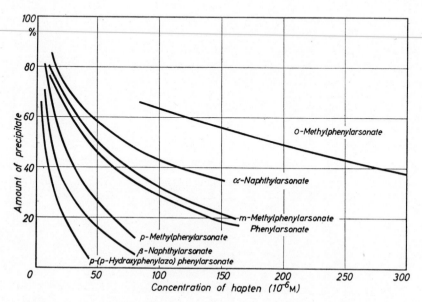

FIGURE 1. Amounts of precipitate formed by anti-*p*-phenylarsonic acid antiserum with homologous test antigen in the presence of varying concentrations of haptens. The amounts of precipitate are expressed as percentages of the amount of precipitate formed when no hapten was present (Pauling and Pressman, 1945). The haptens are designated against the appropriate curves.

In a large number of experiments, Pauling and colleagues have estimated the affinities of homologous and heterologous haptens for antibodies by the degree by which they reduced the amount of precipitate formed by antibody with homologous antigen; the optimum amount of homologous test antigen was added to antiserum in the presence of varying amounts of hapten and the precipitate formed was measured chemically. An example of such inhibition experiments is illustrated in FIGURE 1. For practical purposes the average equilibrium constant of combination of hapten with antibody may be taken to be inversely proportional to the concentration of hapten required to halve the amount of precipitate formed with the test antigen. A relative average equilibrium constant* (K_0') of a hapten may be taken as the

* There is evidence that the antibody molecules in an antiserum differ in their affinity for the determinant; it is, therefore, necessary to consider the average equilibrium constant.

ratio of the 50 per cent inhibiting concentration of a standard hapten to the 50 per cent inhibiting concentration of the hapten under consideration. These experiments are further complicated by the fact that haptens are adsorbed to a varying degree by serum albumin. Since whole serum was used in these groups of experiments the concentration of hapten, available for combining with antibody and inhibiting precipitation, was less than the total concentration. This complication has been studied by Pressman and Siegel (1953a), both by measuring and correcting for the amount of hapten bound by albumin, and by using the serum globulin alone (which does not bind the haptens non-specifically) in place of whole antiserum. On the whole the relative affinities of the haptens, so corrected, do not differ seriously from the uncorrected values. In the discussion that follows, corrected values have been used when available.

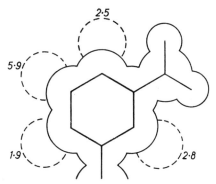

FIGURE 2. Diagram of cavities fitting closely to a m-azo-phenylcarboxylic determinant, showing the dilatation necessary to accommodate a chlorine atom replacing a hydrogen atom of the benzene ring. The K_0' of each chloro-substituted m-(p-hydroxyphenylazo-)phenylcarboxylate hapten is shown in the appropriate position; the value for the unsubstituted compound is 17.

As Pauling and Pressman (1943, 1945) have pointed out, the forces involved in the combination of antigens or haptens with antibodies are of three kinds, namely (i) electrostatic attraction of charged groups; (ii) hydrogen-bond forces; and (iii) van der Waals forces. These are entirely non-specific, short-range forces. The specificity of combination must depend on the close approach of a number of atoms of antigen or hapten to a combining site of the antibody. Pauling and Pressman (1945) suggested that the determinants of the type of antigen which we are considering fit closely into cavities or depressions on the surface of the antibody (FIGURE 2). This concept provides a framework to which the details of the experiments may be related. The radial dilatation of the cavity needed to accommodate various substituents on the benzene ring as estimated by Pauling and Pressman (1945) is given in TABLE 3.

TABLE 3. DILATATION OF CAVITIES

[Degree of dilatation of cavities, that accommodate *o*-, *m*- and *p*-determinants, required to admit various substituents at positions on the benzene ring other than that of the —N=N— group in the homologous determinant (Pauling and Pressman, 1945).]

(All values in Ångstrom units)

Substituent group	*o*-Antigen		*m*-Antigen		*p*-Antigen	
	Position of substituent		Position of substituent		Position of substituent	
	m	*p*	*o*	*p*	*o*	*m*
Phenylazo	>4	>2	2	1	>3	1·5
Nitro	0·9	1·6	0·8	1·0	1·0	0·8
Methyl	0·8	1·2	0·7	0·9	0·8	0·7
Amino	0·8	1·2	0·6	0·9	0·8	0·6

The following conclusions may be drawn from inhibition experiments, such as are illustrated in FIGURE 1; the antibody in this instance was that against an antigen formed from diazotized *p*-aminophenylarsonic acid.

The effect of the position of a second substituent on the benzene ring—A substituent in the position *ortho* to the arsonic group reduces the affinity below that of the unsubstituted phenylarsonic acid, which is taken as the standard; the effect of a small *meta*-group varies, whereas an extension of the area of the hapten in the place on the benzene ring in the *para*-position increases the affinity for antibody. In particular, the azo derivatives *p*-(*p*-hydroxyphenylazo)phenylarsonate ($HO \cdot C_6H_4 \cdot N_2 \cdot C_6H_4 \cdot AsO_3H^-$) and *p*-(*p*-aminophenylazo)phenylarsonate ($NH_2 \cdot C_6H_4 \cdot N_2 \cdot C_6H_4 \cdot AsO_3H^-$) have the highest affinity. Early experiments by Erlenmeyer and Berger (1933) showed that other haptens in which the link connecting the two benzene rings was not an azo link were equally effective inhibitors. In the *β*-naphthyl derivative, in which the second benzene ring may be regarded as a *meta*- and a *para*-substituent, the effect of a *meta*-substituent is outweighed by the effect of increased area; and the *α*-naphthyl derivatives are stronger inhibitors than other haptens that have an *ortho*-substituent.

These effects of the position of a second substituent are those found with the *p*-phenylarsonate antigen and the homologous antiserum. With the *o*-phenylarsonate antigen and homologous antiserum, it is the haptens with a substituent in the *ortho*-position to the arsonate group that inhibit most strongly; those with the substituent in the *para*-position inhibit least. Of the naphthyl derivatives, *α*-naphthyl-arsonate inhibits most strongly. With *m*-phenylarsonate antigen and homologous antiserum the haptens with substituents *meta* to the arsonate group inhibit most strongly and the *para*-hapten least. There is little difference between the two naphthyl derivatives.

A similar series of experiments was made using antigens, made by coupling diazotized *p*-aminobenzoic acid to proteins, and the homologous antisera (Pressman *et al.*, 1944). The results were similar to those obtained with the arsonate system, except there was little difference between the inhibitory effects of *m*- and *o*-hydroxybenzoates, and the order of inhibition by the nitro derivatives was $m > o > p$. In later experiments Pressman, Siegel and Hall (1954) tested the closeness of fit of the supposed cavity to different parts of the determinant. They assumed that the introduction of a chlorine atom at a position, other than that of the azo group of the determinant, would cause the maximum reduction of the K_0' if the cavity fits closely round this position of the determinant, and the minimum if the fit at this position is loose. The results, examples of which are given in FIGURE 2, suggest that the fit is closest in the neighbourhood of the carboxyl group and azo groups, and loosest at positions away from both.

Pressman and Siegel (1957) concluded from inhibition experiments that pyridine and quinoline derivatives act as though they were benzene and naphthalene derivatives with large substituents at the positions occupied by the annular nitrogen atoms. They considered that, as the heat of hydration of pyridine is much greater than the heat of combination of a hapten with antibody, the combination of the pyridine and quinoline derivatives with antibodies takes place with the water of hydration still attached to the nitrogen atoms. This paper is illustrated with van der Waals outlines illustrating the degree of dilatation of the receptor cavities of antibodies needed to accommodate these haptens.

The effect of the ionized group of the determinant—It was evident from the early experiments of Landsteiner, and from experiments such as those of TABLE 1, that the specificity of determinants depended very much on the nature of the charged group. FIGURE 3 illustrates the effect of changes of the nature of a negatively charged group on the inhibitory power of haptens. Replacement of the As of a hapten by P increased the affinity for the anti-arsonate antibody. This agrees with the earlier work of Erlenmeyer and Berger (1932). These workers, and also Haurowitz and Breinl (1933), showed that antibodies against an arsonate antigen formed less precipitate with a stibonate antigen than with the arsonate antigen. Pressman *et al.* (1945) attributed the greater affinity of the phosphonate hapten to the smaller radius of the phosphorus atom, which allows the negative charge to come nearer to the positive charge of the antibody site. With the larger antimony atom in place of arsenic, the positive and negative charges are still further apart and the affinity is much reduced. The phenylmethyl-arsinate $(C_6H_5 \cdot As(CH_3) \cdot O^-)$ hapten inhibited much less than the similar arsonate hapten in the instance illustrated, and in other experiments had practically no inhibitory effect. A sulphonate hapten inhibited to some extent; but it also had little effect in other experiments with the arsonate–antigen–antibody systems. The p-carboxylate system was slightly inhibited by p-(p-hydroxyphenylazo)phenyl sulphonate ($HO \cdot C_6H_4 \cdot N_2 \cdot C_6H_4 \cdot SO_3^-$), but not at all by p-(p-hydroxyphenylazo)phenylarsonate, nor by the smaller compound phenylsulphonate. Replacement of the CO_2^- group by the larger groups $CH_2 \cdot CO_2^-$ and $CH_2 \cdot CH_2 \cdot CO_2^-$ greatly reduced the affinity for antibody.

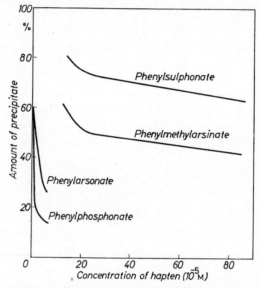

FIGURE 3. Amounts of precipitate formed by anti-p-phenylarsonic acid antiserum with homologous test antigen in the presence of haptens in which the arsonate group was replaced by other negatively charged groups. The amounts of precipitate are expressed as percentages of the amount formed when no hapten was present (Pressman, Bryden and Pauling, 1945).

Erlenmeyer and Berger (1933) found that $0 \cdot 01\text{M}$ phenylselenonate had a considerable inhibitory effect on formation of precipitate by p-aminophenylsulphonate antigen with homologous antiserum, though less than that of phenylsulphonate; phenylsulphinate had very little effect.

In order to study the reactions with the corresponding antisera of antigens that carried a positively charged determinant, and the inhibition of these by haptens, Pressman and colleagues (1946) used, as antigens, proteins coupled to diazotized p-aminophenyltrimethylammonium salts. As before, the order of inhibition by methyl-substituted haptens was $p > m > o$; and, as with the negatively charged determinants, the replacement of the charged group $N(CH_3)_3{}^+$ by larger groups, $N(C_2H_5)_3{}^+$ and $CH_2 \cdot N(CH_3)_3{}^+$, considerably reduced the affinity for antibody ; replacement of nitrogen by the slightly larger arsenic atom halved the affinity.

To test the effect of replacement of a charged group by a neutral group, Pressman and his colleagues (1946) compared the effect of H-acid-p-azo-*tert*.-butylbenzene ($N_2 \cdot C_6H_4 \cdot C(CH_3)_3$)* with that of H-acid-$p$-azophenyltrimethylammonium salt on the amount of precipitate formed by the phenyltrimethylammonium antigen with homologous antiserum ; the neutral $-C(CH_3)_3$ differs little in shape or size from $-N(CH_3)_3{}^+$, but reduces the amount of precipitate much less than does the positively charged ion.

Immunological evidence of the conformation of a determinant—Landsteiner and van der Scheer (1934) had found that the formation of a precipitate by a test antigen made by coupling protein to diazotized p-amino-succinanilic acid ($NH_2 \cdot C_6H_4 \cdot NH \cdot CO \cdot CH_2 \cdot CH_2 \cdot CO_2H$) with the corresponding antibody was inhibited by maleates but not by fumarates, and inferred that the $-CO \cdot CH_2 \cdot CH_2 \cdot CO_2H$ residue in the antigen reacts in the *cis*-conformation. Pressman and his colleagues (1948)

IV

confirmed this, estimating the affinity of haptens by the degree to which they inhibited precipitate formation ; the K_0' of maleanilate was 0·25 (with succinanilate as standard hapten) and that of fumaranilate

| V | VI | VII |

was 0·01. Pressman *et al.* (1948) suggested that an oxygen of the $CO_2{}^-$ group is linked by a hydrogen bond to the NH, as in IV. They also suggested that in β-benzoylpropionate (V) ($K_0' = 0·59$) the *cis*-

* H-acid is 1 : 8-aminonaphthol-3 : 6-disulphonic acid.

conformation is stabilized by the electrostatic attraction of the negative charge of the carboxylate ion for a positive charge on the benzene ring; the resonance structure (VII), which places a significant positive charge in this region, indicates distribution of the partial positive charge shown in structure (VI) from the carbonyl carbon atom.

The K_0's of both malonanilate and glutaranilate compounds, having respectively one carbon less and one carbon more than succinanilate in the chains, are 0·03; either these chains cannot form rings, or the rings formed do not fit the site on the antibody molecule. Pressman and Siegel (1953b) produced further evidence, on similar lines, that β-benzoylpropionate reacts in the *cis* form.

$$\text{H}$$
$$\langle\bigcirc\rangle\!\!-\!\!\overset{\mathbf{H}}{\underset{\mathbf{Me}}{\mathbf{C}}}\!\!-\!\!\text{NH·CO·CH}_2\text{CH}_2\text{·CO}_2\text{H}$$

VIII

The K_0' of the (−)isomer of N-(α-methylbenzyl)-succinamate (VIII) is appreciably higher than that of the (+)isomer. Pressman, Bryden and Pauling (1945) suggested that this difference is ' to be attributed to the presence of optically active amino-acid residues in the antibody γ-globulin, causing stable conformations complementary to the asymmetric hapten group of the immunizing antigen to be asymmetric '. However, there is an alternative explanation. The ring formed by the succinate residue is not symmetrical; if the receptor site of the antibody is a cavity on the surface of the antibody molecule, one face of the ring must lie towards this receptor. If the methyl group of the (−)isomer is on the face opposite to that which fits the antibody receptor, that of the (+)isomer will obstruct the approach of this isomer to the receptor.

Pressman *et al.* (1946) have calculated the distance between the positive charge of the $N(CH_3)_3{}^+$ of the H-acid-p-azophenyltrimethylammonium ion and the charge of the hypothetical negatively charged group of the antibody, from the differences between the K_0' of the H-acid-p-azophenyltrimethylammonium hapten and that of H-acid-p-azophenyl-*tert.*-butylbenzene. By these calculations, the distance between the charges is 2 Å more than the sum of the van der Waals radii of the atoms involved; when allowance is made for the non-specific adsorptions of the haptens by the serum albumin, the calculated distance is greater. A closer approach might be expected if the specificity of the binding of the hapten depends on the accuracy of fit; but owing to the assumptions involved in the estimation of the equilibrium constant and the value of the dielectric constant in the gap between the two charges, an exact value cannot be expected.

It appears that purely steric considerations will account for most of the results of these experiments. There are, however, anomalous effects such as the relatively high affinity of the *o*-hydroxybenzoate hapten for the *p*-hydroxybenzoate antibody. The strength of the attraction of antibody for hapten will depend not only on the closeness of approach of the atoms of one to those of the other, but also on the polarizability of the constituent groups.

The hypothetical cavity must have an opening that accommodates the azo group of the immunizing antigen; replacement of the hydrogen in this position on the benzene ring of a hapten by a substituent should have no steric effect. Pauling and Pressman (1945) calculated the effects that replacement by $\cdot NH \cdot CO \cdot CH_3$, $\cdot NO_2$, $\cdot I$, $\cdot Br$, $\cdot Cl$, $\cdot F$, $\cdot OCH_3$, $\cdot CH_3$, $\cdot OH$ and $\cdot NH_2$ would have—owing to their effects on polarizability—on the standard free energy ($\mathbf{R}T \ln K_0'$) of the combination of an antibody receptor with a hapten if the cavity fits closely in this position. The antibody in this instance was that against a *p*-phenylarsonate antigen. The effects on polarizability were deduced from the differences between the molar refractions of benzene and of benzene in which a hydrogen atom was replaced by these atoms or groups. The calculated differences of interaction energy agreed well with those deduced from the experimentally observed values of K_0', except that the observed effects were somewhat greater than those calculated in the case of $\cdot NH \cdot CO \cdot CH_3$ and $\cdot NO_2$ and less in the case of $\cdot NH_2$. Pauling and Pressman suggested that this may be due to formation of hydrogen bonds with the antibody by $\cdot NH \cdot CO \cdot CH_3$ and $\cdot NO_2$, and with water by $\cdot NH_2$. The difference between the standard free energies of the combination of phenylcarboxylate and *p*-nitrophenylcarboxylate with antibody against a *p*-phenylcarboxylate antigen was similar. In the *p*-succinanilate and 4-azophthalate systems the effects were less (Pressman and Pauling, 1949); it appears that the cavities of these antibodies fit less closely round this position.

When the substituent in the *para* position is larger, as in *p*-(*p*-hydroxyphenylazo)phenylarsonate, a larger area of the hapten may be brought in contact with the antibody, and the increased van der Waals attraction should increase the affinity for antibody. Pauling and Pressman (1945) considered that the K_0' of this hapten was lower than that calculated from the effect on polarizability alone, and concluded that the second ring could not fit into the hypothetical antibody cavity. But the corrected values of K_0' found by Pressman and Siegel (1953a) were considerably higher, so that an increased van der Waals attraction due to the increase of area in contact with antibody cannot be excluded.

When an antibody against an antigen, in which the azo group is in the *para* position, is modified, the replacement of a *meta* hydrogen atom may have various effects on the interaction energy. If the effect on

239

polarizability is high, or a hydrogen bond can be formed, the K_0' is above that of the unsubstituted hapten; otherwise, as, for example, when the substituent is $\cdot CH_3$, the steric effect reduces the K_0'. The relatively high K_0's of the naphthyl derivatives can be ascribed to the high polarizability of the naphthyl rings.

The majority of the determinants used in the studies quoted are not components of the tissues (or fluids) of living organisms. They have been used because they can easily be linked to proteins, and because rabbits form fairly strong antibodies against the antigens so made. Similar antigen–antibody reactions may, however, be involved in other processes not studied experimentally by immunologists, and may show characteristic differences between isomers. For example, Nathan and Stern (1930) reported the case of a person who was sensitive to resorcinol but not to the isomers, catechol and quinol.

CARBOHYDRATES

Since polysaccharides can be built up of monosaccharides each linked to any of four carbon atoms of the next (if this is a hexose) by one of two forms of glycoside link, a very large number of compounds that differ in structure can be built up out of a limited number of units even if these are arranged in the same sequence. The carbohydrate groups that serve as determinants in immunity reactions have the additional interest that, unlike the aromatic determinants, they are not flat; the receptors of the corresponding antibody must have a three-dimensional complementary structure.

The results of experiments made with artificial antigens that have carbohydrate determinants also have a wider application, since the specific parts are constituents of living organisms; although, in order to form antigens by linking them to proteins, an unphysiological unit, viz. an azophenyl group, is introduced between the carbohydrate and the protein.

Monosaccharides and Disaccharides

The specificity of antigens made in this way with mono- and di-saccharides is illustrated in TABLES 4 and 5*. We see the importance of configuration at the C-4 atom; antisera against the glucoside antigen form no precipitate with the galactoside antigen. Since glucose and galactose, with the corresponding hexosamines and hexuronic acids, are the commonest constituents of naturally occurring poly-saccharides, we meet repeatedly instances of this dependence of specificity on the configuration at C-4.

* Individual pyranose rings are shown in that chair conformation which is known (or in some cases may reasonably be assumed) to be preferred (*cf* Reeves, 1950). The conformations shown here in the formulae of di- and poly-saccharides round the oxygen atoms of the hemi-acetal links between monosaccharides are arbitrary.

TABLE 4. REACTIONS OF ANTIGENS CONTAINING CARBOHYDRATE DETERMINANTS

[Amounts of precipitate formed by antisera against antigens, that contain carbohydrates as determinants, with homologous and heterologous test antigens (Avery, Goebel and Babers, 1932; Goebel, Avery and Babers, 1934).]

Antiserum against	Test Antigen			
	α-Glucoside IX	β-Glucoside X	β-Galactoside XI	β-Maltoside XII
α-Glucoside	+++	++	0	++±
β-Glucoside	++	++++	0	±
β-Galactoside	0	0	+++	0
β-Maltoside	+++	+++	0	++++
β-Cellobioside	±	+++±	0	±
β-Lactoside	0	0	++	±
β-Gentiobioside	±	++±	0	±

Antiserum against	Test Antigen		
	β-Cellobioside XIII	β-Lactoside XIIIA	β-Gentiobioside XIV
α-Glucoside	±	0	0
β-Glucoside	+++	0	+++
β-Galactoside	0	+±	0
β-Maltoside	+++	±	++±
β-Cellobioside	++++	±	++±
β-Lactoside	++±	+++±	±
β-Gentiobioside	+++	±	++++

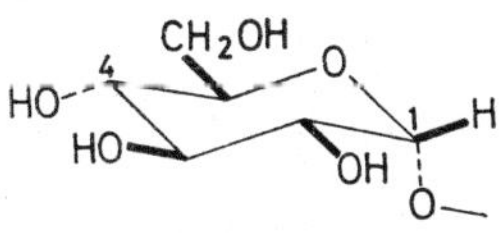

α-Glucoside
IX

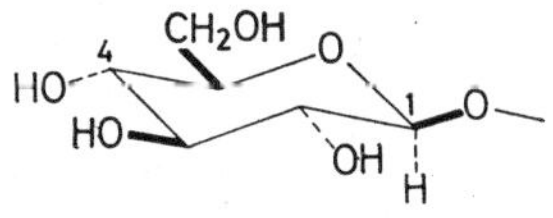

β-Glucoside
X

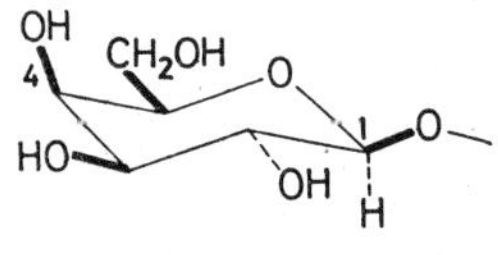

β-Galactoside
XI

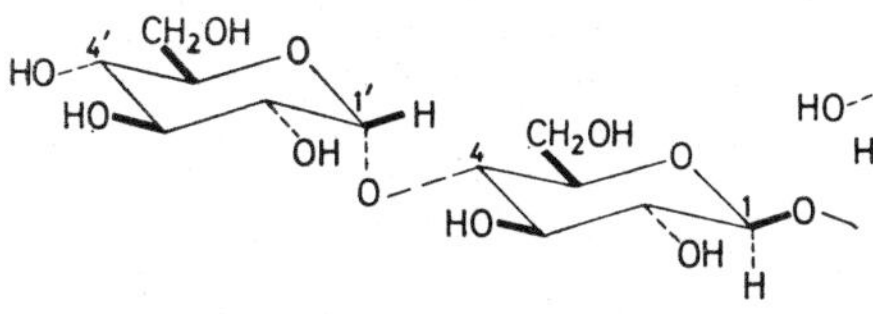

β-Maltoside
XII

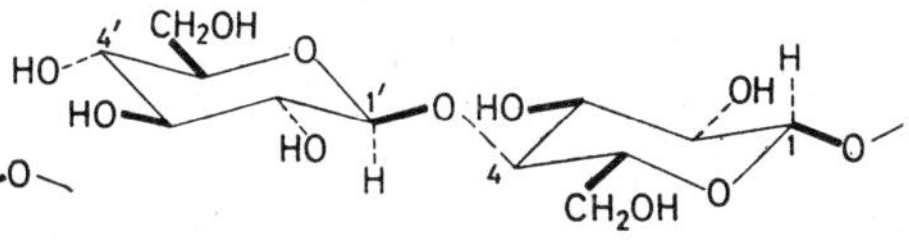

β-Cellobioside
XIII

[XIIIA β-Lactoside has configuration at C-4 inverted]

241

β-Gentiobioside
XIV

TABLE 5. REACTIONS OF CELLOBIOSIDE AND GENTIOBIOSIDE ANTIGENS

[Amounts of precipitate formed by antisera against cellobioside and gentiobioside antigens with homologous and heterologous test antigens, in the presence of homologous and heterologous haptens. The haptens were the p-nitrophenyl-β-glucosides (Goebel, Avery and Babers, 1934).]

Hapten	Anti-cellobioside serum		Anti-gentiobioside serum	
	Test antigen		Test antigen	
	Cellobioside	Gentiobioside	Gentiobioside	Cellobioside
None	+ + + +	+ +	+ + +	+ ±
α-Glucoside	+ + + +	+ ±	+ + ±	+ ±
β-Glucoside	+ + + +	0	+ + ±	0
Galactoside	+ + + +	+ +	+ + ±	+ ±
Cellobioside	0	0	+ + ±	0
Maltoside	+ + + ±	+ ±	+ + ±	+ ±
Lactoside	+ + + ±	+ ±	+ + ±	+ ±
Gentiobioside	+ + + ±	0	0	0

The difference between α- and β-glucosides is less than might be expected. For if the α-glucoside fits a site such as *ABC* (FIGURE 4), the β-glucoside will not fit this site; either the azophenyl ring or the —CH₂OH group will obstruct its approach. Insertion of a second monosaccharide between the terminal monosaccharide and the benzene ring also has a minor influence, if the configuration at the C-1 atom of the terminal monosaccharide is not changed; thus, antiserum against α-glucoside antigen forms a considerable precipitate with the maltoside antigen, but very little with the cellobioside antigen.

Similarly, the specificity of a disaccharide antigen depends mainly on the configuration at the C-4 atom of the terminal monosaccharide; the antiserum against the β-maltoside antigen forms nearly as much precipitate with the β-cellobioside as with the homologous antigen. Nor does the point on the intermediate monosaccharide at which the terminal monosaccharide is attached have much influence; the β-cellobioside antiserum forms a considerable precipitate with the β-gentiobioside antigen, although in the gentiobioside the intermediate glucose unit cannot be in the same plane as the terminal unit.

These reactions are, however, more specific than appears from the visual estimates of the amounts of precipitate. This can be seen from TABLE 5; haptens, that have little effect on the amount of precipitate formed by β-gentiobioside antigen with the homologous antiserum, completely inhibit the formation of a precipitate by β-cellobioside antigen with this antiserum.

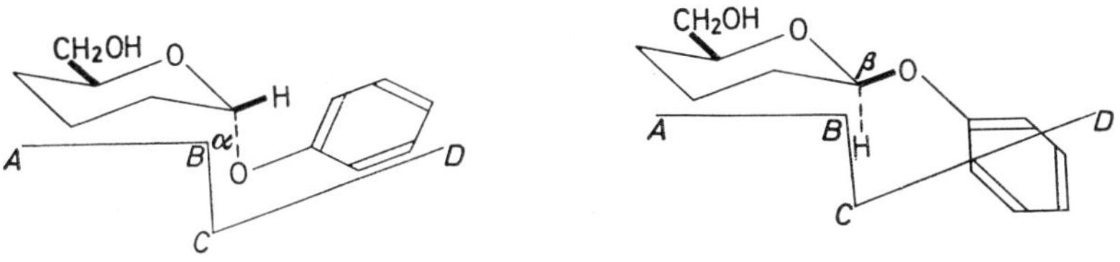

FIGURE 4.

Uronic acids

The uronic acids are important constituents of the polysaccharides of certain types of pneumococci and of vegetable gums. The antisera against glucuronic and galacturonic antigens form little precipitate with the neutral glucose and galactose antigens and vice versa. The specificities of the three uronic-acid antigens that have been studied—glucuronic, galacturonic and cellobiuronic—were very similar to those of the corresponding neutral sugars (Goebel, 1936, 1938; Goebel and Hotchkiss, 1937).

Dextrans

The reactions of the artificial cellobioside and gentiobioside antigens, and their inhibition by haptens, may be compared with the reactions of dextrans. The dextrans considered belong to two series—the $1 \to 6$ or *iso*maltose series and the $1 \to 4$ series (the difference between the two series is comparable to the difference between gentiobioside and cellobioside antigens). The formation of precipitates by dextrans of the $1 \to 6$ series and $1 \to 4$ series with homologous antisera were inhibited by *iso*maltose and maltose respectively (Kabat, 1954).

Kabat availed himself of the opportunity offered by these reactions of dextrans with antisera to form an estimate of the area of a natural antigen involved in combination with antibody. With the artificial antigens we have already seen that the affinity of a phenylarsonate hapten for the homologous antibody is increased if its area is extended by attachment of a second benzene ring through an azo link at the site of the azo group of the immunizing antigen; similarly the p-nitrophenyl glucosides inhibited the formation of precipitates with antisera against the mono- and di-saccharide antigens more efficiently than did the simple mono- or di-saccharides. With $1 \to 6$-dextran and homologous antiserum much smaller amounts of *iso*maltotriose than of *iso*maltose

243

were required to inhibit precipitate formation. With the $1 \rightarrow 4$ dextrans and homologous antiserum the best inhibitors were maltotriose, maltotetraose and maltopentaose; if allowance was made for the possible spontaneous hydrolysis of maltotetraose, it appeared to be the best inhibitor; the tri- and tetra-saccharides, therefore, have the greatest affinity for the antibodies. Kabat inferred that the combining site of each type of antibody is complementary to an open chain of at least three α-D-glucopyranose units of homologous structure ($1 \rightarrow 6$ or $1 \rightarrow 4$) and probably to a part or all of a fourth unit.

Pneumococcal and related polysaccharides

With this estimate of the area of antigen involved in combination with antibody in mind, we may consider the reactions of the pneumococcal and other polysaccharides. The specific polysaccharides of Types I, II, III and VIII pneumococci are of special interest. Type I polysaccharide (SI) contains galacturonic acid; Type II (SII) contains glucuronic acid; Type III (SIII) is a chain polymer of aldobionic acid, cellobiuronic acid ($4\text{-}O\text{-}\beta\text{-}$D-glucosiduronyl-D-glucose). The glucose unit is joined by a β-glucoside link to C-3 of the next glucuronic acid unit (Reeves and Goebel, 1941). The chain therefore is not straight, and the aldobionic acid units are alternately inverted (formula XV).

XV

Type VIII polysaccharide (SVIII) is a chain formed by a series of units of the same aldobionic acid, cellobiuronic acid, with two hexose units between each pair of aldobionic acid units (Goebel, 1935; Heidelberger et al., 1942). Recently Jones and Perry (1957) have worked out the structure of SVIII. They consider that it is a linear chain made up of repeating units of $-O\text{-}\beta\text{-}$D-glucosiduronyl-$(1 \rightarrow 4)$-$O\text{-}\beta\text{-}$D-glucopyranosyl-$(1 \rightarrow 4)$-$O\text{-}\alpha\text{-}$D-glucopyranosyl-$O\text{-}\alpha\text{-}$D-galactopyranosyl-$(1 \rightarrow 4)$-. As all the glycoside links are $(1 \rightarrow 4)$ the chain can assume a conformation that is approximately straight. The aldobionic acid units are not alternately inverted, but are separated by two hexose units. The heavy precipitate formed by Type VIII antiserum with the cellobioside antigen (TABLE 6) is not surprising, since two glucose units are jointed by a β-glucoside link in both cellobiose and SVIII.

The reactions of rabbit and horse antisera against these polysaccharides with artificial antigens and with specific polysaccharides of pneumococci are given in TABLE 6. The rabbit antisera are much the more specific. The importance of the aldobionic acid unit is shown

244

TABLE 6. REACTIONS OF HORSE AND RABBIT ANTI-PNEUMOCOCCAL SERA

[Amounts of precipitate formed by type-specific horse and rabbit anti-pneumo-coccal sera with artificial antigens and with the type-specific polysaccharides (Goebel, 1936, 1938; Goebel and Hotchkiss, 1937).]

Antigen	Horse antisera				Rabbit antisera			
	Anti-I	II	III	VIII	Anti-I	II	III	VIII
Glucoside	0	0	+	0				
Glucuronide	0	++±	++++	++±				
Galacturonide	+++	±	++±	++				
Cellobioside	0	±	+±	+++±	0	0	±	++
Cellobiuronide	0	++++	++++	++±	0	+±	++±	+±
SI	++++	0	0	0	++++	0	0	0
SII	0	+++++	0	0	0	++++	0	0
SIII	0	0	+++++	++	0	0	+++++	Varies
SVIII	0	0	++	++++	0	0	Varies	+++

by the fact that rabbit anti-SII, anti-SIII and anti-SVIII sera form precipitates with the artificial cellobiuronic acid antigen, whereas the anti-SI serum, that reacts with a galacturonic acid containing poly-saccharide SI, does not form a precipitate with this antigen. If the anti-SIII antibody combines with four hexose units (as Kabat concluded in the case of the dextran antigen) this combining area includes two cellobiuronic acid units set at an angle, the CO_2H of one being up and the other down. Now horse anti-SIII serum also forms precipitates with oxidized cotton (Heidelberger and Hobby, 1942), in which, if alternate glucose units are oxidized, cellobiuronic units are joined in a straight chain by α-1 → 4 glycoside links; the CO_2H groups of these are all on the same side of the main plane. Two consecutive cellobiuronic acid units of oxidized cotton cannot fit an antibody site that is complementary to the two consecutive cellobiuronic units of SIII. Since oxidized cotton precipitates about ⅔ of the antibody of a horse anti-SIII serum, affinity of the horse antibody for SIII appears to depend mainly on the presence on the antibody molecules of sites complementary to the two hexose units that form cellobiuronic acid. However, the precipitate (measured chemically) formed by SVIII with anti-SIII horse serum may be about ⅓ of that formed by SIII with the serum; conversely, the precipitate formed by SIII with anti-SVIII serum may be about ⅙ of that formed by SVIII with this serum. As these two polysaccharides, also, both contain the same aldobionic acid, cellobiuronic acid, it appears from this that more than two hexose units are necessary for the maximum affinity for antibody. This applies even more to the more specific rabbit antisera; for these antisera either form no precipitate with the heterologous polysaccharide, or the precipitate formed with the heterologous polysaccharide may be no more than $\frac{1}{20}$ of that formed with the homologous polysaccharide (Heidelberger, Kabat and Shrivavasta, 1937).

Horse anti-SIII serum forms some precipitate with gum acacia, that has been partially hydrolysed by acid with loss of pentose units. The aldobionic acid of this gum is 6-O-β-D-glucosiduronyl-D-galactose; as the glucuronic acid is attached to C-6 of the galactose these two hexose units are not in the same plane, and both units of this aldobionic acid cannot fit a site on an antibody molecule that fits the aldobionic acid of SIII.

Type II pneumococcal polysaccharide (SII) consists of a branched chain of units of D-glucuronic acid, D-glucose and rhamnose. The rhamnose is all in the chain structure, the glucose forms a large proportion of the branch points; some of the glucuronic acid forms the ends of chains with the CO_2H groups free (Butler and Stacey, 1955). Horse anti-SII serum forms a precipitate with partially hydrolysed gum acacia and with other plant gums (TABLE 7).

These gums also contain aldobionic acids, one unit of which is glucuronic acid. Glucuronic acid, bornyl glucuronide, benzoyl-glucuronide (in which the benzoyl group is attached to C-1; Pryde and Williams, 1933; Goebel, 1937-8), chondrosin and the aldobionic acid of gum acacia all inhibit the formation of these precipitates; methyl 2 : 4-di-O-methylglucosuronide does not inhibit. It appears that these cross reactions all depend on the affinity of the horse antibodies for glucuronic acid; and as cherry gum forms most precipitate with anti-SII sera, the aldobionic acid of SII may resemble that of cherry gum.

The precipitates formed by native gum acacia with anti-SIII serum and by this and other native gums with anti-SII serum are much less than the precipitates formed by the residues of these gums left after a partial hydrolysis in which pentoses are split off. In native gum acacia pentose units are attached to the C-4 of the glucuronic acid and the C-3 of the galactose unit. These pentose units presumably obstruct the approach of the gum polysaccharide to the combining sites of anti-SII and anti-SIII antibodies.

We are left with the problem of the erratic specificity of these horse antipneumococcal sera. In general they are remarkably unspecific. Horse anti-SI, anti-SII and anti-SIII sera form precipitates with artificial antigens formed by coupling diazotized aminobenzoic and sulphanilic acids with proteins (Goebel and Hotchkiss, 1937). Anti-SII, anti-SIII and anti-SVIII sera form precipitates not only with the glucuronic but also with the galacturonic acid artificial antigens (TABLE 6). Anti-SII and anti-SIII horse sera both cross react with partially hydrolysed gum acacia. Yet horse anti-SII serum does not form a precipate with SIII, nor anti-SIII serum with SII. This example of a specificity of otherwise relatively unspecific sera may be due to some steric factor, but is, so far, not explained.

TABLE 7. PRECIPITATION OF HORSE TYPE II ANTIBODY BY VEGETABLE GUMS

[Maximum amounts of antibody in precipitates formed by vegetable gums with 1 ml of a horse Type II anti-pneumococcal serum, that contained 8·1 mg of antibody precipitable by SII (Marrack and Carpenter, 1938); with composition of the aldobionic acids of these gums (Jones and Smith, 1949).]

Gum	Aldobionic acids	Maximum antibody precipitated (mg)
Cherry		3·4
Plum	XVI	2·65
Acacia	XVII, R = H	1·8
Mesquite	XVIII and XIX (= XVII with R — Me)	1·8
Ghatti		2·3

BLOOD-GROUP SUBSTANCES

The term 'blood-group substances' includes both those antigens on red blood cells that differentiate bloods of different groups of individuals of the same species from one another, and similar substances that are detectable in the tissues and body fluids of animals of the same and other species. The best known of these groups are the A, B and O groups, because the serum of a B group person naturally contains an antibody that agglutinates A group red blood cells and the serum of an A group person contains an antibody that agglutinates B group red blood cells; neither A nor B serum agglutinates O group cells, but O group serum agglutinates both A and B cells.

It has not been possible to isolate significant amounts of the actual antigens directly from red blood cells; the substances that have been studied have been prepared from human ovarian cysts or from gastric mucin, mainly obtained from pigs. These substances are immunologically similar to the actual blood cell antigens, for they specifically inhibit the agglutination of red blood cells by the corresponding agglutinins (e.g. a group A substance derived from pig gastric mucin inhibits agglutination of A group cells by B group serum); also these substances form precipitates, specifically, with strong antisera. The substances that have been fully studied are the A and B substances; H substance, which is supposed to be a primary substance from which the A and B substances are developed; and the Le (Lewis) substance which is completely independent of the ABO system.

TABLE 8. RELATIVE PROPORTIONS OF THE MAIN CONSTITUENTS OF A, B AND H BLOOD GROUP SUBSTANCES (Gibbons, Morgan and Gibbons, 1955)

Group substance	Ratio		
	Galactose : Hexosamine	Glucosamine : Galactosamine	Fucose : Galactose
A	0·6	1·0 to 1·5	Up to 0·96
B	1·5	3	0·44
H	1·2	3 to 12	0·66 to 0·86

In composition these substances are all very similar; they all contain D-galactose, N-acetyl-D-glucosamine, and N-acetyl-D-galactosamine with variable amounts of fucose (TABLE 8). The immunological differences between them must depend on differences in the proportions and arrangement of these constituents.

Apart from their reactions with specific sera, blood group substances react with other unrelated sera and with some seed extracts. These cross reactions afford interesting examples of the relation of combining affinity to structure and composition in a reaction of the antigen-antibody type. Group O red blood cells are agglutinated by serum of the eel, *Anguilla anguilla* (Watkins and Morgan, 1952) and by extracts of the seeds of *Lotus tetragonolobus* (Morgan and Watkins, 1953). Very high dilutions of H substance inhibit this agglutination; the eel serum and seed extract, therefore, react specifically with the H substance on the cells. As seen in TABLE 9, methyl α-L-fucopyranoside is the most efficient of the carbohydrates and their derivatives tested in inhibiting agglutination of O cells by either eel serum or seed extract. The pentose L-fucose was nearly as effective as its methyl derivative.

TABLE 9

[Dilutions of H substances and of monosaccharides and their derivatives required to inhibit the agglutination of group-O red blood cells by eel serum and by extract of the seeds of *Lotus tetragonolobus* (Morgan and Watkins, 1953).]

D-Glucosamine, D-galactosamine, *N*-acetyl-D-galactosamine, sucrose, D- and L-glucose, D-galactose, D-mannose, L-sorbose, L-rhamnose, L-arabinose, D- and L-xylose, D-altrose, L-gulomethylose, L-glucomethylose, D-gala- and L-galaheptose were inactive.

	Dilutions	
	Lotus tetra-gonolobus extract	Eel serum
Human H-substance	25,600	819,200
Pig H-substance	25,600	1,638,400
Methyl α-L-fucopyranoside	51,200	51,200
L-Fucose (XXA)	25,600	12,800
Methyl β-L-fucopyranoside	12,800	3,200
2-Deoxy-L-fucose (XXD)	12,800	6,400
L-Galactose (XXB)	3,200	< 50
6-Deoxytalose (XXI)	400	800
D-Arabinose (XXc)	200	400
D-Digitoxose (XXII)	200	< 50
N-Acetyl-D-glucosamine	200	< 50
D-Ribose	100	< 50
D-Fructose (XXIII)	< 50	200
D-Fucose (Mirror image of XXA)	< 50	< 50

Reversal of the configuration at C-2 and C-3, as in 6-deoxy-L-talose, greatly reduced the inhibitory power—more so than replacement of the hydroxyl at C-2 by hydrogen. Replacement of CH_3 by CH_2OH, as in L-galactose, and inversion of the configuration at C-5, as in D-digitoxose, affected inhibition of the reaction with eel serum considerably more than it affected inhibition of the reaction with seed extract. It seems, therefore, that the reacting protein (the equivalent of an antibody) in eel serum fits much more closely round the

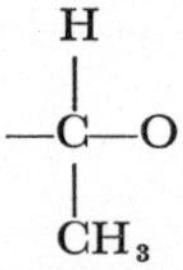

$$-\overset{\overset{\displaystyle H}{|}}{\underset{\underset{\displaystyle CH_3}{|}}{C}}-O$$

group (C-5) than does the reacting protein in *Lotus* extract.

Human red blood cells of groups A, B and O are agglutinated by horse antisera against Type XIV pneumococci, and the blood group substances form precipitates with these antipneumococcal sera. This

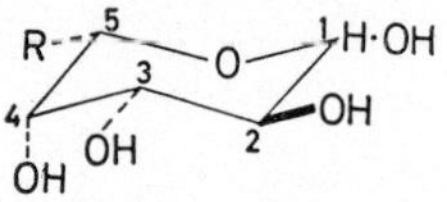

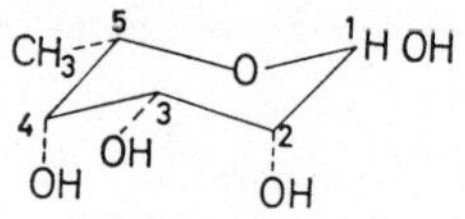

XX_A R = CH₃, L-Fucose
XX_B R = CH₂OH, L-Galactose
XX_C R = H, D-Arabinose
XX_D R = CH₃, and H for OH at C-2, 2-Deoxy-L-fucose

6-Deoxy-L-talose
XXI

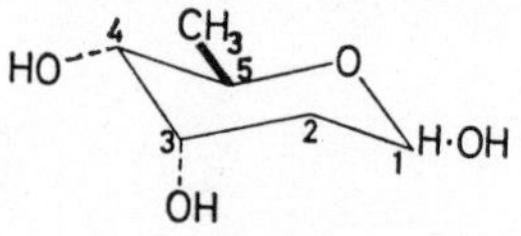

D-Digitose
XXII

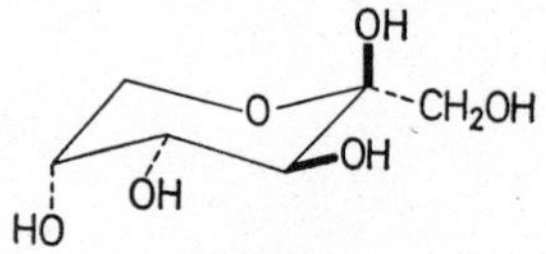

D-Fructose
XXIII

ability to form a precipitate with Type XIV antisera is enhanced by mild acid hydrolysis of the group substance; whereas the ability of the substance to inhibit agglutination of homologous red blood cells by the corresponding antisera is progressively lost. Fucose, D-glucosamine and, from group B substance, some galactose are split off by the hydrolysis. There is an inverse correlation between the fucose content of pig A and H substances and the amount of precipitate formed with Type XIV antiserum (Baer *et al.*, 1948); and the A substance with the highest fucose content, prepared from human ovarian cysts, did not react at all with Type XIV antiserum until hydrolysed (Aminoff *et al.*, 1950). Type XIV polysaccharide contains *N*-acetyl-D-glucosamine, D-galactose and some D-glucose, but no fucose; the non-dialysable substances left after the acid-hydrolysis of the blood-group substances contain galactose and hexosamine units in much the same proportions as in the original substance, together with some residual fucose. Bray *et al.* (1946) have shown that fucose and some glucosamine residues are non-reducing end groups. It appears that fucose and some glucosamine and galactose units are on labile branches of a central chain of galactose, *N*-acetylglucosamine and *N*-acetyl-galactosamine units, and that the cross reaction with Type XIV

250

polysaccharide is due to a common pattern of N-acetylglucosamine and galactose units in the fundamental chain. The pentose-containing side branches interfere with the approach of the Type XIV antibody to the determinant part of the group substance, much as the pentose intervenes between the Types II and III antibodies and glucuronic acid of undegraded gum acacia (see p. 246).

Kabat and Leskowitz (1955) have attempted to identify the specific constituents of the B and A substances. They found that the formation of precipitates by these substances with corresponding antisera was inhibited by oligosaccharides obtained by hydrolysis of the substances; and sought to identify the inhibiting oligosaccharide. The oligo-saccharides that were most effective in inhibiting the formation of a precipitate by B substance with the serum of a woman who was carrying a B-group foetus were the disaccharide melibiose (α-galactosyl-$1 \rightarrow 6$ glucose), the trisaccharide raffinose (α-galactosyl-$1 \rightarrow 6$-α-glucosyl-$1 \rightarrow 2$-β-fructopyranoside), and the tetrasaccharide stachyose (α-galac-tosyl-$1 \rightarrow 6$-α-galactosyl-$1 \rightarrow 2$-α-glucosyl-$1 \rightarrow 2$-β-fructopyranoside); these were followed in order of efficiency by methyl α-galactoside, galactose and methyl β-galactoside. Lactose did not inhibit, nor did a range of oligosaccharides including neolactose, galactosyl $(1\beta \rightarrow 4)$-N-acetylglucosamine, N-acetylgalactosamine, gentiobiose and sucrose, also fucose. This indicates that the B specificity is determined by an oligosaccharide with a terminal non-reducing galactose linked to the next sugar in α-$1 \rightarrow 6$-galactoside linkage. As the agglutination of B group blood cells is slightly inhibited by glucosamine this is probably the second monosaccharide unit.

The relation of galactose units to the specific activity of the B substances was also shown by the studies of Morgan and Watkins (1955) on the effects of an enzyme derived from *Trichomonas foetus*. This enzyme destroys the specific activities of the blood-group sub-stances; D-galactose, methyl α- and β-D-galactopyranoside, lactose and melibiose protect the B substance against this enzyme, presumably by competitive inhibition.

None of the carbohydrate derivatives which were tested fully inhibited the formation of a precipitate by A substance (derived from pig gastric mucin) with rabbit antisera against pig A substance or against human group A saliva. Of those tried, galactosamine had a weak inhibitory effect on precipitate formation with antiserum against human A substance, but not with antiserum against pig A substance. From comparison of the relative inhibitions of dextran-antidextran interaction by oligosaccharides (Kabat, 1954), Kabat and Leskowitz (1953) inferred that (supposing dimensions of antibody-combining sites are similar, and bond strengths of the same magnitude) the active A and B determinants of the A and B substances are of the order of tri- to penta- or hexa-saccharides.

Both group A and B cells are agglutinated by extracts of the seeds of *Sophora japonica* in high dilutions; and agglutination is inhibited by the blood group substances and by some mono- and di-saccharides (Morgan and Watkins, 1953). The most effective of the mono-saccharides tested in inhibiting agglutination of cells of both groups was *N*-acetyl-D-galactosamine; *N*-acetyl-D-glucosamine did not inhibit. Agglutination was also inhibited by higher concentrations of D-galactose, melibiose and lactose. Group A cells are agglutinated by extracts of seeds of *Vicia cracca* in dilutions higher than those which will agglutinate B cells. This agglutination of A cells is inhibited by *N*-acetyl-D-galactosamine but not by *N*-acetyl-D-glucosamine.

We can draw the interesting conclusion that different antibodies and antibody-like substances combine with different parts of the blood group substances. The specific antibodies combine with branch chains. In the case of the B substance, the essential group seems to be a terminal non-reducing D-galactose joined to a *N*-acetyl-D-glucosamine unit by a $1 \to 6$ glucoside link. *N*-Acetyl-D-galactosamine appears to be a constituent of the parts of A and B substances with which the extracts of *Sophora japonica* and *Vicia cracca* combine, and may also be a constituent of the part of human A substance with which the specific antibody combines. There is no evidence that fucose is involved in combination with the specific antibodies, but an α-L-fucopyranoside is an essential of that part of H substance with which the antibody-like substance of *Lotus tetragonolobus* seeds combines. Type XIV antibody combines with the fundamental chain and not with the branches.

THE RECEPTORS OF ANTIBODIES

The theory of the nature of the combination between antigen (or hapten) and antibody postulates the presence on an antibody molecule of receptor sites, which may consist either of a pattern of positively and negatively charged groups complementary to the pattern of negatively and positively charged groups of the antigen determinant, and/or a cavity that fits the determinant closely.

The combination of determinants with antibodies may be compared with the strong non-specific adsorption of various anions by serum albumin. Karush (1950) suggested that there are a number of sites on an albumin molecule, each associated with several amino-acid side-chains, which can to a varying extent assume a large number of conformations, in equilibrium with each other and of approximately equal potential energy; in the presence of an organic anion, the conformation that fits the anion is stabilized. In contrast with this, the specificity of an antibody is to be attributed to a similar but relatively rigid and therefore selective conformation, associated with the antibody receptor-site.

This selective conformation may be determined :

1. By a suitable number and sequence of the various amino-acids of which the antibody is composed ; when a peptide chain with a given sequence has been synthesized, it adopts a conformation of low potential energy, with parts of the molecule complementary to the determinant of the antibody.

2. By suitable folding of the peptide chain without variation in the number or sequence of the constituent amino acids ; the conformation of the peptide chain may be set to fit a complementary template in order to form the receptor sites, and, once so set, be fixed in a metastable structure. This theory has the merit that the template on which the pattern of the receptor is set is similar to that of the determinant with which it eventually will combine, and may actually be the determinant of the immunizing antigen ; whereas, if the amino-acids are first arranged in order on a template, and the chain thus formed is then coiled up to form the antibody molecule, the template will not resemble the structure to which the receptor is finally adapted ; in this case the antigen determinant cannot serve as the primary template. The receptor sites of antibodies are adapted to structures that are much more varied than those of the substances that are adsorbed by serum albumin ; it seems improbable that this variety of sites could be formed merely by varying the conformations of the amino-acid side-chains without differences in folding of the peptide chains*.

Pauling (1940), taking the second view, suggested that, in the formation of an antibody, a globulin peptide chain is synthesized first, and that then, without any change in the sequence of the amino-acids, the two ends of the peptide chain are coiled in a form adapted to the determinant of the antigen. On the face of it, this seems improbable, as the two ends of a peptide chain differ, one ending in a NH_2 group and the other is a CO_2H group. It is, however, claimed (e.g. Haurowitz, 1953 ; Smith et al., 1955), that antibodies do not differ one from another or from 'normal' γ-globulin† either in composition or in the sequence of the amino-acids of which they are composed ; and that the various receptor sites are formed by different conformations of the peptide chain, though not necessarily situated at the ends as Pauling suggested. Until 1955 there was no evidence to support even the first claim ; in the only analysis that had been made (Calvery, 1935-36) a difference, that was considered to be outside the limits of error, was found between the amounts of cystine in Type I and Type II horse antipneumococcal antibodies.

Recently, Smith et al. (1955) reported analyses of rabbit antibodies against the polysaccharides of Types I, III, VIII and XIV pneumo-

* Differences of conformation would have to account also for differences of electrophoretic mobility (Cann et al., 1951), and of adsorption (Humphrey and Porter, 1951 ; Porter, 1955).

† It is possible that the γ-globulin of serum is wholly composed of antibodies, and that there should be no division between antibodies and 'inert' or 'normal' γ-globulin.

cocci; the amounts of aspartic and glutamic acids, of glycine, alanine, leucine, tyrosine, histidine, lysine, arginine and tryptophan were the same in the different antibodies, within the limits of error of the estimations. The larger differences between the amounts of other amino-acids could be accounted for by uncertainties concerning the degree of destruction in hydrolysis, the rate of liberation, and the separation of the amino-acids.

Although these analyses put on a much sounder basis the claim that antibodies do not differ in composition, they still leave open the possibility that the latter may differ in the nature of the amino-acids at or near the receptor sites. It is generally accepted that antibody molecules do not have more than two receptors for antigens. These receptors may be no larger than is required to accommodate four hexose residues. On the surface of a molecule formed by parallel α-helices (see Figure 2 in Pauling et al., 1951) this would involve some 10 amino-acids at each receptor. An antibody molecule contains 50 or more residues of aspartic and glutamic acids, of threonine, serine, proline, glycine, alanine, valine, isoleucine, leucine, tyrosine, lysine and arginine. It is doubtful whether differences of two more or less per molecule (one for each receptor) of these amino-acids could be detected with certainty by present methods of analysis.

For the second claim, that the sequence of the amino-acids is the same in different antibodies, there is no evidence whatsoever. Porter (1950) found that both rabbit antibody against ovalbumin and inert rabbit γ-globulin had a single N-terminal amino acid—alanine—per molecule. Alanine is also the only N-terminal amino-acid of rabbit antibody against bovine serum albumin (Orlans, 1955); also of the rabbit antibodies against Types I, II, III, IV, VII, VIII and XIV pneumococci and the inert rabbit γ-globulins (McFadden and Smith, 1955). Porter and McFadden and Smith also concluded that the terminal sequence is alanyl—leucyl—valyl—aspartyl—glutamyl—. It is, however, preposterous to infer the sequence of some 1,500 amino-acids from that of the terminal 5. If the number of possible forms in which peptide chains can be coiled is as limited as Pauling et al. (1951) and Bragg et al. (1950) have indicated, the great range of antibody receptors cannot be caused by variations of the coiling of the peptide chain alone. However, great variations of patterns of amino-acid side-chains exposed on the surface of a molecule could be introduced by rotating two adjacent parallel α-helices and by shifting one longitudinally with respect to the other. Such rotation and longitudinal shift would involve an alteration of the point at which the peptide chain bent through an angle of 180°*; the possibility of such variations would depend on the nature of these bends. A great variety of

---

* The antibody molecules are compact; if, as appears, each is composed of a single peptide chain, this must be bent back on itself some 16 times.

conformations could be introduced by varying the positions in the chain of the 119 proline residues of rabbit γ-globulin.

THE STRUCTURE OF ANTIGEN–ANTIBODY AGGREGATES

A steric problem on a larger scale arises in connection with the aggregates formed by antigens with antibodies. These aggregates are usually insoluble if the ratio of antigen to antibody lies within certain limits, and they have special properties—among others the ' fixation ' of complement, the release of histamine from some form of combination in cells and, possibly, the activation of certain proteolytic enzymes. The question arises whether some special conformation of combined antibody, or some feature of the structure of an antigen–antibody aggregate, accounts for these phenomena.

Complement is by definition a collection of properties of fresh serum. The most familiar of these is that of ' complementing ' the action of an antibody against red corpuscles; that is, red corpuscles that have been treated with such an antibody are haemolysed by complement. Another important property is that complement is ' fixed ' in the course of many antigen–antibody reactions—that is, the haemolysing property of serum is removed by most antibodies interacting with antigen or by a pre-formed precipitate of antibody and antigen. This ' fixation ' of complement is associated with the incorporation of protein into the antigen–antibody complex; presumably this protein is the substance that has the complementary properties. The incorporation of this protein into antigen–antibody complexes is particularly interesting, as, on the whole, the precipitates formed by antigen with antibody are remarkably ' clean '. They do not adsorb unrelated proteins from the solution in which they combine. It is true that the ' complementing ' properties of serum can be removed by various particles, e.g. particles of heat-coagulated protein. But the processes differ qualitatively and quantitatively; complement has several components, and the components taken up preferentially by antigen–antibody aggregates are not the same as those taken up by other particles; and much smaller amounts of antigen–antibody aggregates than of other particles are needed to fix a given amount of complement. The weight of complement protein taken up by an antigen–antibody precipitate may amount to over $\frac{1}{3}$ of the weight of the precipitate (Heidelberger et al., 1941). Lanni (1946) considered that antigen–antibody precipitates are made up of antigen and antibody combined by their specific valences into particles with diameters of the order of 0.2μ; further aggregation of these particles is, in part at least, non-specific. He has suggested the name ' seromicron ' for these particles. If the molecules of complement protein are 200 Å long and are closely packed on the surface of these seromicrons, the amount added would only be some

6 per cent of the total precipitates. The complement, therefore, enters into the structure of the aggregate. It is not merely entrapped as the antigen–antibody aggregates are formed, for the protein is also fixed, though more slowly, by pre-formed antigen–antibody precipitates. We may, therefore, suggest that in the antigen–antibody aggregates spaces are formed which are specially shaped to accommodate the molecules of complement—that complement is a *clathrate*. The remarkable point is that complement is fixed by the aggregates formed by a great variety of antigens (ranging from proteins of various sizes to polysaccharides and the lipid particles used in the Wassermann reaction) with the antibodies of various species. The aggregates formed by horse antibodies with polysaccharides do not fix complement; the molecules of these antibodies are considerably larger than most rabbit and human antibodies. The failure is not, however, solely due to the size of the antibody molecules, and the aggregates formed by the polysaccharides with bovine antibodies, which are equally large, do fix complement (Kabat, 1939).

It is unlikely that free antibody or combined antibody, which has not formed an aggregate, has the property of fixing complement; for complement is not fixed by the complexes consisting of one antibody molecule and one or two antigen molecules, formed when antigen is in considerable excess (Osler and Heidelberger, 1948); a minimum complexity of structure is necessary.

One antigen molecule can combine with several antibody molecules and one antibody molecule with two antigen molecules; large aggregates can therefore be built up by specific combinations between antigen and antibody molecules. Two kinds of structure have been proposed. Marrack (1934) and Pauling (1940) suggested that cyclic structures form a three-dimensional network, commonly spoken of as a lattice; Goldberg (1952), on the other hand, on the analogy of polymers formed by smaller molecules, ruled out cyclic structures and considered that the aggregates are composed only of branched chains without cross-links between the chains. The question whether or not cyclic structures can be formed depends mainly on the sizes and shapes of antigen and antibody molecules and on the relative orientations of these molecules when combined. We may start with the basic unit— that is, one antigen molecule combined with one antibody molecule— and take an actual example, bovine serum albumin combined with rabbit antibody. The antigen has a molecular weight of about 70,000, and, if its shape is the same in solution as in crystals, it is a prism 144 Å in length, with a prism height of 45 Å and 20 or 16 Å wide in the centre (Low, 1952). The antibody, which has a molecular weight of about 160,000, is more elongated; its length seems to be of the order of 200 Å and its breadth about 40 Å.

The union will occur at definite sites on each molecule—at one or the other of the two possible sites on the antibody molecule and at one of several sites on the antigen molecule. The antibody combines with antigen by a multipoint attachment, so that no rotation about the actual site of attachment is possible; also there is nothing to suggest that these sites of attachment are on branches of the molecules that might rotate about a single bond. We now have, as the basic unit, an antibody molecule projecting at a fixed angle from one of several sites of an antigen molecule.

Attempts have been made to deduce the relative positions of combined antigen and antibody from studies of the soluble and relatively small complexes formed when antigen is in considerable excess. Singer and Campbell (1952) found that the sedimentation constant of the complex, which they considered to be composed of two bovine serum albumin molecules combined with one antibody molecule,

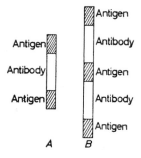

A   B

was 8·7 S. As the molecular weight of this compound is approximately 300,000, the frictional ratio is 1·8. This large value indicates that the compound is strongly asymmetric and 'suggests that the antigen molecules are situated near the opposite poles of the elongated antibody-molecule'. They also considered that another complex which was detected consisted of two antibody molecules combined with three antigen molecules; that the frictional ratio of this was 1·9; and that this ratio was smaller than that of a linear array of 3 antigen and 2 antibody molecules.

Becker (1952) also estimated that the sedimentation constant of a complex formed by excess of bovine serum albumin with rabbit antibody was 8·8 S. He found that the sedimentation constants of the compounds formed with horse antibodies were higher than those of the compounds formed with rabbit antibodies. He suggested that this might be due to differences of location of the combining sites on the two types of antibody molecule. This is plausible, as it appears that the combining sites of one horse antibody (diphtheria antitoxin) are distributed asymmetrically on the molecule. By treatment with proteo-lytic enzymes at pH about 4·0, the molecules are split transversely into two bits, one of which, with a molecular weight of about 90,000, carries

257

both the combining sites. As the properties of the horse antibody considered by Becker resembled those of diphtheria antitoxin and differed from those of rabbit antibodies, the combining sites of these antibodies may be similarly asymmetrically distributed.

Unlike the antibodies of rabbits and most other species, certain of the antibodies of horse antisera, particularly diphtheria antitoxin, do not form precipitates with antigen when antibody is in great excess. Goldberg (1952), applying the method used by Stockmayer (1943) in the study of the molecular sizes of three-dimensional polymers, concluded that aggregates of antigen and antibody will combine to grow up to a *critical point*, at which a few large aggregates are formed by the union of aggregates of moderate size ; the large aggregates precipitate. This *critical point* can be reached only when the ratio of antibody to antigen in the mixture lies within certain limits ; precipitates will not be formed in this way when antibody is in great excess*. It is possible that the orientation of rabbit antibodies, with respect to antigen molecules, is such that cyclic structures are inevitably formed by cross-links between chains, and that this formation of cyclic structures accounts for the formation of precipitates into the region of extreme antibody excess. The cross-links between chains may be specific bonds between antigen and antibody molecules of two separate chains that are brought together owing to the relative orientations of the molecules, or the non-specific attraction between any oppositely charged groups, or hydrogen bonds between appropriately juxtaposed atoms. The ratio of antibody to antigen molecules in the precipitates formed by bovine serum albumin with rabbit antibodies in antibody excess may be 6 to 1 or possibly more. It seems highly probable that, in an aggregate formed of branching chains in which the ratio of bulky antibody molecules to antigen molecules is as high as this, some of the molecules will be in positions suitable for the formation of such non-specific bonds.

The molecules are not tightly packed in the aggregates. Over 80 per cent of an antigen–antibody precipitate is water, which is available for solution of small molecules or ions (chloride or glucose) and, in part, available for solution of haemoglobin (Marrack and Grant, 1952). These secondary properties of antigen–antibody aggregates may well be *in vitro* analogues of reactions that occur in living tissues. For their elucidation we must await a better understanding of the detailed and over-all structure of proteins.

---

* Goldberg (1952) attributed the difference between the reactions of rabbit and horse antibodies to the lower solubility of rabbit antibody, quoting Boyd (1941). However, Boyd referred to solubility of antibody in concentrated solutions of ammonium sulphate; this does not, necessarily, have any relation to the solubility of the antigen–antibody compounds in the customary medium—0.15M-NaCl solution. Anyhow, Burtin (1954) has disposed of this argument, as he has found that horse antibodies which are less soluble than rabbit antibodies in concentrated ammonium sulphate solutions still do not form precipitates with the homologous antigen (human serum albumin) when the antibody is in great excess.

REFERENCES

Aminoff, D., Morgan, W. T. J. and Watkins, W. M. (1950) *Biochem. J.* **46,** 426
Avery, O. T., Goebel, W. F. and Babers, F. H. (1932) *J. exp. Med.* **55,** 769
Baer, H., Dische, Z. and Kabat, E. A. (1948) *ibid* **88,** 59
Becker, E. L. (1952) *J. Immunol.* **70,** 372
Boyd, W. C. (1941) *J. exp. Med.* **74,** 369
Bragg, L., Kendrew, J. C. and Perutz, M. F. (1950) *Proc. roy. Soc.* **A203,** 321
Bray, H. G., Henry, H. and Stacey, M. (1946) *Biochem. J.* **40,** 124
Burtin, P. (1954) *Bull. Soc. Chim. biol.* **36,** 335
Butler, K. and Stacey, M. (1955) *J. chem. Soc.* 1537
Cann, J. R., Campbell, D. H., Brown, R. A. and Kirkwood, J. M. (1951) *J. Amer. chem. Soc.* **73,** 4611
Calvery, H. O. (1935-36) *J. biol. Chem.* **112,** 167
Cohn, M., Wetter, L. R. and Deutsch, H. F. (1949) *J. Immunol.* **61,** 282
Erlenmeyer, H. and Berger, E. (1932) *Biochem. Z.* **255,** 429 ; (1933) *ibid* **262,** 196
Gibbons, R. A., Morgan, W. T. J. and Gibbons, M. (1955) *Biochem. J.* **60,** 428
Goebel, W. F. (1935) *J. biol. Chem.* **110,** 391 ; (1936) *J. exp. Med.* **64,** 29 ; (1937-38) *J. biol. Chem.* **122,** 649 ; (1938) *J. exp. Med.* **68,** 469
— Avery, O. T. and Babers, F. H. (1934) *J. exp. Med.* **60,** 599
— and Hotchkiss, R. D. (1937) *ibid* **66,** 191
Goldberg, R. J. (1952) *J. Amer. chem. Soc.* **74,** 5715
Haurowitz, F. (1953) *The Nature and Significance of the Antibody Response,* New York, Columbia University Press, p. 3
— and Breinl, F. (1933) *Hoppe-Seyl. Z.* **214,** 111
Heidelberger, M. and Adams, J. (1956) *J. exp. Med.* **103,** 189
— and Hobby, G. L. (1942) *Proc. nat. Acad. Sci., Wash.* **28,** 516
— Kabat, E. A. and Mayer, M. (1942) *J. exp. Med.* **75,** 35
— — and Shrivavasta, D. L. (1937) *ibid* **65,** 487
— Rocha E Silva, H. and Treffers, H. P. (1941) *ibid* **73,** 695
Humphrey, J. H. and Porter, R. R. (1956) *Biochem. J.* **62,** 93
Jones, J. K. N. and Perry, M. B. (1957) *J. Amer. chem. Soc.* **79,** 2787
— and Smith, F. (1949) *Advanc. Carbohyd. Chem.* **4,** 243
Kabat, E. A. (1939) *J. exp. Med.* **69,** 103 ; (1949) *Bact. Rev.* **13,** 189 ; (1954) *J. Amer. chem. Soc.* **76,** 3709 ; (1956) *Blood Group Substances,* New York, Academic Press
— and Leskowitz, S. (1955) *J. Amer. chem. Soc.* **77,** 5159
Karush, F. (1950) *ibid* **72,** 2705
Landsteiner, K. and Lampl, H. (1917) *Z. ImmunForsch.* **26,** 293
— and van der Scheer, J. (1927) *J. exp. Med.* **45,** 1045 ; (1929) *ibid* **50,** 407 ; (1934) *ibid* **59,** 75 ; (1936) *ibid* **63,** 325
Lanni, F. (1946) *ibid* **84,** 167
Low, B. W. (1952) *J. Amer. chem. Soc.* **74,** 4830
Marrack, J. R. (1934) *The Chemistry of Antigens and Antibodies,* Medical Research Council Special Report No. 194
— and Carpenter, B. R. (1938) *Brit. J. exp. Path.* **19,** 53
— and Grant, R. A. (1952) *ibid* **33,** 506
Marucci, A. A. and Mayer, M. M. (1955) *Arch. Biochem. Biophys.* **54,** 350
McFadden, M. L. and Smith, E. L. (1955) *J. biol. Chem.* **214,** 185
Morgan, W. T. J. and Watkins, W. M. (1953) *Brit. J. exp. Path.* **34,** 94 ; (1955) *Nature, Lond.* **175,** 676
Nathan, E. and Stern, F. (1930) *Dermat. Wschr.* **91,** 1471
Nuttall, G. H. F. and Strangeways, T. S. P. (1904) *Blood Immunity and Blood Relationship,* Cambridge

Orlans, E. S. (1955) *Nature, Lond.* **175**, 728

Osler, A. G. and Heidelberger, M. (1948) *J. Immunol.* **60**, 327

Pauling, L. (1940) *J. Amer. chem. Soc.* **62**, 2643

— Corey, R. B. and Branson, H. R. (1951) *Proc. nat. Acad. Sci., Wash.* **37**, 205

— and Pressman, D. (1943) *Physiol. Rev.* **23**, 203 ; (1945) *J. Amer. chem. Soc.* **67**, 1003

Percival, E. G. V. (1950) *Structural Chemistry of the Polysaccharides*, London, Frederick Muller

Porter, R. R. (1950) *Biochem. J.* **46**, 473 ; (1955) *ibid* **59**, 405

Pressman, D., Bryden, J. H. and Pauling, L. (1945) *J. Amer. chem. Soc.* **67**, 1219 ; (1948) *ibid* **70**, 1352

— Grossberg, A. L., Pence, L. H. and Pauling, L. (1946) *ibid* **68**, 250

— Pardee, A. B. and Pauling, L. (1945) *ibid* **67**, 1602

— and Pauling, L. (1949) *ibid* **71**, 2893

— and Siegel, M. (1953a) *ibid* **75**, 686 ; (1953b) *ibid* **75**, 1376 ; (1957) *ibid* **79**, 994

— — and Hall, L. A. R. (1954) *ibid* **76**, 6336

— Swingle, S. M., Grossberg, A. L. and Pauling, L. (1944) *ibid* **66**, 1731

Pryde, J. and Williams, R. T. (1933) *Biochem. J.* **27**, 1205, 1210

Reeves, R. E. (1950) *J. Amer. chem. Soc.* **72**, 1499

— and Goebel, W. F. (1941) *J. biol. Chem.* **139**, 511

Singer, S. J. and Campbell, D. (1952) *J. Amer. chem. Soc.* **74**, 1794

Smith, E. L., McFadden, M. L., Stockwell, A. and Buettner-Janusch, V. (1955) *J. biol. Chem.* **214**, 197

Stockmayer, W. H. (1943) *J. chem. Phys.* **11**, 45

Tomcsik, J. (1953) *Annu. Rev. Biochem.* **22**, 352

Watkins, W. M. and Morgan, W. T. J. (1952) *Nature, Lond.* **169**, 852

8

THE STEREOCHEMISTRY OF INORGANIC
MOLECULES AND COMPLEX IONS

R. J. Gillespie and R. S. Nyholm

THE stereochemistry of inorganic molecules is usually discussed in terms of the valence-bond method or a modified form of this employing localized molecular orbitals (valence or bond orbitals). The recent theoretical work of Lennard-Jones, Pople, Linnett and others enables the problem of directed valency to be approached in a manner that differs somewhat from the conventional valence-bond treatment although it employs essentially the same fundamental ideas. This recent work provides considerable justification for the very simple idea that the arrangement of bonds around an atom is determined by the tendency of the pairs of electrons in the valency shell to avoid each other and thus to dispose themselves as far apart as possible. It shows that the stereochemistry of an atom is determined by the size of its valency shell including the lone pairs, and it emphasizes that the lone pairs are equally as important as the bonding pairs in this respect. By taking account of the differences in the electrostatic repulsions between lone pairs, between lone pairs and bonds, and between bonds themselves, the simple theory can be refined to explain, for example, changes in bond angles in related series of molecules. This work also provides a clear explanation of the significance of hybrid orbitals.

In connection with the transition metal complexes the ligand (crystal) field theory has recently come into prominence, primarily owing to its value in the interpretation of the spectra and magnetic properties of transition-metal compounds. Whereas the valence-bond theory is concerned primarily with the bonding electrons, the ligand field theory deals mainly with the effect of the electric field arising from the surrounding ligands upon the properties of the non-bonding electrons of the central atom. The way in which the energy levels of the various d orbitals are separated by the ligand field is reflected in the magnetic behaviour, and in the frequency and the intensity of spectral transitions. Conversely, a study of the latter leads one to information concerning the geometric arrangement of the ligands about the central atom.

THE ARRANGEMENT OF ELECTRON PAIRS IN VALENCY SHELLS

In an excellent survey of inorganic stereochemistry known at that time, Sidgwick and Powell (1940) pointed out that the arrangements in space of the covalencies of polycovalent atoms are very simply related to the size of the valency shell of electrons. The pairs of electrons in a valency shell, irrespective of whether they are shared (i.e. bonding) pairs or unshared (i.e. non-bonding) pairs, are always arranged in the same way which depends only on their number. Thus two pairs are arranged linearly; three pairs in the form of a plane triangle; four pairs tetrahedrally; five pairs in the form of a trigonal pyramid; and six pairs octahedrally. FIGURE 1 gives the various possible molecular shapes that can arise from these different electron arrangements. These arrangements appear to hold without exception for the non-transitional elements, i.e. those elements which do not use inner d orbitals for bond formation. To these we can add a further arrangement, namely that of seven electron pairs in a pentagonal bipyramid. Valency shells containing more than seven electron pairs are not known among the non-transitional elements.

It should be noted that exactly regular shapes will be obtained only if all the electron pairs are forming bonds with identical atoms or groups. If some of the electrons are lone pairs, or if there are two or more different attached atoms or groups, deviations from the completely regular structures are to be expected. Some of these are discussed later.

In certain cases (marked with an asterisk in FIGURE 1) alternative molecular shapes are possible, since there are alternative positions for the one or more lone pairs. The choice has been made on the basis of considerations that are discussed later. For example, we cannot say whether ClF_3, would be planar T-shaped with 90° bond angles (I), planar and symmetrical with 120° bond angles (II), or pyramidal (III).

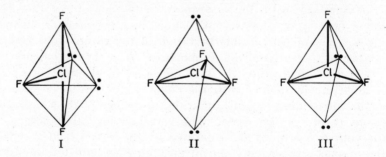

FIGURE 1 includes almost all the possible shapes, if it is assumed, as seems from the available evidence to be the case, that a given number of bonding pairs and a given number of lone pairs of electrons always give rise to the same shape. Only the rather improbable cases of more than two lone pairs in a total of six electron pairs and more than one lone pair in a total of seven electron pairs have been omitted. The case of the pentagonal bipyramidal arrangement of six bonding

FIGURE 1. Shapes of molecules (non-transitional elements)

No. of electron pairs and corresponding hybrid orbitals	Number of lone pairs			
	0	1	2	3
2 sp	 Linear e.g. $HgCl_2$			
3 sp^2	 Triangular plane e.g. BCl_3	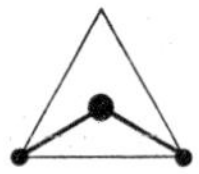 V-shape e.g. $SnCl_2$ gas		
4 sp^3	 Tetrahedron e.g. CH_4	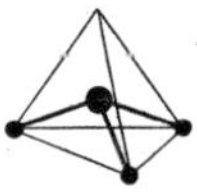 Trigonal pyramid e.g. NH_3	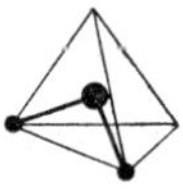 V-shape e.g. H_2O	
5 $sp^3d_{z^2}$	 Trigonal bipyramid e.g. PCl_5	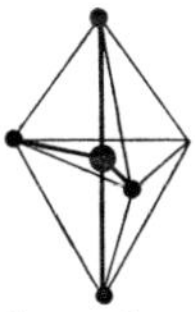 Irregular tetrahedron* e.g. $TeCl_4$	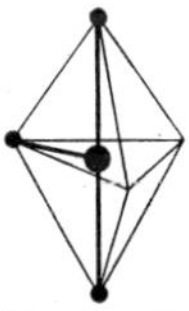 T-shape* e.g. ClF_3	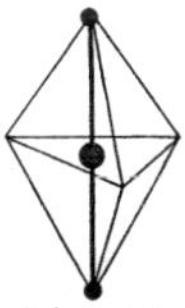 Linear* e.g. $[ICl_2]^-$
6 $sp^3d_{z^2}d_{x^2-y^2}$	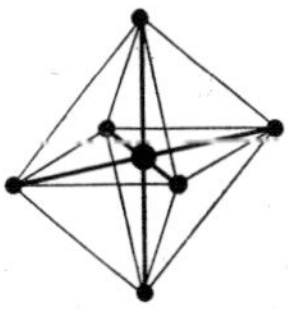 Octahedron e.g. SF_6	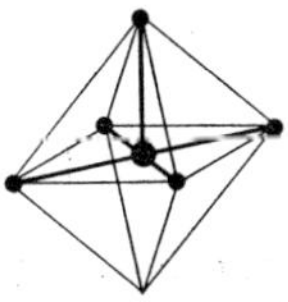 Square pyramid e.g. IF_5	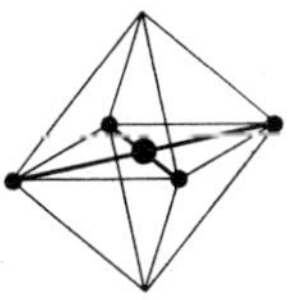 Square plane* e.g. $[ICl_4]^-$	
7 $sp^3d_{z^2}d_{x^2-y^2}d_{xy}$	 Pentagonal bipyramid e.g. IF_7	 Irregular octahedron e.g. $[SbBr_6]^{3-}$		

pairs and one lone pair is the only one in FIGURE 1 that is at all uncertain. The only known example whose structure has been investigated is the $[SbBr_6]^{3-}$ ion, which has been reported as having a regular and not an irregular octahedral structure (Hoard and Dickinson, 1933). A reinvestigation of this structure and an investigation of the structure of the related $[SeBr_6]^{2-}$ ion would obviously be of interest.

The shapes of molecules containing double bonds and triple bonds can be predicted similarly. This can be done by considering all the electron pairs independently, and assuming that they can be arranged as shown in FIGURE 1. Thus, for example, a tetrahedral arrangement of four pairs leads to a trigonal planar molecule if there is one double bond as in $COCl_2$ (IV), and to a linear molecule as in CO_2 (V) if

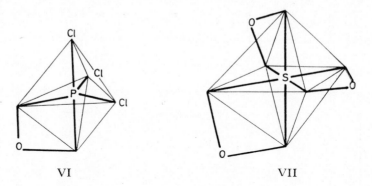

IV   V

there are two double bonds. This method can be extended to five electron pairs as in $POCl_3$ (VI) which is approximately tetrahedral in shape, and to six pairs as for example in SO_3 (VII) which is planar.

VI   VII

The shapes of many other molecules containing double bonds can be similarly predicted at least approximately in this manner, but the method is rather clumsy, and a somewhat more accurate and simpler picture is obtained by considering the two pairs of electrons in a double bond and the three pairs in a triple bond as together occupying only one of the positions in the various arrangements given in FIGURE 1. In this way the shapes listed in TABLE 1 may be predicted.

Alternatively, one may describe double and triple bonds in terms of σ and π orbitals, in which case only the σ electrons are effective in determining molecular shape. It is worthwhile pointing out that it may be shown (cf e.g. Pitzer, 1953) that the 'classical' description of

TABLE 1. THE SHAPES OF MOLECULES CONTAINING MULTIPLE BONDS

No. of bonding plus lone pairs	Arrangement in space	Corresponding hybrid orbitals	No. of bonds	No. of lone pairs	Shape of molecule	Examples
2	Linear	sp	2	0	Linear	$O{=}C{=}O$ $H{-}C{\equiv}N$
3	Triangular plane	sp^2	3	0	Triangular plane	(canonical structures)
			2	1	V-shape	(canonical structures)
4	Tetrahedron	sp^3	4	0	Tetrahedral	(canonical structures)
			3	1	Triangular pyramid	(canonical structures)
			2	2	V-shape	(canonical structures)
5	Trigonal bipyramid	sp^3d	5	0	Trigonal bipyramid	(canonical structures)
			4	1	Irregular tetrahedron	(canonical structures)
6	Octahedron	sp^3d^2	6	0	Octahedron	(canonical structures)

Note: Some of the formulae represent only one of several contributing canonical structures.

265

a double bond (e.g. IV–VII) and the ' modern ' description in terms of a σ- and a π-orbital are entirely equivalent.

The arrangements of electron pairs, on which the molecular shapes given in FIGURE 1 and TABLE 1 are based, are just those that might be predicted if it is assumed that there is a tendency for the electron pairs to arrange themselves as far apart as possible. Quantum-mechanical justification of this very simple idea has been provided by the recent work of Lennard-Jones and others, and is discussed later. It is noteworthy that it is thus predicted, for example, that CH_4 should be tetrahedral and that NH_3 and H_2O should also have bond angles of 109° 28′. Since the bond angles in these molecules are respectively 109° 28′, 106° 7′, and 104° 27′, this is a more satisfactory result than that given by a simple valence-bond treatment, which, as is discussed later, predicts that the bond angles should be 90° in NH_3 and H_2O, and that three of the bond angles in CH_4 should be 90°. This difficulty is generally overcome in the valence-bond method by the introduction of the concept of hybrid orbitals in the case of CH_4 and of hybrid orbitals and/or repulsions between the bond electrons and the hydrogen atoms in the cases of NH_3 and H_2O.

ELECTROSTATIC EFFECTS

The simple theory that we have described above can be considerably improved in a qualitative manner by the introduction of a second simple idea that is justified, for example, by the results of the detailed theoretical treatment of the water molecule by Pople (1950). It is assumed that electrostatic repulsions between the electron pairs in a valency shell decrease in magnitude in the order :

lone-pair : lone-pair >lone-pair : bond-pair >bond-pair : bond-pair

This can be understood if it is imagined that the lone pairs are closer to the nucleus than the bonding pairs, which may be imagined as being pulled out to a greater or lesser extent by the other nucleus with which they are forming a bond. Thus the lone pairs will be closer together than the bonding pairs and hence they will repel each other more strongly. This assumption enables one to give a qualitatively correct account of the variation of the bond angles in a series such as CH_4, NH_3, H_2O, and to understand somewhat better the shapes of those molecules that could not be predicted unambiguously in FIGURE 1. Thus in passing from CH_4 to NH_3 we replace one bonding pair by one lone pair, which repels the remaining three bond pairs somewhat more than the original bond pair, and hence causes the bond angle to decrease from the tetrahedral value of 109° 28′. In passing from NH_3 to H_2O another bond pair is replaced by a lone pair and the bond angle decreases correspondingly again.

266

In ICl_4^- the two lone pairs can either be at an angle of 180° as in VIII or at an angle of 90° as in IX. Repulsions between the lone pairs will evidently be minimized in VIII and this is the observed structure.

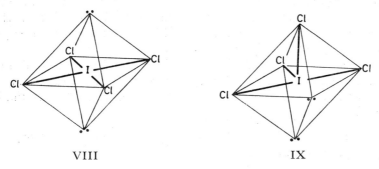

VIII   IX

In $TeCl_4$ there is only one lone pair, and it is necessary to consider the lone-pair : bond-pair repulsions. In the structure in which the lone pair is placed in one of the equatorial positions of the trigonal bipyramid (X) the lone pair is at an angle of 90° to two of the bonding pairs ; but in the other structure (XI) the lone pair is at one of the apices, and therefore is at an angle of 90° to three of the bond pairs. It is to be expected, therefore, that lone-pair : bond-pair repulsions will be less in structure X than in XI, in agreement with the fact that X is the observed structure.

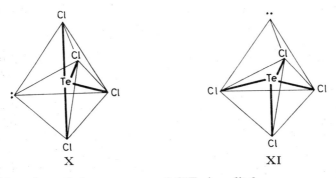

X   XI

Consideration of the structure of ClF_3 is a little more complicated, and the actual structure cannot be predicted with as much confidence as in the above cases. There are three possible structures in this case (I, II and III, p. 262) in which the two lone pairs are at angles of 120°, 180°, and 90° respectively. Considering only the lone-pair : lone-pair repulsions it would be predicted that the planar structure II would be preferred to I or III. The actual structure is, however, I ; and it appears, therefore, that one must also take the lone-pair : bond-pair repulsions into account. In II there are six lone-pair : bond-pair angles, all of 90°, whereas in I, two of these angles are 120°, and only four of them are 90°. It appears that this reduction in the lone-pair : bond-pair repulsions more than offsets the increased lone-pair : lone-pair repulsion caused by decreasing the angle between them from 180° to 120°. The two bond angles in the molecule are actually only 87° 29′, which means that the angles between the lone pairs and the fluorine atoms are slightly greater than 90°, which is consistent with the assumption that lone-pair : lone-pair repulsions are greater than bond-pair : bond-pair repulsions.

The variations in the bond angle in various series of related molecules can be satisfactorily interpreted by a slight extension of the above ideas. Thus, in the following two series of molecules, the bond angles vary in the manner shown :

$$NH_3, 106° 45′: PH_3, 93° 50′: AsH_3, 91° 35′: SbH_3, 91° 30′;$$
$$H_2O, 104° 27′: H_2S, 92° 20′$$

These trends can be attributed to the decreasing electronegativity of the central atom in both series. This allows the bonding pairs to be drawn further away from the central nucleus by the hydrogen atoms, thereby increasing their distance apart and decreasing the repulsions between them. A quite similar effect is obtained by replacing hydrogen by the more electronegative fluorine, which decreases the bond angle ; compare the following examples with NH_3 and H_2O above :

$$NF_3, 102° 9′; OF_2, 101° 30′$$

Similarly the decrease in the bond angle F—C—F in the series :

$$CF_4, 109° 28′; CHF_3, 108° 48′; CH_2F_2, 108°$$

can be attributed to the fact that on replacing fluorine by hydrogen the electrons in the remaining C—F bonds are enabled to move farther out towards the fluorine atoms.

In the above discussion all electrostatic interactions involving the nuclei and the electrons of the attached atoms have been ignored for simplicity, and only the electrons of the valency shell of the central atom have been considered. Detailed calculations for the water molecule (Pople, 1950) show that consideration of all the electrostatic interactions reinforces the conclusions that were reached above on the basis of the valency-shell interactions alone.

In molecules in which atoms other than hydrogen are bonded to the central atom, it is also necessary to take into account interactions between their lone-pair electrons. Thus for example Cl_2O has a bond angle of 110° 48′, which is greater than the bond angle in water. Here, it appears that the repulsions between the lone-pairs of the large chlorine atoms more than offset the effect of their electro-negativity in decreasing the repulsion between the bond electrons. It is interesting to note than on replacing the oxygen by sulphur we obtain the expected decrease in bond angle (Cl_2S, 102°).

THE VALENCE-BOND METHOD

In the valence-bond method, the description given by Heitler and London of the covalent bond in the hydrogen molecule is extended to covalent bonds in general. A covalent bond is imagined as being formed when an electron in a singly occupied orbital (i.e. an unpaired electron) is paired with an electron of opposite spin in a singly occupied orbital of another atom, the strength of the resulting bond being roughly proportional to the extent of overlap of the two atomic orbitals. Orbitals that have directional character (e.g. p and d orbitals, see FIGURE 7) are assumed to form bonds in the directions in which they are concentrated, since this will give maximum overlap. The pair of electrons constituting a bond may be conveniently imagined as occupying a localized (valence or bond) orbital that is to a reasonable approximation simply a linear combination of the singly occupied orbitals.

The water molecule may be considered as an example. The electronic configuration of the oxygen atom may be written $(1s)^2$ $(2s)^2$ $(2p_x)^2$ $(2p_y)(2p_z)$, with an unpaired electron in each of the $2p_y$ and $2p_z$ orbitals. If it is assumed that these are the orbitals used in bond-formation, as was assumed originally by Slater (1931), then it may be seen in FIGURE 2 that maximum overlap with the hydrogen $1s$ orbitals will be obtained if the two bonds are formed along the axes of the two singly occupied $2p$ orbitals, that is at an angle of 90°. Similar considerations lead one to expect that the ammonia molecule would have a triangular pyramidal structure with bond angles of 90°.

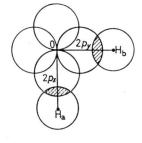

FIGURE 2. The water molecule

According to the valence-bond theory, the valency of an atom should be equal to the number of its unpaired electrons. The ground state of the beryllium atom is $(1s)^2$ $(2s)^2$ which indicates that it should have a zero valency. In fact beryllium is known to be divalent, at least in the majority of its compounds. This may be accounted for by assuming that, under the perturbing influence of the atoms with which it combines, one of the $2s$ electrons is unpaired and promoted to one of the vacant $2p$ orbitals to give the configuration $(1s)^2$ $(2s)(2p_x)$ with two unpaired electrons. A fairly large amount of energy is needed to achieve this promotion but it is more than recovered in the energy resulting from the formation of two bonds.

For simplicity the structure of the unknown monomeric beryllium hydride molecule BeH_2 will be considered. The electron in the $1s$ orbital of one of the hydrogen atoms (H_a) may be paired with the electron in the beryllium $2p$ orbital, and maximum overlap and greatest bond strength will be obtained if the hydrogen nucleus is located on the axis of symmetry of the $2p$ orbital. The electron in the $1s$ orbital of the other hydrogen atom (H_b) will then have to be paired with the electron in the beryllium $2s$ orbital (Structure (a) in FIGURE 3).

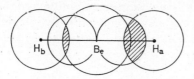 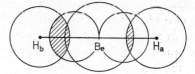

(a) H_b $1s$: $2s$ Be $2p$: $1s$ H_a (b) H_b $1s$: $2p$ Be $2s$: $1s$ H_a

FIGURE 3. The BeH_2 molecule: atomic orbital description

Since the $2s$ orbital has no directional character, it will not give better overlap in any one preferred direction, and therefore we cannot from these considerations alone predict the shape of the molecule. This picture of the molecule is also unsatisfactory in so far as the expected equality of the two Be—H bonds is not apparent. Thus the bond formed by the $2p$ orbital might be expected to differ, for example, in both length and strength from that formed by the $2s$ orbital. It is customary in such cases to introduce the idea of hybrid orbitals in order that the description of the molecule should correspond to the expected equality of the two Be—H bonds. It will first, however, be instructive to discuss why the above description is unsatisfactory and to show how it may be improved *without* the introduction of the concept of hybrid orbitals. One reason for the unsatisfactory nature of the above description of the molecule is that it is not justifiable to consider only this particular way of pairing the electrons. It is evident that although the $1s$ electron of H_a was paired with the $2p$ electron of beryllium, since the $1s$ orbital of H_a also overlaps with the $2s$ orbital of beryllium, the possibility that H_a is paired with the $2s$ electron of beryllium and H_b with the $2p$ electron of beryllium should also be considered. Thus it may be seen that the pairing scheme represented by (a) is not unique, and in fact that represented by (b) (FIGURE 3) is equally probable, and must be of the same energy. A good approximation to the actual structure may then be obtained by imagining it to be a mixture or resonance hybrid of (a) and (b) taken with equal weights; a still better description of the molecule would also include ionic and other structures of lesser importance. Since maximum overlap with the $2p$ orbital of beryllium is achieved if both the hydrogen nuclei lie on the axis of symmetry of the $2p$ orbital of beryllium, it may now be predicted that the two Be—H bonds will be collinear. Moreover, because of the equivalence of structures (a) and (b), the two bonds would also be expected to be identical. This is a valid but nevertheless somewhat unsatisfactory description of the molecule, as it does not seem to be very obviously related to the generally accepted view of such a molecule as containing two nearly independent bonds, each made up of a pair of shared electrons.

In order to be able to identify each bond with a single pair of electrons, it is customary to introduce the idea of *hybrid orbitals*. Thus instead of pairing each of the electrons of hydrogen with both of the unpaired electrons of beryllium in two separate resonance structures, the atomic orbitals of beryllium are first mixed or hybridized in such a way as to obtain two new hybrid orbitals, each of which—because they are more localized and strongly directed than the atomic orbitals—can, to a good approximation, be paired exclusively with only one of the hydrogen atoms.

Such hybrid orbitals are obtained by taking appropriate linear combinations of atomic orbitals. In the case under consideration, the two orbitals must be equivalent (so that they may form equivalent bonds) and they must therefore be constructed from equal amounts of the $2s$ and $2p$ orbitals. Only two such linear combinations are possible :

$$\psi_{sp}' = \frac{1}{\sqrt{2}}(\psi_{2s} + \psi_{2p})$$

$$\psi_{sp}'' = \frac{1}{\sqrt{2}}(\psi_{2s} - \psi_{2p})$$

The factor $\dfrac{1}{\sqrt{2}}$ is a normalizing factor inserted to ensure that the total probability of finding an electron in one of these orbitals is unity, i.e.

$$\int \psi_{sp}'^2 \, d\tau = \int \psi_{sp}''^2 \, d\tau = 1$$

These two orbitals are known as sp or digonal hybrid orbitals. The linear combinations taken to form hybrid orbitals must be chosen so that the hybrid orbitals are independent of each other, that is, it must not be possible to express any one of a set of hybrid orbitals in terms of the others. This independence is ensured if the orbitals are made orthogonal to each other, i.e. $\int \psi_i \, \psi_j \, d\tau = 0$. It is easily verified that the two orbitals above are orthogonal and therefore independent. The form of the two sp hybrid orbitals can easily be visualized by superimposing the $2s$ and $2p$ orbitals and either adding or subtracting them as shown in FIGURE 4.

It may be seen that on the right-hand side of the diagram the two wave functions are of the same sign and on adding they reinforce each other; thus in the hybrid orbital the magnitude of the wave function is increased in this region. On the left-hand side of the diagram, however, the two wave functions are of opposite sign, and hence neutralize each other. Thus in the hybrid orbital the magnitude of the wave function is decreased in this region. The other linear combination is easily seen to give rise to an orbital of the same shape directed along the same axis, but in the opposite direction (FIGURE 4).

(a) Atomic orbitals   (b) Hybrid orbitals (sp)

FIGURE 4. The beryllium atom

It may be seen that these sp hybrid orbitals are strongly directed in space, and hence they can overlap well and form strong bonds in these particular directions. Thus the electron in the orbital ψ_{sp}' may be paired with the electron in the $1s$ orbital of one of the hydrogen atoms, say H_a, maximum overlap and maximum bond-strength being achieved by placing the hydrogen atom on the axis of symmetry of the hybrid orbital (FIGURE 5).. It may be seen that this hydrogen orbital overlaps very little with the other beryllium hybrid orbital ψ_{sp}'',

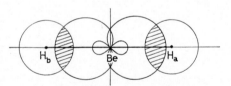

H_b $1s : sp''$ Be $sp' : 1s$ H_a

FIGURE 5. The BeH$_2$ molecule: hybrid orbital description

and hence pairing with the electron in this orbital can be justifiably neglected. Similarly the electron in the $1s$ orbital of H_b may be paired exclusively with the electron in the beryllium ψ_{sp}'' orbital, and maximum overlap and bond strength may be obtained by placing the hydrogen atom on the axis of symmetry of ψ_{sp}''. Thus the molecule would be expected to be linear.

In the case of the carbon atom, which has the configuration $(1s)^2(2s)^2(2p_x)(2p_y)$ in the ground state, it is necessary to promote one of the $2s$ electrons to the vacant $2p$ orbital in order to obtain a configuration with four unpaired electrons, i.e. $(1s)^2(2s)(2p_x)(2p_y)(2p_z)$. Application of the criterion of maximum overlap would lead one to expect that the $2p$ orbitals would form three bonds at 90°, and that the $2s$ orbital would form a bond in some other direction which cannot be predicted. This is evidently an unsatisfactory description of the valencies of the carbon atom which are known to be arranged tetrahedrally. Again, this is because other equally probable pairing schemes have been neglected. Although a molecule such as CH_4 could be described in terms of resonance between, in this case, a rather large number of possible pairing schemes, it is more convenient to use hybrid orbitals, each of which, because of its more localized and directional character, overlaps appreciably with only one of the combining atoms. In this case these are the sp^3 orbitals which are strongly directed towards the corners of a tetrahedron.

The advantage of using hybrid orbitals is always that a molecule can be reasonably accurately described by only one structure, in which a pair of electrons corresponds to each of the bonds. It is necessary to be clear that the use of hybrid orbitals is merely a matter of convenience, and that a molecule can always be equally correctly, although less conveniently, described in terms of resonance between structures corresponding to different pairing schemes between the singly occupied atomic orbitals of the combining atoms.

THE EXCLUSION PRINCIPLE AND MOLECULAR SHAPE

It is a fundamental property of electrons that they conform to the exclusion principle. It is not possible, at least at present, to prove the exclusion principle from any theory, and it must be accepted as a fundamental fact concerning the behaviour of electrons. In its original form, due to Pauli, it states that no two electrons can have both the same space wave function (i.e. occupy the same orbital), and the same spin. It is another fundamental property of electrons that they are indistinguishable. Because of their indistinguishability the interchange of any two electrons in a system does not produce any observable change in the system. This means that the square of the wave-function, ψ^2, which represents the probability that the electrons are found at any given positions, must remain unchanged when the space- and spin-coordinates of any two electrons are interchanged. This places a restriction on the wave function itself; either it must remain unchanged, or it must change sign when the coordinates of any two electrons are interchanged, i.e. it must be either symmetrical or antisymmetrical to the interchange of the coordinates of any two electrons. In fact only antisymmetrical wave-functions are found to represent the properties of electrons, and it may be shown that this is an alternative and more general statement of the exclusion principle, namely that the complete wave function for any system must be antisymmetrical to electron interchange.

Systems of Electrons with the Same Spin

As we shall see, the physical manifestation of the exclusion principle is that two electrons of the same spin cannot occupy the same orbital, and that more generally electrons of the same spin tend to avoid each other as much as possible. In particular, it is found that if all the electrons in a system have the same spin, the most probable distribution of the electrons is that in which they are as far apart as possible. This is an extremely important conclusion, and follows directly from writing the complete wave function so that it conforms to the exclusion principle and the principle of the indistinguishability of electrons; it does not require for its derivation a consideration, for example, of the electrostatic repulsion between the electrons. This is well brought out by an example discussed by Lennard-Jones (1954) in which he considers the distribution of three particles of the same spin, but between which there are no force fields of any kind, confined to move in a circular ring. It is found that the most probable arrangement is that in which the three particles are arranged at equal intervals around the ring (i.e. at the corners of an equilateral triangle), and that there is zero probability of any two particles being found at the same point. It can also be shown that for any arrangement of two particles the most probable position of the third is that in which it is as far as possible from the other two (FIGURE 6).

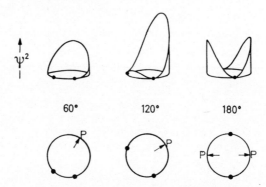

FIGURE 6. The distribution of a particle relative to two others (Lennard-Jones, 1954)

Similar conclusions are reached for atoms. Let us consider the beryllium atom in the configuration $(1s)^2(2s)(2p)$ in which the spins of the two unpaired electrons are the same. An approximation to the complete wave function for a system may be obtained by taking an antisymmetrical linear combination of an appropriate set of single-electron wave-functions. Because there is little interaction between the spin and orbital motions of an electron, a single-electron wave-function may be written as the product of a space wave-function and a spin wave-function, i.e. $\psi = \psi_{space}\psi_{spin}$. The spin wave-function can only have one of two values, which are generally denoted by α and β. The complete wave function for the valency electrons of the beryllium atom in the above configuration may thus be written

$$\psi = \psi_{2s}(1)\alpha(1)\ \psi_{2p}(2)\alpha(2) - \psi_{2s}(2)\alpha(1)\ \psi_{2p}(1)\alpha(2),$$

and this can be rearranged as the product of an antisymmetrical space wave-function and a symmetrical spin wave-function, i.e.

$$\psi = [\psi_{2s}(1)\ \psi_{2p}(2) - \psi_2(2)\ \psi_{2p}(1)]\alpha(1)\alpha(2)$$

The probability of finding the electrons with any given set of space coordinates is given by ψ^2. As our interest is mainly in the angular distribution of the electrons, we may for simplicity use hydrogen-like wave functions and take their radial parts to be identical. Thus we may write $\psi_{2s} = R$ and $\psi_{2p} = \sqrt{3}R\cos\theta$. The angular distribution of the electrons is then given by

$$\psi^2(\theta) = (\cos\theta_2 - \cos\theta_1)^2$$

It is readily seen that this expression has a maximum value when $\theta_1 = 0°$ and $\theta_2 = 180°$, or when $\theta_1 = 180°$ and $\theta_2 = 0°$. Thus we conclude that there is a maximum probability of finding the two electrons on opposite sides of the nucleus on a straight line passing through the nucleus. For the configuration $(1s)^2(2s)(2p_x)(2p_y)(2p_z)$ of the carbon atom, in which all the spins of the unpaired electrons are the same, Zimmermann and van Rysselberghe (1949) have shown that the most probable arrangement of the four electrons is at the corners of a regular tetrahedron. Similarly, in the configuration $(1s)^2(2s)$ $(2p_x)(2p_y)$ of the boron atom, in which the spins of the unpaired electrons are the same, their most probable arrangement is at the corners of an equilateral triangle. Now it seems reasonable to suppose that the directions in which an atom will form bonds will be the directions in which there is a maximum probability of finding its unpaired electrons when they have the same spin. Thus we would expect to find bond angles of 180°, 120°, and 109° 28′ in single-bonded molecules of beryllium, boron, and carbon respectively.

It should be noted that in the actual valence-state of an atom, the spins of the electrons must be considered to be random, and not necessarily all parallel. Such a valence state may be described by a linear combination of appropriate atomic states. Thus, in the case of the beryllium atom, the valence state is given by a linear combination of the triplet (^{3}P) state that we have been considering, in which the spins of the electrons are the same, and the singlet (^{1}P) state, in which the spins of the electrons are opposite, and in which the electron distribution of maximum probability is that in which the electrons are on the same side of the nucleus. However, the triplet state has a

275

weight of 3/4 in the valence state, and it will therefore determine the electron distribution of maximum probability. Similar considerations apply in the other cases that we have discussed.

Neon-like Closed Shells

It is more difficult to make similar calculations for atoms, such as nitrogen and oxygen, in which not only are there electrons of opposite spin in the valency shell, but also the numbers of electrons with opposite spin are different (Linnett and Poë, 1951), and we shall not discuss them. It will be simpler and more convenient for our present purpose to pass on to a consideration of closed shells in which there are equal numbers of electrons of opposite spin. Thus, for example, in the neon atom there are four electrons of one spin, and four with the opposite spin, and the exclusion principle leads to the conclusion that the most probable arrangement is that in which there are four close pairs of electrons of opposite spins at the corners of a regular tetrahedron (Lennard-Jones, 1949; Linnett and Poë, 1951; Brickstock and Pople, 1953; Dickens and Linnett, 1957). In other atoms whose valency shells have been completed in molecule formation the eight valency-shell electrons would be expected to have the same most probable arrangement. This arrangement would be expected in CH_4, for example, and, moreover, in such a molecule the electrostatic attractions of the hydrogen nuclei for the valency-shell electrons will increase the probability of the tetrahedral arrangement of the four pairs of electrons. The same arrangement will also be found in molecules such as NH_3 and H_2O, except that in these cases one or two of the pairs of electrons will be lone pairs. Thus, solely, as a consequence of the exclusion principle and the indistinguishability of electrons, it is found that the most probable arrangement of four pairs of electrons in a valency shell is at the corners of a tetrahedron, and hence one may predict that the bond angles in molecules such as CH_4, NH_3 and H_2O should have the tetrahedral value of 109°.

Valency Shells of more than Eight Electrons; d Orbitals

In valency shells containing more than eight electrons, d orbitals are used. These have properties which differ in some important respects from those of p orbitals.

Unlike p orbitals, the d orbitals are not all equivalent in shape, nor do they all have the same relative orientation in space. Thus the d_{z^2} orbital differs in shape from the four equivalent $d_{x^2-y^2}$, d_{xy}, d_{xz}, and d_{yz} orbitals; and the d_{z^2} and the $d_{x^2-y^2}$ orbitals are directed along the same x, y and z orbitals as the p orbitals, whereas the d_{xy}, d_{xz}, and d_{yz} orbitals have their maxima in directions at 45° to the x, y, and z axes and have nodes in the directions of these axes (FIGURE 7). The differences in the relative orientation of the d orbitals are of the greatest importance for stereochemistry, and, following the usual practice in ligand-field theory, we shall sometimes find it convenient to refer to the $d_{x^2-y^2}$ and the d_{z^2} orbitals as d_γ orbitals and the d_{xy}, etc. orbitals as d_ε orbitals. The arrangements of the electron pairs in valency shells and the shapes of molecules depend on the particular d orbitals that are used for bond formation, as well as on the number that are used.

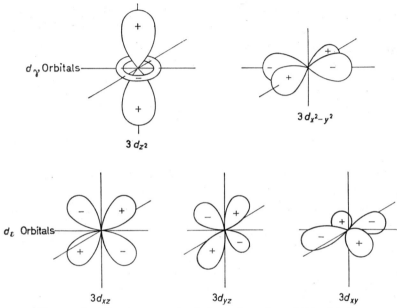

FIGURE 7. The shapes and relative orientation of $3d$ orbitals

It is evident that, as the d_ε orbitals have their maxima in directions between the p orbitals and have nodes in the directions of the p orbitals, they cannot form bonds in the directions of the p orbitals and they will therefore tend not to be used for bond formation simultaneously with the p orbitals. On the other hand, the d_γ orbitals have their maxima in the directions of the p orbitals, and they can form bonds in these directions. There will be a tendency, therefore, for the d_γ orbitals to be used simultaneously with the p orbitals for bond formation. It is convenient at this point to make a distinction between the transitional elements and the non-transitional elements, and for the moment we shall discuss only the latter. These elements use only outer d orbitals, which are of higher energy than s and p orbitals, in bond formation. Thus d orbitals are only used in addition to the one s and the three p orbitals. One, two and three d orbitals are, therefore, used in five-, six-, and seven-coordinated molecules respectively. Higher coordination numbers than seven are not known among the non-transitional elements using outer d orbitals.

It seems reasonable, therefore, that when only one d orbital is used in bond formation it will be a d_γ orbital. Linnett and Mellish (1954) have shown from a consideration of the complete wave function that the most probable arrangement of five electrons with the same spin in the configuration, $(s)(p)^3(d_{z^2})$ is at the corners of a pentagonal bipyramid. The most probable arrangement for the configuration $(s)(p)^3(d_{x^2-y^2})$, on the other hand, is the square pyramid. The former is found to be slightly more probable than the latter, and it will also probably be favoured by the fact that inter-electronic repulsions will be somewhat smaller in this structure. By an argument similar to that given above for CH_4, it may be concluded that, in any molecule in which there are five pairs of electrons in the valency shell of an atom of a non-transitional element, these electron pairs will be arranged at the corners of a trigonal bipyramid. The trigonal bipyramid and structures derived from it are the only structures that have been observed for molecules of non-transitional elements with ten electrons in their valency shells.

When two d orbitals are used for bond formation, they will be the two d_γ orbitals. Linnett and Mellish (1954) have shown that the most probable arrangement of six electrons with the same spin in the configuration $(s)(p)^3(d_{x^2-y^2})(d_{z^2})$ is at the corners of an octahedron. Similarly, in any molecule in which there are six pairs of electrons in the valency shell of an atom of a non-transitional element, the pairs of electrons will have the octahedral arrangement. The octahedron and structures derived from it are the only structures that have been observed for molecules of non-transitional elements with twelve electrons in their valency shells.

When three d orbitals are used for bond formation, these will be the two d_γ and one of the d_ε orbitals. The most probable arrangement of seven electrons with the same spin in the configuration $(s)(p)^3(d_\gamma)^2(d_\varepsilon)$ has not been discussed previously, but it may be shown to be the pentagonal bipyramid. In the only known example of a seven-coordinated molecule of a non-transitional element, namely IF_7, a pentagonal bipyramidal structure has been observed (Lord, Lynch, Schumb and Slowinski, 1950). The probability that the ion $[SbBr_6]^{3-}$ also has a structure based on the pentagonal bipyramid has been discussed earlier (p. 264).

It may be noted that these most probable arrangements of electron pairs in the valency shell of an atom are exactly the arrangements that form the basis of FIGURE 1.

PROMOTION ENERGY

No consideration has been given in the preceding discussion to the possible effects of any differences in energy between the various electrons in a valency shell. In a free atom the order of the energies of orbitals with the same principal quantum number is $s < p < d$, and consequently the average distance of an electron in these orbitals from the nucleus increases in the order $s < p < d$. However, in order for these orbitals to be used simultaneously to form a set of bonds with a number of atoms situated at the same or nearly the same distance from the central atom, they must have their maximum values at approximately the same distance from the nucleus, otherwise they cannot all overlap well with the orbitals of the combining atoms; in other words, all the electrons that are being used to form a set of equivalent or nearly equivalent bonds must be at the same average distance from the nucleus. Craig and Magnusson (1956) have suggested that the electric field of the combining atoms may cause the outer orbitals, which would otherwise extend outside the combining atoms, to contract, so that they become compatible in size with the inner orbitals. In the preceding discussion of the most probable arrangements of electron pairs in a valency shell, only the angular distribution was considered, and it was thus implicitly assumed that all the pairs of electrons are at the same distance from the nucleus. The good agreement between the predictions of this method and the known shapes of molecules lends some further support to the suggestion that in a molecule the energies and the average distances from the nucleus of all the electrons in a valency shell are approximately the same. This implies that the energy of promoting an electron from an s to a p or a d orbital is not such an important factor in determining molecular shape as has hitherto often been supposed. Some further consideration of the shape of the water molecule is of interest in this connection.

There would not at first sight appear to be any need for electron promotion in the oxygen atom, since it has two unpaired electrons in its ground state (A) $(1s)^2(2s)^2(2p_x)^2(2p_y)(2p_z)$. It has been shown earlier that the two singly occupied p orbitals would be expected to form two bonds at 90° (FIGURE 8 (a)). It is known, however, that the bond angle is in fact $104\frac{1}{2}°$. In order to account for this, it is necessary to assume that electron-promotion from the $2s$ orbital to one of the half-filled $2p$ orbitals does, in fact, occur. Let us first assume that there is complete promotion of one electron, giving the configuration (B) $(1s)^2(2s)(2p_x)(2p_y)^2(2p_z)^2$. The singly filled $2s$ and $2p_x$ orbitals in this configuration would be expected to form two collinear bonds (c) which may best be described in terms of sp digonal hybrid orbitals (d). Thus on the basis of this configuration a bond angle of 180° would be predicted. Intermediate bond angles between 90° and 180° correspond to partial promotion of an electron from a $2s$ to a $2p$ orbital. Such a partial promotion corresponds, for example, to a configuration (C) in which all the electrons are in tetrahedral hybrid orbitals $(sp_1^3)^2$ $(sp_2^3)^2(sp_3^3)(sp_4^3)$, since in this configuration there are effectively $1\frac{1}{2}$

electrons in the $2s$ orbital and $4\frac{1}{2}$ electrons in the $2p$ orbitals. Thus there has been an effective promotion of half an electron from the

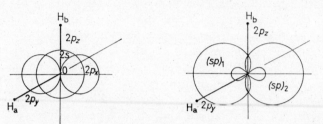

(a) O : $(1s)^2\ (2s)^2\ \underbrace{(2p_x)^2}_{\text{lone pair electrons}}\ \overbrace{(2p_y)\ (2p_z)}^{\text{bond electrons}}$

(b) O : $(1s)^2\ \underbrace{(sp_1)^2\ (sp_2)^2}_{\text{lone pair electrons}}\ \overbrace{(2p_y)\ (2p_z)}^{\text{bond electrons}}$

A. Bond angle 90°

(c) O : $(1s)^2\ \overbrace{(2s)\ (2p_x)}^{}\ \underbrace{(2p_y)^2\ (2p_z)^2}_{}$

lone pair electrons (above), bond electrons (below)

(d) O : $(1s)^2\ \overbrace{(sp_1)\ (sp_2)}^{}\ \underbrace{(2p_y)^2\ (2p_z)^2}_{}$

lone pair electrons (above), bond electrons (below)

B. Bond angle 180°

(e) O : $(1s)^2\ \underbrace{(sp_1^3)^2\ (sp_2^3)^2}_{\text{lone pair electrons}}\ \overbrace{(sp_3^3)\ (sp_4^3)}^{\text{bond electrons}}$

C. Bond angle 109½°

FIGURE 8. Shape of the water molecule

$2s$ to a $2p$ orbital. This tetrahedral hybridization corresponds to a bond angle of $109\frac{1}{2}°$ (e), which is closer to the observed bond-angle in water. The actual state of the oxygen atom of the water molecule can be described by a degree of hybridization and of corresponding electron promotion between the electron configurations (C) and (A). Since the use of hybrid orbitals gives better overlap, and hence stronger bonds, than would the p orbitals of the oxygen atom in the electronic configuration (A), the actual structure of the water molecule may be regarded as being determined by a compromise between the tendency to achieve maximum overlap, which would be greatest for configuration (B), and a tendency for one of the lone pairs of electrons to remain in the $2s$ orbital (of the oxygen atom), as in configuration (A). This tendency has usually been ascribed to the energy difference between the $2s$ and the $2p$ orbitals, and it is evident that, if this separation were large, it would be an important factor in determining the structure of the water molecule. Similarly it has been suggested that the reason for the decrease in the bond angle in the series H_2O, H_2S, H_2Se and H_2Te, is the increasing tendency of one of the lone-pair electrons to occupy the s orbital. This explanation however, meets with the difficulty that it would imply that the separation of the s and the p levels increases with increasing principal quantum number, whereas the reverse is certainly the case for the free atoms. Although we have argued above that these energy differences may all be much smaller in molecules than in atoms, we have no reason for supposing that they could be reversed. It seems probable, therefore, that this apparent increase in the difficulty of promoting an electron from an s to a p orbital is not the reason for the decrease in the bond angle in the above series, and in view of our previous discussion, it seems reasonable to suppose in fact that there is probably only a small difference between the energies of the s and p orbitals of the central atom in the molecule.

The tendency of one of the lone pairs to occupy the s orbital may instead be regarded as an alternative but equivalent description of electron pair repulsion. Thus, for example, if in the water molecule the oxygen has the configuration (A), one of the lone pairs may be described as occupying the $2s$ orbital and the other the $2p$ orbital (a). These lone pair electrons may alternatively be described as occupying two equivalent sp hybrid orbitals (b) and it may then be seen that they are at the maximum possible angle apart, i.e. 180°. This corresponds to a case in which lone-pair : lone-pair repulsions are very much greater than bond : bond repulsions. On the other hand, if both the lone pairs are in $2p$ orbitals, as in configuration (c), then the lone pairs will be at the minimum angle of 90° apart, and the bonds will be at 180° [(c) and (d)]. This corresponds to a case in which lone-pair : lone-pair repulsions are very much less than bond : bond repulsions. The actual structure of the water molecule is intermediate between these two extremes, and corresponds to that in which lone-pair : lone-pair repulsions are comparable with, although slightly greater than, bond : bond repulsions, and in which there has been a partial promotion of an electron from the $2s$ to a $2p$ orbital (e). We see, then, that increasing the bond angle in water from 90°, and thereby at least partially promoting an electron from the $2s$ to a $2p$ orbital, involves bringing the lone-pair electrons closer together, and thus increasing the repulsion between them. If, as suggested above, the energy difference between the $2s$ and the $2p$ orbitals of the oxygen atom in the water molecule is relatively small, the tendency of the lone-pair electrons to remain in the $2s$ orbital can be adequately interpreted simply in terms of electrostatic repulsion between the lone-pairs. In the series H_2O, H_2S, H_2Se, H_2Te, it is to be expected that the inter-electronic repulsions will decrease with increasing size of the central atom, and that the bond : bond repulsions will decrease rather more rapidly than the lone-pair repulsions. Thus the effect of the lone pairs will become increasingly more important, the angle between them will open out towards 180°, and the bond angle will decrease correspondingly towards 90°.

It is always possible to describe the effects of repulsions between electron pairs alternatively in terms of a tendency for the non-bonding electrons in the valency shell of an atom to remain in its lowest available atomic orbital. Thus in the case of five electron pairs with the trigonal bipyramidal arrangement, it was concluded earlier (p. 267) that as a result of the repulsions between electron pairs, the lone pairs always occupy the equatorial positions (as, for example, in $TeCl_4$, ClF_3, and $[ICl_2]^-$, FIGURE 1). Alternatively one may say that there is a tendency for the lone-pair electrons to utilize the s orbital as far as possible. In the limiting case the lone pairs may be regarded as occupying one or more of a set of three coplanar trigonal sp^2 hybrid orbitals, with two of the bonding pairs occupying the two collinear pd_{z^2} hybrid orbitals, perpendicular to the plane of the sp^2 orbitals.

HYBRID ORBITALS

The most probable arrangement of single electrons with the same spin, or of pairs of electrons with opposite spins, in the valency shell of an atom is not immediately apparent from the usual description in terms of a set of hydrogen-like atomic orbitals. It is apparent, however, that the directions of the maxima of the hybrid sp orbitals for the beryllium atom, i.e. $\mu = (1/\sqrt{2})(s + p)$, $\eta = (1/\sqrt{2})(s - p)$, where we have written s for ψ_{2s} and μ for ψ_{sp}', etc. for simplicity, correspond to the directions of the most probable arrangement of its valency electrons if these have the same spin (FIGURE 5). These orbitals thus give a clearer picture of the most probable arrangement of the electrons than do the atomic orbitals from which they are obtained. It will now be shown that this is a consequence of the smaller overlap, i.e. greater localization of the hybrid orbitals. For the atomic orbital description, ψ^2, the probability that the two electrons will be found simultaneously in any given positions, is given by

$$\psi^2 = (s_1 p_2 - s_2 p_1)^2$$
$$= (s_1{}^2 p_2{}^2 + s_2{}^2 p_1{}^2) - 2s_1 p_2 s_2 p_1$$
$$= P_c - P_e$$

The term P_c may be regarded as corresponding to a classical interpretation of the electron in each of the continuous distributions s^2 and p^2 (allowing for each electron to be in both these orbitals). The last term P_e corresponds to the non-classical or 'exchange' contribution to the probability distribution. Its magnitude, which is proportional to the overlap between the two orbitals, determines the amount by which the true distribution differs from the 'classical' distribution. The electrons will be close together if they are both in the same region of overlap of the two orbitals; in this case P_e is large and positive, and hence the probability ψ^2 is small. On the other hand, if the two electrons are in different regions of overlap, then P_e is negative and the probability ψ^2 is large. Again we see the tendency for the electrons to keep apart. Now for the hybrid orbital description the probability function is given by

$$\psi^2 = (\mu_1 \eta_2 - \mu_2 \eta_1)^2$$
$$= (\mu_1{}^2 \eta_2{}^2 + \mu_2{}^2 \eta_1{}^2) - 2\mu_1 \eta_2 \mu_2 \eta_1$$
$$= p_c - p_e$$

The total probability function ψ^2 is of course identical with that calculated from atomic orbitals, but the relative contribution of P_e and P_e are not the same as those of p_c and p_e. In this latter case, the first term, p_c, may again be regarded as corresponding to a classical interpretation of the distribution of the electrons, with one in each orbital, and the second term, p_e, is the non-classical or 'exchange' contribution which determines the amount by which the true distribution differs from the classical distribution. Again the 'exchange' term p_e depends on the overlap of the two orbitals, and, as this is small, p_e is small, and hence the classical distribution corresponds reasonably well to the true distribution, ψ^2. Lennard-Jones and Pople (1950) have treated a similar case quantitatively, and have concluded that a classical interpretation of the two electrons in hybrid orbitals gives a good approximation to the actual distribution.

A further advantage of the use of hybrid orbitals is illustrated by Lennard-Jones and Pople's calculation of the interaction energy for two electrons with the same spin in the $(1s)^2(2s)(2p)$ configuration of the beryllium atom. They used Slater-type $2s$ and $2p$ functions, and calculated the interaction energy for both the atomic-orbital and the hybrid-orbital description of the atom. The total interaction energy is necessarily the same for both descriptions, of course, and it may be expressed as the sum of terms which can be described as classical coulomb repulsion-energy terms and non-classical or exchange-energy terms. The magnitude of the latter depends on the overlap of the component orbitals, and thus they are greater for the atomic orbital description than for the hybrid orbital description. Lennard-Jones and Pople found that, whereas for atomic orbitals the exchange energy was 28 per cent of the total interaction energy, for hybrid orbitals it was only 2·4 per cent. Thus, if the electrons are described in terms of hybrid orbitals, their interaction energy may to a reasonable approximation be regarded entirely as electrostatic repulsion-energy between charge distributions corresponding to the hybrid orbitals.

In general, then, a classical interpretation of the distribution of electrons in hybrid orbitals corresponds more closely to the most probable distribution than does a similar classical interpretation of the distribution of electrons in atomic orbitals. This is because the hybrid orbitals are more localized, i.e. overlap each other less than the corresponding atomic orbitals. As a consequence of the exclusion principle, electrons of the same spin tend to avoid being simultaneously in a region of overlap, and hence, the greater is the overlap of the orbitals, the more will a classical interpretation of their distribution differ from the most probable distribution. In the limiting case, in which there is no overlap at all between hybrid orbitals, then the arrangement of greatest probability is one in which the electrons so dispose themselves that when one electron is in one of the hybrid orbitals, an electron of the same spin will only be found in one of the other hybrid orbitals.

Similar considerations apply to the electrons in the completed valency shells of molecules. Thus the electrons in the valency shell of, for example, the methane molecule are most conveniently regarded as occupying, in pairs, localized valence- or bond-orbitals that are linear combinations of one of the sp^3 hybrid orbitals of the carbon atom and the $1s$ orbital of a hydrogen atom. There will evidently be four such entirely equivalent bond orbitals in methane.

Similarly, to a first approximation, the water molecule may be most conveniently described in terms of two bond orbitals, each containing two electrons of opposite spin, and each of which is a linear combination of one of the hybrid sp^3 orbitals on the oxygen atom and a hydrogen $1s$ atomic orbital; and two lone-pair orbitals which each then contain two electrons, and are just the two remaining hybrid sp^3 orbitals. Such a description of the water molecule in terms of localized orbitals is entirely equivalent to the molecular (non-localized) orbital description (see e.g. Walsh, 1953) but, because of the smaller overlap of the localized orbitals, it gives a clearer picture of the electron distribution in the molecule in terms of classical ideas than does the molecular orbital description. As was pointed out above, when electrons in a valency shell are described in terms of such localized orbitals, their energy of interaction is almost entirely classical electrostatic repulsion energy between charge-clouds corresponding to the localized orbitals. This provides the justification for treatment of the interaction energy between pairs of electrons simply in terms of the electrostatic repulsions between them.

Similarly, in all the cases considered in FIGURE 1, the pairs of electrons in the valency shell may be regarded as occupying localized bond orbitals, each of which is a linear combination of a hybrid orbital on the central atom and a singly occupied orbital of one of the combining atoms. The hybrid orbitals corresponding to different valency shells are also given in FIGURE 1. These hybrid orbitals may either be combined with a singly occupied orbital of another atom to form a localized-bond orbital containing a bonding pair of electrons, or they may contain a lone pair of electrons.

TRANSITION METALS

The stereochemistry of the transitional metals is more fully discussed in the following section on the ligand field theory. Here, a brief discussion, only, will be given of the stereochemical effects of non-bonding d electrons and the stereochemistry of transition-metal complexes with coordination numbers greater than six.

The Stereochemical Effects of Non-bonding d Electrons

It has been emphasized earlier that lone pairs or non-bonding electrons are of great importance in determining the shapes of molecules. This is, however, not necessarily so for the transition metals, which may use inner d orbitals for bond formation and also often have non-bonding electrons in such inner d orbitals. Thus non-bonding electrons in d_γ orbitals may affect the shape of a molecule in the same way as has been described for s and p electrons, whilst electrons in d_ε orbitals often have very little effect on the stereochemistry. Thus, for example, $[Fe(CN)_6]^{4-}$ is octahedral, although it has nine pairs of electrons in its valency shell with the configuration $(d)^{10}(s)^2(p)^6$. This can be understood by considering the most probable arrangement of nine electrons with the same spin in the configuration $(d)^5(s)(p)^3$ which is that in which there are six electrons at the corners of an octahedron, and the remaining three having an equal probability of being found at the mid-points of each of the three sets of four coplanar edges of the octahedron (FIGURE 9) (Linnett and Mellish, 1954).

The six electrons which have a maximum probability of being found at the corners of an octahedron can be most conveniently described as occupying d^2sp^3 hybrid orbitals, and the three remaining electrons then occupy the three 'unhybridized' d_ε orbitals which, of course, have maxima directed towards the mid-points of the edges of the octahedron. Similarly the eighteen electrons in the configuration $(d)^{10}(s)^2(p)^6$ may be regarded as occupying the same orbitals in pairs. In $[Fe(CN)_6]^{4-}$, the six bonding pairs may be described as occupying localized bond orbitals that are linear combinations of one of the hybrid d^2sp^3 orbitals and a singly occupied orbital on the carbon atom of the CN group; the three lone pairs then occupy the d_ε orbitals.

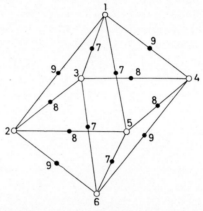

FIGURE 9. The most probable arrangement of nine electrons with the same spin in the configuration $(d)^5(s)(p)^3$.

It is evident from their shape and from the symmetry of the set of the three d_ε orbitals that the three pairs of non-bonding electrons occupying these orbitals can have no effect on the shape of the molecule. The same conclusion will hold also for the configuration $(d)^7(s)^2(p)^6$ and to a reasonably good approximation for the configurations $(d)^9(s)^2(p)^6$, $(d)^8(s)^2(p)^6$, $(d)^6(s)^2(p)^6$ and $(d)^5(s)^2(p)^6$. Because of the shape of the d_ε orbitals, and the fact that they are relatively delocalized, even if they are incompletely occupied, the effects of electrostatic repulsions between non-bonding electrons in these orbitals and the bonding pairs will only be slight; they cannot lead to any deviations from the 90° bond angles of the octahedron, but may cause two of the bonds to be slightly longer or slightly shorter than the other four (see p. 294). The exceedingly common occurrence of the octahedral structure among six-coordinated compounds of the transition elements is thus understandable.

If only five of the pairs of electrons in a completed shell with the configuration $(d)^{10}(s)^2(p)^6$ are bonding pairs, then these five, together with one of the non-bonding pairs, will be arranged at the corners of an octahedron, giving a square pyramidal structure to the molecule, and the other three lone pairs will be in the d_ε orbitals. Configurations in which the d_ε orbitals are incompletely occupied will also have the same arrangement of bonding pairs. In the molecule $NiBr_3.2PEt_3$, the valency shell of the nickel atom has the configuration $(d)^9(s)^2(p)^6$, and, in agreement with the above ideas, dipole moment measurements suggest that it has the square pyramidal structure (Jensen and Nygaard, 1949). The iron atom in $Fe(CO)_5$ has the configuration $(d)^{10}(s)^2(p)^6$, and this molecule would therefore be expected to have the square pyramidal structure, a conclusion which is in agreement with its finite dipole moment (Bergmann and Engel, 1931), but not with the results of an electron-diffraction study of the molecule (Ewens and Lister, 1939), which indicated a trigonal bi-pyramidal structure. The structure of this molecule would evidently merit further study.

If only four of the pairs of electrons, in a completed shell with the configuration $(d)^{10}(s)^2(p)^6$, are bonding pairs, then the five non-bonding pairs will completely occupy the d orbitals and will therefore have an overall spherical symmetry, and hence will have no effect on the orientation of the four bonding pairs, which will therefore be arranged at the corners of a tetrahedron.

Coordination Numbers greater than Six

The most probable arrangement of seven bonding pairs of electrons in the configuration $(d_\varepsilon)^2(d_y)^4(s)^2(p)^6$ is the pentagonal bipyramid. Recently, Zachariason (1954) has shown that $[ZrF_7]^{3-}$, which had previously been reported to have a distorted octahedral structure with an additional bond at the centre of one of the triangular faces (Hampson and Pauling, 1938), has a pentagonal bipyramidal structure (FIGURE 10A), as also have $[UO_2F_5]^{3-}$ and $[UF_7]^{3-}$. However, $[TaF_7]^{2-}$ which, like $[ZrF_7]^{3-}$, also has 14 electrons in its valency shell, apparently has the structure of a distorted trigonal prism (FIGURE 10B) with an extra bond at the centre of one of the rectangular faces. In $[ZrF_7]^{3-}$, the two remaining d_ε orbitals must be empty, although in seven-coordinated molecules with larger valency shells it would be possible for these d_ε orbitals to contain non-bonding electrons without seriously affecting the shape of the molecule.

Two structures have so far been observed for eight-coordinated molecules; the square antiprism as found in $[TaF_8]^{3-}$ and $[Sr(H_2O)_8]^{2+}$ (FIGURE 10C), and the $[Mo(CN)_8]^{4-}$ structure (Hoard and Nordsieck, 1939) (FIGURE 10D). The former arises from the configuration $(d_\varepsilon)^6(d_{x^2-y^2})^2(s)^2(p)^6$ and the latter from the configuration $(d_\varepsilon)^4(d_y)^4$ $(s)^2(p)^6$ (Duffey, 1950a, b). In $[TaF_8]^{3-}$ and $[Sr(H_2O)_8]^{2+}$ the d_{z^2} orbital is empty, but in $[Mo(CN)_8]^{4-}$ the d_ε orbital that is not used in bonding is occupied by a non-bonding pair, which, because of its symmetrical situation with respect to the bonding pairs, will not have any appreciable effect on their arrangement.

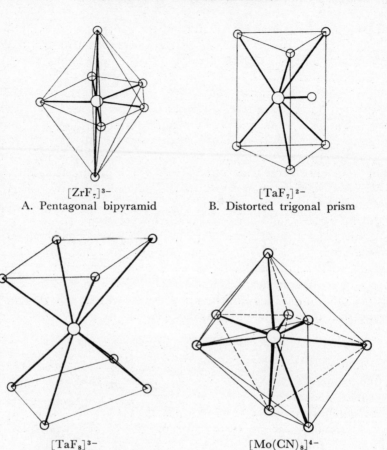

[ZrF₇]³⁻
A. Pentagonal bipyramid

[TaF₇]²⁻
B. Distorted trigonal prism

[TaF₈]³⁻
C. Square antiprism

[Mo(CN)₈]⁴⁻
D

FIGURE 10. Observed structures of transitional metal complexes with coordination numbers greater than six

STEREOCHEMISTRY AND THE LIGAND-FIELD THEORY

As mentioned earlier, ligand-field theory is concerned with the way in which the behaviour of the non-bonding electrons of an atom is affected by the symmetry and strength of the electric field arising from the surrounding atoms. We shall confine our attention to that electric field which arises from the ligands directly attached to a metal atom. Second-order effects arising from more distant charges are not considered in this discussion.

The term ' ligand-field theory ' rather than the more usual term, ' crystal-field theory ', is adopted here because it is considered to be a better description of the method. The use of the word ' crystal ' is likely to give rise to the impression of electrical fields extending throughout the whole crystal, with the usual implication of ionic binding. In fact, the theory is concerned with charges (e.g. lone pairs of electrons) on the ligands which are attached to the metal atom. To a first approximation effects arising from more distant charges are ignored. The unsuitability of the term ' crystal field ' is illustrated when it is realized that this theory is applied to the interpretation of the magnetic properties and stereochemistry of covalent non-electrolytes.

Ligand-field theory is based in the first instance on a model which assumes that the central metal atom or ion retains the same charge that it would have if it were in a field-free state and were surrounded by a number of electrically charged ligands or electric dipoles. It is implicitly assumed that there is no covalent bonding between the metal atom and the ligands. In an actual molecule there is generally some charge transfer from the ligands to the metal atom; i.e. the metal-ligand bonds have some covalent character.

Ligand-field theory is of interest to the chemist because of its relationship with (a) valency theory, (b) stereochemistry, (c) magnetic behaviour (paramagnetism of ions), and (d) absorption spectra of compounds of the transition metals, lanthanides and actinides. Following the fundamental work of Bethe (1929, 1930), Penney and Schlapp (1932, 1933) examined its implications in connection with the magnetic behaviour of paramagnetic ions in hydrated salts. Van Vleck (1932) and Stoner (1934) have summarized and discussed early work. Immediately after the second world war the development of paramagnetic-resonance techniques and their application to transition-metal salts resulted in a renewed application of crystal-field theory in general. This work was summarized recently by Bowers and Owen (1955). During the last seven years, interest in the application of crystal-field theory to the stereochemistry and spectra of transition-metal complexes has developed rapidly. Detailed references to the latter are given by Jorgensen (1956) and Orgel (1956) in their reports to the 1956 Solvay Conference in Brussels: whilst Nyholm (1956) and also Orgel (1956) discussed some of the problems of stereochemistry. Specially relevant individual papers will be mentioned in the survey which follows. Attention is directed particularly to Orgel (1952) and to subsequent work of this author.

We shall confine this survey to those metal complexes of the first transition series which contain one or more non-bonding $3d$ electrons. It is found on examination that many stereochemical arrangements give rise to a ligand field that may be regarded as derived from the perfect cubic field by suitable distortion. Hence an examination of the effect of an octahedral arrangement of ligands upon the energy levels of the d orbitals of an atom is a convenient starting point. There are five of these independent d orbitals divided into a group of three (d_ε orbitals) and a group of two (d_y orbitals). The three d_ε orbitals (d_{xy}, d_{xz}, and d_{yz}) each have four lobes ; these point in between the various x, y and z axes (FIGURE 7). The two d_y orbitals ($d_{x^2-y^2}$ and d_{z^2}) however, both point *along* the directions of the x, y and z axes. In a field-free atom these five d orbitals are degenerate. To appreciate the way in which they are affected by an electric field, it is convenient to consider an ion with one unpaired electron in each orbital, i.e. $d^5(d_\varepsilon^3 d_y^2)$ configuration ; this is illustrated by the Fe^{3+} ion. We shall bring up towards this ion six F^- charges along the x, y and z axes, keeping all six equidistant from the iron atom. When the distance of approach becomes a few Å units, a splitting of the degeneracy of five d orbitals begins to take place. Since in the three d_ε orbitals the lobes of electron density are further from the approaching charges than in the two d_y orbitals, the energy levels of the latter will be displaced upwards owing to greater electrostatic repulsion. In the more general case there will be some slight departure from perfect octahedral symmetry, and the three d_ε and two d_y orbitals will be split apart slightly also, but the separation of these will be, in the octahedral case, negligibly small as compared with the separation between the d_ε and d_y degenerate levels. The situation, shown diagrammatically in FIGURE 11, is one in which no pairing of the d electrons occurs (known as a ' weak field case '). In complex ions, such as the $[FeF_6]^{3-}$ ion, the separation (Δ) between the triply degenerate d_ε levels and the doubly degenerate d_y

FIGURE 11. SPLITTING OF d ORBITALS IN ELECTRIC FIELD OF OCTAHEDRALLY ARRANGED NEGATIVE CHARGES

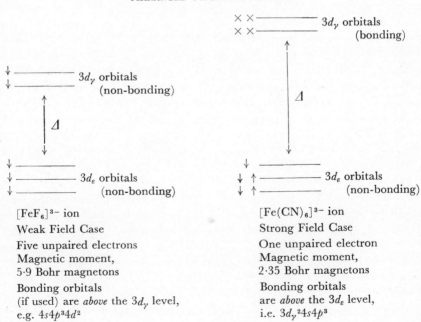

[FeF$_6$]$^{3-}$ ion

Weak Field Case

Five unpaired electrons

Magnetic moment,
5·9 Bohr magnetons

Bonding orbitals
(if used) are *above* the 3d_y level,
e.g. $4s4p^34d^2$

[Fe(CN)$_6$]$^{3-}$ ion

Strong Field Case

One unpaired electron

Magnetic moment,
2·35 Bohr magnetons

Bonding orbitals
are *above* the 3d_ε level,
i.e. $3d_y^2 4s4p^3$

levels is of the order of 20,000 cm^{-1} for a tervalent ion, and 10,000 cm^{-1} for a bivalent ion (Orgel, 1955a). This energy separation is not large enough to force electron-pairing in the d_ε orbitals.

In the octahedral complexes of the first transition series one finds that the magnitude of $\varDelta$ is affected by each of the following factors :— (i) the nature of the metal ; (ii) the charge on the metal ion ; (iii) the nature of the attached ligand. The effects of the first two for the hexahydrates of metal ions of the first transition elements are summarized in TABLE 2 (Jorgensen, 1956). These values show how much the electric field due to the six attached water molecules separates the d_ε and d_γ levels. They have been obtained from studies

TABLE 2. ENERGY SEPARATION $\varDelta$ (cm^{-1}) OF d_ε AND d_γ ORBITALS FOR HEXAHYDRATED METAL IONS

	Hexahydrated Metal Ion :	Ti	V	Cr	Mn	Fe	Co	Ni	Cu
Bivalent ion	Energy separation $\varDelta$	—	12600	13900	7800	10400	9700	8500	12600
	Configuration	d^2	d^3	d^4	d^5	d^6	d^7	d^8	d^9
Tervalent ion	Energy separation $\varDelta$	20300	18600	17400	21000	13700	19100	—	—
	Configuration	d^1	d^2	d^3	d^4	d^5	d^6	d^7	d^8

of the spectra of these hydrated ions. Attention is drawn to certain relationships between $\varDelta$ and the electronic configuration of the metal ion. For the notably stable electronic configuration $(d_\varepsilon)^3(d_\gamma)^2$, the value of $\varDelta$ is smaller compared with other values in each series [cf Mn(II) and Fe(III)]. This may be pictured roughly as meaning that the ligand field is relatively less effective in this case in splitting the d_ε and d_γ levels apart because of the electrical symmetry of the $(d)^5$ arrangement. With $(d)^4$, however, a large $\varDelta$ is obtained. In this case the symmetrical $(d_\varepsilon)^3$ sub-shell is readily separated from the single occupied d_γ orbital by the ligand field. Electron pairing occurs only in the ion $[Co(H_2O)_6]^{3+}$ causing diamagnetism owing to the large value of $\varDelta$.

If one now varies the ligand, it is found that the splitting $\varDelta$ is in all cases affected by the same ligands in the same general order. The order of increasing ability to split apart the d_ε and d_γ degenerate levels for some common ligands is I$^-$< Br$^-$< Cl$^-$< OH$^-$< F$^-$< H$_2$O< SNC$^-$< NH$_3$< En< NO$_2$$^-$< o-Phen*, and Dipy†< CN$^-$ (Orgel, 1955b). With certain exceptions, notably the position of the Br$^-$ and I$^-$ ligands, this sequence follows the order of polarizability of the ligands. As was

* o-Phenanthroline.
† 2 : 2′-Dipyridyl.

291

pointed out by Orgel (1952), the important factor in deciding field strength is the polarizability of the ligand rather than the charge on it; hence as we pass from F^- to CN^- the intensity of the field increases and the splitting, Δ, steadily rises. It is probable that the order of $I^- < Br^- < Cl^- < F^-$ is determined by double bonding between metal and halide ion and by the size of ions; if the electronegativity or polarizability were the determining factor, the opposite order would be expected.

We shall return presently to consider other aspects of the weak-field situation, but we now wish to examine the implications of a large splitting of the energy levels upon the location of the d electrons when the number of these exceeds three, that is to say when there are unpaired d electrons in both d_ε and d_γ orbitals. The complexes of Fe^{3+} are again convenient for discussion. If we bring up a ligand which results in the energy separation Δ being sufficiently large, then a stage will be reached where the electronic configuration in which all five electrons remain in d_ε orbitals becomes the more stable. In essence, we have two competing effects—the electrostatic repulsion of paired electrons in d_ε orbitals, which will tend to cause the electrons to occupy separate orbitals (Hund's rule of maximum multiplicity), and the work which must be done to lift two electrons through the energy separation Δ. In the sequence of ligands referred to above, only the CN^- is known to be capable of causing electron pairing for Fe^{3+}. This change over from a 'spin-free' to a 'spin-paired' complex is conveniently represented as shown in FIGURE 12 (Orgel, 1952).

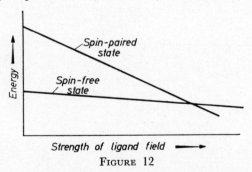

FIGURE 12

In this diagram we represent the way in which the energy levels of the spin-free and spin-paired states vary as the field strength increases. As the strength of the ligand field increases, a stage is reached where the spin-paired state becomes the one of lower energy.

We may picture the situation in another way, which shows the relationship between ligand-field and valence-bond approaches. As the readily polarizable CN^- ions approach the Fe^{3+} metal ion, a stage is reached at which the lone pairs of electrons on the CN^- ions come so close to the iron atom that they make use of the two d_γ orbitals for σ bond formation. This involves the transfer elsewhere of the two non-bonding electrons formerly occupying these two d_y orbitals; and, of course, they are forced into d_ε orbitals where pairing takes place (see p. 290). This utilization of d_y orbitals for bond formation with consequent electron pairing when the number of non-bonding d-electrons exceeds three is favoured by the following: (i) low electronegativity of the ligand; (ii) high polarizability of the ligand; (iii) overlap, where possible, of vacant p_π or d_π orbitals of the ligand with filled d_ε orbitals of the metal atom; (iv) high valency of the metal atom; and (v) increasing atomic number of the metal atom, passing from the first to the second and third transition series, The effects referred to in (ii), (iv) and (v) are all associated with a high electronegativity of the metal atom. Pauling (1945) originally suggested that metal complexes were of two types: ' ionic ' (in which no electron pairing occurs and the magnetic moment is large) and ' covalent ' (in which electron pairing occurs and the magnetic moment is small). In a subsequent modification of the theory, the spin-paired complexes were regarded as strongly covalent, and the spin-free complexes as weakly covalent or ionic. The present picture may be summarized as follows: if the magnetic moment indicates spin pairing, then the binding is strongly covalent, and ' inner ' d_y orbitals of the metal are used; if there is no spin pairing, then the bonding may be anything from purely electrostatic to moderately covalent using ' outer ' d orbitals, depending upon the polarizability of the ligand and the electronegativity of the metal ion.

The effect of placing four negative charges about the metal atom at the corners of a regular tetrahedron will now be considered. The effect of such an arrangement is in fact identical with an octahedral arrangement of six *positive* charges of somewhat smaller magnitude. As a result, the pattern of energy levels shown in FIGURE 11 is inverted and the splitting between the d_ε and the d_y levels is only about a quarter as large as in the octahedral case. One result of this is that spin-paired octahedral complexes are rare; perhaps the only example may be the $[ReCl_4]^-$ ion. This is diamagnetic, but as yet its stereo-chemistry has not been determined (Orgel, 1956).

Stereochemistry of Complexes with d Electrons

In this section the stereochemistry expected for each of the transition metal ions in both the weak-field and the strong-field cases will be considered. In many cases small deviations from a perfect octahedral arrangement are to be expected as a result of electrostatic repulsions between non-bonding electrons and the bonding electrons. In practice, however, these small deviations may be obscured by thermal vibrations. The predicted stereochemistry of transition metal complexes is summarized in advance in TABLE 3.

TABLE 3. PREDICTED DERIVATIVES OF TRANSITION METAL COMPLEXES FROM A PERFECT OCTAHEDRAL STRUCTURE

Number of non-bonding d electrons	Strength of field	Number of unpaired d electrons	Configuration	Predicted variation from perfect octahedron arrangement (with reference to structure in parenthesis)*
1	Weak	1	$d_\varepsilon^1(d_{xy})$	V. slight lengthening along x and y axes (cf with d^0)
	Strong	1	$d_\varepsilon^1(d_{xy})$	V. slight lengthening along x and y axes (cf with d^0)
2	Weak	2	$d_\varepsilon^2(d_{xy}, d_{xz})$	V. slight shortening along y and z axes (cf with d_ε^3)
	Strong	2	$d_\varepsilon^2(d_{xy}, d_{xz})$	V. slight shortening along y and z axes (cf with d_ε^3)
3	Weak or strong	3	$d_\varepsilon^3(d_{xy}, d_{xz}, d_{yz})$	Nil
4	Weak	4	$d_\varepsilon^3 d_\gamma^1(d_{xy}, d_{xz}, d_{yz}, d_{z^2})$	Marked lengthening along z axis (cf with d_ε^3)
	Strong	2	$d_\varepsilon^4(d^2{}_{xy}, d_{xz}, d_{yz})$	V. slight shortening along z axis (cf with d_ε^6)
5	Weak	5	$d_\varepsilon^3 d_\gamma^2(d_{xy}, d_{xz}, d_{yz}, d_{z^2}, d_{x^2-y^2})$	Nil
	Strong	1	$d_\varepsilon^5(d^2{}_{xy}, d^2{}_{xz}, d_{yz})$	V. slight shortening along y axis (cf with d_ε^6)

TABLE 3 (contd.)

6	Weak	4	$d_\varepsilon^4 d_\gamma^2 (d^2_{xy}, d_{xz}, d_{yz}, d_{z^2}, d_{x^2-y^2})$	V. slight lengthening along x and y axes (cf with $d_\varepsilon^3 d_\gamma^2$)
	Strong	0	$d_\varepsilon^6 (d^2_{xy}, d^2_{xz}, d^2_{yz})$	Nil
7	Weak	3	$d_\varepsilon^5 d_\gamma^2 (d^2_{xy}, d^2_{xz}, d_{yz}, d_{z^2}, d_{x^2-y^2})$	V. slight lengthening along y and z axes (cf with $d_\varepsilon^6 d_\gamma^2$)
	Strong	1	$d_\varepsilon^6 d_\gamma^1 (d^2_{xy}, d^2_{xz}, d^2_{yz}, d_{z^2})$	Marked lengthening along z axis (cf with d_ε^6)
			or $d_\varepsilon^6 5s (d^2_{xy}, d^2_{xz}, d^2_{yz}, 5s^1)$	Nil†
8	Weak	2	$d_\varepsilon^6 d_\gamma^2 (d^2_{xy}, d^2_{xz}, d^2_{yz}, d_{z^2}, d_{x^2-y^2})$	Nil
	Strong	0	$d_\varepsilon^6 d_\gamma^2 (d^2_{xy}, d^2_{xz}, d^2_{yz}, d^2_{z^2})$	Marked lengthening along z axis (cf with d_ε^6) tending to give a square-planar arrangement
		0	$d_\varepsilon^6 5s^2 (d^2_{xy}, d^2_{xz}, d^2_{yz}, 5s^2)$	Nil†
9	Weak or strong	1	$d_\varepsilon^6 d_\gamma^3 (d^2_{xy}, d^2_{xz}, d^2_{yz}, d^2_{x^2-y^2}, d^2_{z^2})$	Marked increase in length along z axis (cf with d_ε^6) tending to give square-planar arrangements

* In each case the lengthening or shortening of bonds is with reference to suitable empty, half-filled or filled d_ε and d_γ shells with perfect octahedral arrangements.

† See discussion on p. 299 as to possible location of unpaired electron(s).

It must be emphasized that the configurations shown are for ideal ground states. In fact, some mixing of other electronic arrangements must be assumed in certain cases, in order to explain experimental observations, such as magnetic data. This mixing arises because we must set inter-electronic repulsions between individual d_ε electrons ($\sim 10,000$ cm^{-1}) against the value of Δ. Thus although for d^1 only the d_ε^1 configuration need be considered, for *two* d electrons we must postulate that $d_\varepsilon^1 d_\gamma^1$ may contribute to the actual state in addition to d_ε^2. For d_ε^3 we have a half-filled d_ε sub-shell of relatively high stability and the contribution of $d_\varepsilon^2 d_\gamma^1$ is negligible. Similarly in the case of $d_\varepsilon^3 d_\gamma^1$ we may safely ignore $d_\varepsilon^2 d_\gamma^2$. With $d_\varepsilon^3 d_\gamma^2$ a stable half-filled shell again arises and no other configuration need be entertained. For d^6 both $d_\varepsilon^3 d_\gamma^3$ and the more likely $d_\varepsilon^4 d_\gamma^2$ must be considered. It is of interest to note that the magnetic moments of octahedral Ni(II) complexes (d^8, $\mu_{\text{eff}} \simeq 3\cdot1$–$3\cdot2$ B.M.) are higher than the figure for spin only ($2\cdot83$ B.M.); the spin-only value is expected for $d_\varepsilon^6 d_\gamma^2$ since d_γ electrons are in a non-magnetic doublet. Hence we have some support for the view that the configuration $d_\varepsilon^5 d_\gamma^3$ makes some contribution to the final state.

Finally, for d^9 complexes the contribution of $d_\varepsilon^5 d_\gamma^4$ must be considered in addition to the ground state $d_\varepsilon^6 d_\gamma^3$. Once again support for this view is given by magnetic data; the moments of Cu(II) complexes ($\sim 2\cdot1$ B.M.) exceed the spin-only value ($1\cdot73$ B.M.). A single unpaired d_γ electron should have no orbital contribution and therefore we invoke $d_\varepsilon^5 d_\gamma^4$ to explain the existence of orbital magnetism.

d^1

This case is illustrated by Ti(III) complexes. All the known complexes appear to be six-covalent and are presumably octahedral. The single d electron is in a d_ε orbital; apart from a very slight increase in length along the x and y axes, no departure from a perfect octahedron is expected.

d^2

Ti(II) and V(III) complexes are of this configuration. The only distortion likely in an octahedral complex is a very slight shortening along the y and z axes.

d^3

Examples of this are V(II) and Cr(III) complexes. The half-filled d_ε level gives a perfectly symmetrical electron shell, and hence perfect octahedral symmetry is expected in six-covalent complexes. In the strong-field case, the occupation of the d_γ orbitals by bonding electrons is to be expected, but this will not affect the magnetic behaviour. In the case of [Cr(H$_2$O)$_6$]$^{3+}$ and other Cr(III) complexes the occupation of inner orbitals by bonding electron pairs is suggested by the covalent character of these complexes (Hunt and Taube, 1951).

d^4

Both the Cr^{2+} and Mn^{3+} ions have this configuration. In the weak-field case there will be a half-filled d_ε triplet lying lowest, and a single electron in one of the d_γ orbitals. This is expected to make the two axial bonds along the z axis longer than the other four because of repulsion, assuming that the single electron occupies the d_{z^2} orbital*. The structure of MnF_3 (Hepworth, Jack and Nyholm, 1957) is in agreement with this expectation. If this repulsion is strong enough it can easily lead to the formation of square complexes. The common occurrence of $Cr(II)$ compounds in which the coordination number may be *four* suggests that this is very probable, and the subject warrants detailed examination by x-ray methods. In the strong-field case, electron pairing will occur, leading to a configuration with one d_ε doubly filled and the other two d_ε orbitals each half filled. The likely effect of this is a slight bond-shortening along the z axis. Data on complexes of this type, e.g. the $[Cr(Dipyridyl)_3]^{2+}$ and $[Cr(CN)_6]^{4-}$ ions are not available.

d^5

This configuration occurs in Mn^{2+} and Fe^{3+}. In the weak-field case we have an ion with five unpaired electrons and a perfectly spherical electron distribution. Therefore in the octahedral arrangement a perfectly symmetrical octahedron is expected. The tetrahedral arrangement does arise in the $[FeCl_4]^-$ ion and in gaseous Fe_2Cl_6; the stereochemical arrangement which is assumed is at least partly dependent upon the charge on the complex. With non-charged ligands in cationic complexes the maximum coordination number of six is observed. This also holds for the very electronegative fluoride ion in anionic complexes like $[FeF_6]^{3-}$; with this ligand the negative charge remains largely on the ligand owing to its high electronegativity. However, if six chlorine atoms are used as ligands, the relative electronegativities of Fe and Cl would result in a smaller positive (or a larger negative charge) on the Fe atom making the $[FeCl_6]^{3-}$ ion less stable than the $[FeF_6]^{3-}$. At the same time it is possible that the larger size of the chloride ion may be important; the effect of size in determining whether a tetrahedral or an octahedral complex ion is formed is illustrated by a comparison of crystalline PCl_5 and PBr_5. The former contains $[PCl_6]^-$ and $[PCl_4]^+$ ions; the latter contains $[PBr_4]^+$ and Br^- ions. In the strong-field case (d_ε^5, e.g. $[Fe(CN)_6]^{3-}$) a slight shortening is expected along one axis.

d^6

Both $Fe(II)$ and $Co(III)$ complexes fall into this class. In the weak-field spin-free case, exemplified by many spin-free iron complexes

---

* It is assumed that the single electron would tend to occupy the d_{z^2} orbital, because in this orbital it is repelling *two* ligands and not four as when in the $d_{x^2-y^2}$ orbital.

such as the $[Fe(H_2O)_6]^{2+}$ ion, and by the Co(III) complex, K_3CoF_6, only a slight lengthening along two axes should occur. When a strong field is operating, as in all other Co(III) complexes or complex ions such as $[Fe(Dipyridyl)_3]^{2+}$, a completely filled $3d_\varepsilon$ sub-shell is obtained and a perfect octahedron is expected.

Complexes with Seven, Eight and Nine Non-bonding d Electrons

These cases involve more than the number of electrons required to fill the three d_ε orbitals in an octahedral spin-paired complex. FIGURE 13 gives the electronic configurations for the spin-free complexes in each case.

FIGURE 13

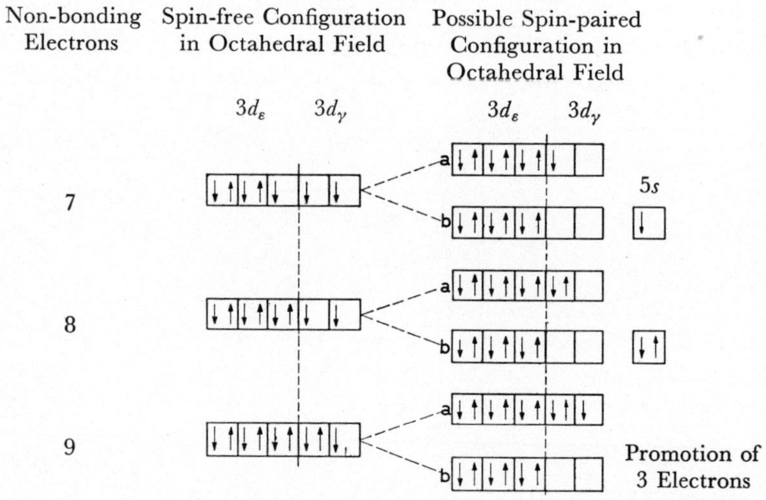

If an octahedral complex is formed, there are respectively one, two and three electrons 'too many' for inner orbital $(3d_\gamma^2 4s^4 4p^3)$ binding. In the case of spin-paired Co(III) complexes (e.g. $[Co(NO_2)_6]^{4-}$), Pauling (1945) suggested 'promotion' of the single unpaired electron to a $5s$ orbital: similarly for six-covalent complexes containing two electrons too many (e.g. $[Ni(Diarsine)_3]^{2+}$), Burstall and Nyholm (1952) suggested that these might be promoted to a $5s$ orbital in which they are paired off, explaining the diamagnetism. It was pointed out in each case that the fact that these compounds could be oxidized to higher valency states gave some support for the proposal. However, the isolation of six-covalent complexes of Pd(II) and Au(III) (Harris, Nyholm and Stephenson, 1956), where no evidence of such ease of oxidation is available, suggests that in these

298

two examples at least, the hypothesis of promotion is unlikely. Finally, six-covalent d^9 complexes [e.g. Cu(III) with six NH_3 ligands (Peyronel, 1941)] are known to exist, and here the promotion of three electrons is probably untenable. It will be observed that in each case the two occupied d_y orbitals point in the direction of the ligands. If one of these e.g., $(d_{x^2-y^2})$ could be made available for bond-formation by spin-pairing, then a complex of the dsp^2 square-planar type might be envisaged. This indeed, is precisely what we commonly find with d^7 and d^8 complexes with suitable ligands where the preference is for 4 rather than 6 covalency. Nevertheless, should the charge on the metal atom still be sufficient to hold the two further ligands required for an octahedral complex, one might expect that these would suffer some repulsion from the electron (or electron pair) in the d_{z^2} orbital. Some evidence to support this is available, Harris, Nyholm and Stephenson (1956) having observed this effect in $[Pd(Diarsine)_2I_2]^0$ (see p. 301). Finally, in the d^9 complexes no inner $(3d_y)$ orbitals are available for bond formation. The use of the outer orbitals will mean that, in general, more electronegative ligands will be required to form complexes; furthermore, since one of the d_y orbitals is doubly and one singly filled, two longer bonds along one axis might be expected. Many Cu(II) complexes have been examined, and it is common to find four coplanar bonds of equal length and two longer bonds normal to this plane (Wells, 1945; Dunitz and Orgel, 1957).

d^7

The only spin-free complexes of this configuration are those of Co(II). These are of two types; octahedral complexes which are generally pink (or violet), and tetrahedral complexes, which are usually blue. It will be observed by reference to FIGURE 13 that in the octahedral case there are two doubly filled d_ε orbitals and one singly filled d_ε orbital; both d_y orbitals are singly filled. This is expected to lead to a slight lengthening along two axes. When the pattern shown in FIGURE 11 is inverted, however, the configuration involves two doubly filled d_y orbitals and three half-filled d_ε orbitals. This is an electrically symmetrical arrangement and one expects a perfect tetrahedron as a result.

The spin-paired case is found in octahedral complexes of both Co(III) e.g. $[Co(NO_2)_6]^{4-}$ ion, and in the Ni(III) complexes of the type $[NiCl_2(Diarsine)_2]^+$. No exact structural data are available for complexes of this type; if the unpaired electron is in a $3d$ orbital in each case, one expects four square-planar $3d4s4p^2$ bonds and two others normal to this plane and appreciably longer. We prefer to regard these as $4p4d$ hybrid bonds, but ligand-field theory provides no guidance on this point. The alternative theory of promotion of the unpaired electron to a $5s$ orbital would enable six equivalent $3d^24s4p^3$

bonds to be formed. As pointed out elsewhere, the promotion of the unpaired electron to a $5s$ orbital is expected to lead to (a) ease of oxidation; (b) a negligibly small orbital contribution to the magnetic moment. Both of these have been observed. However, the really important information will be provided by accurate bond-length data on complexes of the type $[\mathrm{Co(NO_2)_6}]^{4-}$. Support for the view that no promotion occurs may also be obtained from a study of the paramagnetic resonance spectrum. Finally, it is interesting to note that Dwyer (1956) has shown that in aqueous solution it is the $[\mathrm{Co(NO_2)_5}]^{3-}$ ion which is formed; this, of course, may also contain a coordinated molecule of water, but it is more likely to reflect the reluctance of the $\mathrm{Co(II)}$ atom to assume an *octahedral* spin-paired configuration.

As might be expected from the presence of an electron in one of the d_γ orbitals (presumably the d_{z^2} orbital normal to the square), both square four-covalent and (presumably) square pyramidal five-covalent molecules may be prepared. These may be considered to involve the ultimate stage in the effect of the electron repulsion from the non-bonding d_{z^2} orbital. The energy-level splitting is then given in FIGURE 14. The d_{z^2} orbital may well fall *below* the d_ε level. Such a postulate is necessary to explain the high orbital-contribution to the magnetic moment of square spin-paired $\mathrm{Co(II)}$ complexes (Figgis and Nyholm, unpublished).

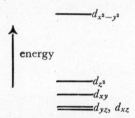

FIGURE 14. Splitting of d orbital energy levels in square complexes

Five-covalency almost certainly occurs in complexes such as $[\mathrm{CoBr_2},$ triarsine$]^0$ (Barclay and Nyholm, 1953) and $[\mathrm{NiBr_3, 2PEt_3}]^0$ (Jensen and Nygaard, 1949), at least in solution. They are probably square-pyramidal in shape, being derived from the octahedron with the single non-bonding electron in the sixth position (FIGURE 15) and probably best described as occupying a $3d_{z^2}4p$ hybrid orbital.

d^8

The six-covalent complexes of d^8 closely resemble d^7, except that the extra non-bonding electron pairs off in the d_{z^2} orbital (or, less likely in the $5s$ orbital). It is of interest to note that, if the $5s$ orbital were intermediate in energy between the d_ε triplet and the d_γ bonding doublet levels, then the hypothesis of promotion and ligand-field theory might be reconciled. Strong support for the view, however, that the

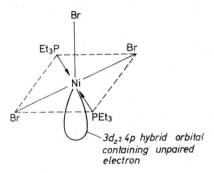

FIGURE 15.   Possible structure of NiBr$_3$, 2Et$_3$P

ligand-field interpretation is the correct one is provided by the x-ray crystal structure investigation of complexes of the type Pd(Diarsine)$_2$I$_2$ (FIGURE 16) (Harris, Nyholm and Stephenson, 1956).

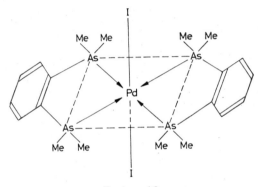

FIGURE 16

Compounds of this type were first prepared by Chatt and Mann (1939). Their properties have been investigated recently in more detail as part of an extensive study of the valence states stabilized by this chelate group, and of the stereochemistry of the complexes so formed. Pd(Diarsine)$_2$I$_2$ is found to be a uni-univalent electrolyte in nitrobenzene solution; the single iodide ion may be replaced by the perchlorate ion. The structure of these (presumably) five-covalent Pd(II) compounds of the type [Pd(Diarsine)$_2$I]$^+$[ClO$_4$]$^-$ is being investigated. In the solid state, the compound Pd(Diarsine)$_2$I$_2$ is found to contain an octahedrally coordinated Pd(II) atom; the Pd—I bonds are unusually long (3·52 Å; calculated for covalent bond, 2·65 Å), being almost of the length which one expects for a purely ionic link. On the ligand-field theory, this indicates that the electronic configuration of the non-bonding electrons is that shown in FIGURE 11. A diagrammatic representation of the bond hybridization which has been proposed is shown in FIGURE 17.

Other compounds which fall into the d^8 spin-paired category are [Ni(Diarsine)$_3$]$^{2+}$, and the Au(III) complexes of the type [Au(Di-arsine)$_2$I$_2$]$^+$. The structures of the latter are still being investigated. They are almost certain to have the distorted octahedral configuration shown in FIGURE 17.

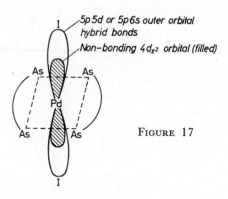

FIGURE 17

d^9

The complex compounds of Cu(II) and Ni(I) fall into this category. Cu(II) readily forms square complexes with ligands of high electronegativity, e.g. [Cu(H$_2$O)$_4$]$^{2+}$ and [Cu(NH$_3$)$_4$]$^{2+}$; these can attach two extra molecules of ligand in suitable circumstances to form a distorted octahedral configuration. In the solid state, the square complexes crystallize as a rule in such a way as to complete the octahedral arrangement, but the two extra bonds are longer than the other four. An example of this is the complex [CuEn$_2$]$^{2+}$[Hg(SCN)$_4$]$^{2-}$, the crystal structure of which has been determined by Scouladi (1953). The lengths of the Cu—N bonds to the N atoms of the En groups are considerably shorter than the Cu—N bonds to the N of the NCS groups. Without even considering any *bonding* orbitals, the ligand-field theory provides the interpretation that the repulsion in the xy plane, arising from the electron density in the half-filled $d_{x^2-y^2}$ orbital in the plane, is less than that due to the doubly filled d_{z^2} orbital normal to the plane. Paramagnetic resonance measurements on cupric complexes provide good support for the view that some degree of covalent binding occurs (Bleaney and Stevens, 1953), implying that outer-orbital overlap occurs at least to some extent. This is consistent with the view expressed earlier that Cu(II) octahedral complexes may be conveniently regarded as containing four $4s4p^24d$ square bonds in the plane, and two $4p4d$ linear hybrid bonds normal to the latter. Cu(II) shows a great reluctance to form stable complexes with ligands of low electronegativity. Ni(I) complexes include the presumably dimeric K$_4$Ni$_2$(CN)$_6$, which is diamagnetic (Craig and Mellor, 1940), and the recently prepared K$_3$Ni(CN)$_4$, which contains the expected unpaired

Periodic table of the elements | H (1)

0	I	II	III	IV	V	VI	VII
He (2)	Li (3)	Be (4)	B (5)	C (6)	N (7)	O (8)	F (9)
Ne (10)	Na (11)	Mg (12)	Al (13)	Si (14)	P (15)	S (16)	Cl (17)

0	Ia	IIa	IIIa	IVa	Va	VIa	VIIa	VIII			Ib	IIb	IIIb	IVb	Vb	VIb	VIIb
A (18)	K (19)	Ca (20)	Sc (21)	Ti (22)	V (23)	Cr (24)	Mn (25)	Fe (26)	Co (27)	Ni (28)	Cu (29)	Zn (30)	Ga (31)	Ge (32)	As (33)	Se (34)	Br (35)
Kr (36)	Rb (37)	Sr (38)	Yt (39)	Zr (40)	Nb (41)	Mo (42)	Tc (43)	Ru (44)	Rh (45)	Pd (46)	Ag (47)	Cd (48)	In (49)	Sn (50)	Sb (51)	Te (52)	I (53)
Xe (54)	Cs (55)	Ba (56)	La (57) * / Hf (72)	Ta (73)	W (74)	Re (75)	Os (76)	Ir (77)	Pt (78)	Au (79)	Hg (80)	Tl (81)	Pb (82)	Bi (83)	Po (84)	At (85)	
Rn (86)	Fr (87)	Ra (88)	Ac (89) **														

* Lanthanides: Ce (58) Pr (59) Nd (60) Pm (61) Sm (62) Eu (63) Gd (64) Tb (65) Dy (66) Ho (67) Er (68) Tm (69) Yb (70) Lu (71)

** Actinides: Th (90) Pa (91) U (92) Np (93) Pu (94) Am (95) Cm (96) Bk (97) Cf (98) E (99) Fm (100) Mv (101) No (102)

electron (Nast and Krakkay, 1954). Preliminary investigations using x-ray methods by Nast and Pfab (1952) lead to the postulation of a bridged structure. Infra-red studies show one C—N stretching frequency (El-Sayed and Sheline, 1956) throwing doubt upon the structure assigned by Nast and Pfab. Nothing is known of the structure of the highly reactive $K_3Ni(CN)_4$.

Summary

The application of the ligand-field theory to transition-metal complexes involves the following assumptions and leads to the following conclusions :

(i) For six ligands the octahedron is the most commonly occurring arrangement.

(ii) Distortions of this octahedron may occur owing to the inter-electronic repulsions between the lone pairs and the ligands.

(iii) Metal ions with seven, eight or nine non-bonding d electrons tend to form square complexes with strongly bound ligands, because the other two ligands are more readily ' lost ' as the result of the strong repulsion from electrons in the d_{z^2} orbital pointing in their direction.

(iv) If the electronegativity of the metal atom and/or the charge on the complex ion is large enough, octahedral spin-paired complexes may still be formed from metal ions with more than six d electrons; but two bonds of unusual length must complete the octahedron.

(v) The tetrahedral is less common than the octahedral arrangement. It is favoured by electronic configurations involving completely empty, half-filled, or doubly-filled d_γ orbitals and d_ε orbitals which are empty, half-filled, or doubly-filled; in short, by any electrically symmetrical configuration with the two d_γ orbitals lying lowest. TABLE 4 illustrates these six possibilities both for spin-free and for spin-paired complexes.

TABLE 4

Number of Non-Bonding d Electrons	Electronic Configuration	Type	d_γ Orbitals	d_ε Orbitals	Example
0	—	Spin-free or Spin-paired	Empty	Empty	$[TiCl_4]^{0*}$
2	$d_\gamma{}^1 d_\gamma{}^1$	Spin-free	Half-full	Empty	$[FeO_4]^{2-}$
4	$d_\gamma{}^2 d_\gamma{}^2$	Spin-paired	Full	Empty	$[ReCl_4]^{-}$?
5	$d_\gamma{}^1 d_\gamma{}^1 d_\varepsilon{}^1 d_\varepsilon{}^1 d_\varepsilon{}^1$	Spin-free	Half-full	Half-full	$[FeCl_4]^{-}$ MnII Complexes
7	$d_\gamma{}^2 d_\gamma{}^2 d_\varepsilon{}^1 d_\varepsilon{}^1 d_\varepsilon{}^1$	Spin-free	Full	Half-full	$[CoCl_4]^{2-}$
10	$d_\gamma{}^2 d_\gamma{}^2 d_\varepsilon{}^2 d_\varepsilon{}^2 d_\varepsilon{}^2$	Spin-paired	Full	Full	$[ZnCl_4]^{2-}$

* Tetrahedral oxyanions such as the $CrO_4{}^{2-}$ and $MnO_4{}^{-}$ ions may be formally regarded in this category if the oxygen ligands are regarded as O^{2-} ions.

REFERENCES

Barclay, G. A. and Nyholm, R. S. (1953) *Chem. & Ind.* 378
Bergmann, E. and Engel, L. (1931) *Z. phys. Chem.* **B13**, 232
Bethe, H. (1929) *Ann. Phys.* **3**, 133; (1930) *Z. Phys.* **60**, 218
Bleaney, B. and Stevens, K. W. H. (1953) *Rep. Progr. Phys.* **16**, 108
Bose, A. and Mitra, C. S. (1952) *Indian J. Phys.* **26**, 393, 543
Bowers, K. D. and Owen, J. (1955) *Rep. Progr. Phys.* **18**, 305
Brickstock, A. and Pople, J. A. (1953) *Phil. Mag.* **44**, 705
Burstall, F. H. and Nyholm, R. S. (1952) *J. chem. Soc.* 3570
Chatt, J. and Mann, F. G. (1939) *ibid* 1622
Craig, D. P. and Magnusson, E. A. (1956) *ibid* 4895
—— and Mellor, D. P. (1940) *J. Proc. roy. Soc. N.S.W.* **74**, 495
Dickens, P. G. and Linnett, J. W. (1957) *Trans. Faraday Soc.* **53**, 1037
Duffey, G. H. (1950a) *J. chem. Phys.* **18**, 746; (1950b) *ibid* **18**, 1445
Dunitz, J. D. and Orgel, L. E. (1957) *Nature, Lond.* **179**, 462
Dwyer, F. P. (1956) Personal communication
El-Sayed, M. F. A. and Sheline, R. K. (1956) *J. Amer. chem. Soc.* **78**, 702
Ewens, R. V. G. and Lister, M. W. (1939) *Trans. Faraday Soc.* **35**, 681
Figgis, B. N. and Nyholm, R. S. (1954) *J. chem. Soc.* 12; (1957) Unpublished
Hampson, G. C. and Pauling, L. (1938) *J. Amer. chem. Soc.* **60**, 2702

Harris, C. M. and Nyholm, R. S. (1956) *J. chem. Soc.* 4375
— — and Stephenson, N. C. (1956) *Rec. Trav. chim. Pays-Bas* **75**, 687 ; *Nature, Lond.* **177,** 1127
Hepworth, M. A., Jack, K. H. and Nyholm, R. S. (1957) *Nature, Lond.* **179,** 211
Hoard, J. L. and Dickinson, R. G. (1933) *Z. Kristallogr.* **84,** 436
— and Nordsieck, H. H. (1939) *J. Amer. chem. Soc.* **61,** 2853
Hunt, J. P. and Taube, H. (1951) *J. chem. Phys.* **19,** 602
Jensen, K. A. and Nygaard, B. (1949) *Acta chem. scand.* **3,** 474 ; see also Jensen, K. A. (1937) *Z. anorg. Chem.* **231,** 365
Jorgensen, K. (1956) 10ᵉ *Conseil de Chimie*, Institut International de Chimie Solvay. " Quelques Problems de Chimie Minerale," R. Stoops, Brussels, 1956, 355
Lennard-Jones, J. (1949) *Proc. roy. Soc.* **A198,** 14 ; (1954) *Advanc. Sci., Lond.* **11,** 136
— and Pople, J. A. (1950) *ibid* **A202,** 166
Linnett, J. W. and Mellish, C. E. (1954) *Trans. Faraday Soc.* **50,** 655
— and Poë, A. J. (1951) *ibid* **47,** 1033
Lord, R. C., Lynch, M. A., Schumb, W. C. and Slowinski, E. J. (1950) *J. Amer. chem. Soc.* **72,** 522
Nast, R. and Pfab, W. (1952) *Naturwissenschaften* **39,** 300
— and von Krakkay, T. (1954) *Z. Naturforsch* **9b,** 798
Nyholm, R. S. (1954) *Rev. pure appl. Chem. (Austr.)* **4,** 15 ; (1956) 10ᵉ *Conseil de Chimie*, Institut International de Chimie Solvay. " Quelques Problems de Chimie Minerale," R. Stoops, Brussels, 1956, 215
Orgel, L. E. (1952) *J. chem. Soc.* 4756 ; (1955a) *J. chem. Phys.* **23,** 1004 ; (1955b) *ibid* **23,** 1819 ; (1956) 10ᵉ *Conseil de Chimie*, Institut International de Chimie Solvay. " Quelques Problems de Chimie Minerale," R. Stoops, Brussels, 1956, 289
— and Sutton, L. E. (1954) *Proc. Copenhagen Conf. on Coordination Compounds*
Pauling, L. (1945) *Nature of the Chemical Bond*, Cornell Univ. Press, Ithaca, N.Y. and earlier references therein.
Penney, W. and Schlapp, R. (1932) *Phys. Rev.* 41, 194 ; **42,** 666 ; (1933) *ibid* **43,** 486
Peyronel, G. (1941) *Gazz. chim. ital.* **71,** 363
Pitzer, K. S. (1953) *Quantum Chemistry*, New York, Prentice-Hall
Pople, J. A. (1950) *Proc. roy. Soc.* **A202,** 323
Scouladi, H. (1953) *Acta. cryst. Camb.* **6,** 651
Sidgwick, N. V. (1950) *The Chemical Elements and their Compounds*, Oxford University Press
— and Powell, H. M. (1940) *Proc. roy. Soc.* **A176,** 153
Slater, J. C. (1931) *Phys. Rev.* **37,** 481
Stoner, E. C. (1934) *Magnetism and Matter*, London, Methuen
Van Vleck, J. H. (1932) *Theory of Electric and Magnetic Susceptibilities*, Oxford University Press
Walsh, A. D. (1953) *Progress in Stereochemistry*, Vol. 1, London, Butterworths
Wells, A. F. (1945) *Structural Inorganic Chemistry*, Oxford University Press
Zachariason, W. H. (1954) *Acta. cryst. Cop.* **7,** 792
Zimmermann, H.K. and Van Rysselberghe, P. (1949) *J. chem. Phys.* **17,** 598

AUTHOR INDEX

The page numbers in heavy type refer to chapters in this volume. The page numbers in italics refer to names given in the lists of references at the ends of the chapters. The other numbers refer to pages on which the authorities' work is mentioned even though their names may not be given in the text.

SUBJECT INDEX

315